Medical Office Billing

Lynn Berry
Cindy Johnston-Laplante
Sandy Miller

emp
2015
Emond Montgomery Publications
Toronto, Canada

DEDICATION

To our families who are our tireless cheerleaders!
To all our students past and present — you inspire us to keep learning.
Thank you to June Bujold, Jennifer Dunn, and Brenda Mulder for your support.

Emond Montgomery Publications Limited
60 Shaftesbury Avenue
Toronto ON M4T 1A3
http://www.emp.ca/highered

Printed in Canada.

We acknowledge the financial support of the Government of Canada through the Canada Book Fund for our publishing activities.

Permission has been received from QHR Technologies Inc.

Physician names, billing numbers, CPSO numbers, patient names, and scenarios used within the projects and workbook documents are intended to be fictional and are for educational purposes only.

Publisher: Mike Thompson
Managing editor, development: Kelly Dickson
Director, editorial and production: Jim Lyons
Production editor: Laura Bast
Production: First Image Graphic Design
Cover design: Tara Wells
Cover image: iStockphoto.com/Maudib

Library and Archives Canada Cataloguing in Publication

Berry, Lynn M., author
Medical office billing / Lynn Berry, Cindy Johnston-Laplante, and Sandy Miller.

ISBN 978-1-55239-657-5 (pbk.)

1. Medical fees. 2. Health insurance claims. 3. Medical offices.
I. Johnston-Laplante, Cindy, author II. Miller, Sandy (Sandy J.), 1961-, author
III. Title.

R728.5.M43 2014 610.68 C2014-907543-X

TABLE OF CONTENTS

Appendices

INTRODUCTION TO BROOKLANE MEDICAL CENTRE

Welcome to Brooklane Medical Centre!

You are about to embark on a rewarding medical administrative career, which involves medical billing.

Brooklane Medical Centre is a comprehensive clinic with a full complement of medical services to meet individual and family needs.

You are the medical assistant for the entire clinic, and you are responsible for assisting the medical director, the clinical director, and their teams. Generally, in community medical centres, there would be more administrative staff; however, for the purposes of this workbook, you are a one-person administrative team!

Your daily duties may consist of reception, appointment management, medical correspondence and requisitions, triaging patients, taking medical histories, patient records management, document production, faxing, problem solving, stakeholder relations, patient education, and billing.

This workbook is focusing on the medical billing function of your position. Medical assistants may also be referred to as medical billing clerks when their sole responsibility is medical billing.

It is crucial that you be familiar with all facets of medical billing including:

- Provider payment
- Health cards
- Schedule of Benefits
- Resource Manual for Physicians
- Claims generation

- Claims submission
- Troubleshooting error codes
- Reconciliation
- Resubmission
- Insured services
- Uninsured services
- Out-of-province billing (reciprocal billing)
- Quebec billing

See Appendix A for the organization chart. There is a copy of the organization chart on your USB key where you can enter your own information.

See Appendix B for the clinical specialists. This is your team! They have hospital privileges at Hope General Hospital.

Two patient spreadsheets have been created: a Brooklane Medical Centre patient spreadsheet and a template for a student patient spreadsheet. You will be creating new clinical patients in the student spreadsheet; these are the patients for which you will be submitting claims to the Ministry. See Appendix C.

For the purposes of this workbook, Brooklane Medical Centre is located in Ottawa, Ontario; as a result, all medical references for medical billing will relate to Ontario.

Clinics across Canada use many different types of medical software. Other medical software programs could be adapted for use within the projects. We have chosen Accuro®EMR from QHR Technologies Inc. as the medical software for this workbook.

Ensure that you take time in each exercise to save your work regularly.

Mission Statement

Brooklane Medical Centre's mission statement is to treat each person as an individual, with respect, confidentiality, efficiency, and empathy. This includes patients, clinical specialists, colleagues, and other stakeholders within the medical environment.

We endeavour to instill confidence in our patients by delivering competent and professional health care.

We work in a team environment, using each person's talents and areas of expertise to his or her fullest potential. We provide a quality and caring environment for our staff and patients alike.

Motto

Our motto is: "*We put your needs first.*"

The contact information for the clinic is:

33 Brooklane Avenue

Ottawa, ON K2B 6M7

 613-224-2308

 613-224-2300

info@bmc.emp.ca

www.bmc.emp.ca

Facility No. 3003

Master No. 0001

For the purposes of this workbook, Brooklane Medical Centre, which is a **fictitious clinic**, is an Independent Health Facility registered with the province.

Hope General Hospital

Hope General Hospital is the hospital nearest to our clinic; it is a fictitious hospital.

Clinics may opt to use hard copy forms from local medical facilities. For the purpose of this workbook, electronic forms have been created for Hope General Hospital.

The contact information for Hope General is:

77 Gladview Avenue

Ottawa, ON K2S 3G8

 613-813-1234

 613-813-1235

info@hgh.emp.ca

www.hgh.emp.ca

Facility No. 1001

Master No. 7001 (Emergency Department)

Overview of Workbook

This workbook will integrate medical billing theory and practice assignments designed to enable you to learn and practise your medical billing skills.

Each project will be divided into tasks that may involve the use of MS Word®, MS Excel®, or Accuro®EMR.

The workbook is divided into projects as follows:

Project 1 – **Introduction to Medical Billing**

Project 2 – **Uninsured Medical Billing**

Project 3 – **Health Cards**

Project 4 – **Codes**

Project 5 – **Schedule of Benefits and Resource Manual for Physicians**

Project 6 – **Creating Claims**

Project 7 – **Generating Claims from Scenarios**

Project 8 – **Creating Claims from Day Sheets, Patient Records, and Physician Notes**

Project 9 – **Claims Submission**

Project 10 – **Ministry Feedback**

Project 11 – **Reconciliation and Resubmission**

Patients within the projects are referred to by number rather than name, without reference to gender (Patient 3).

When dates are represented as 20xx, you are to use the current year.

Your instructor will determine the tasks you will be undertaking, the method of presentation for evaluation (printed or electronically provided), and the evaluation weighting for each task.

Resources

Each task within the project may have resources identified. Always preview the resources before commencing the tasks.

Appendices

To function effectively within Brooklane Medical Centre, the following resources are available to you:

- A **Organization Chart**
- B **Clinical Specialists**
- C **Patients – Brooklane Medical Centre and Student Spreadsheets**
- D **Templates**
- E **Sample Documents**
- F **Accuro®EMR Instructions**
- G **Accuro®EMR Instructions for Medical Billing**
- H **Ministry Claims Submission Software**
- I **Electronic Documents**
- J **Related Task Documents**

Project 1

INTRODUCTION TO MEDICAL BILLING

LEARNING OBJECTIVES

- Explaining medical billing and why you bill
- Discussing health care legislation
- Explaining health care regulators and programs
- Discussing specialist associations
- Understanding who can bill for medical services
- Discussing who is responsible for medical services
- Describing who can bill
- Defining types of billing
- Discussing insured billing
- Describing types of billing
- Understanding physician records
- Describing how physicians get paid
- Discussing how each encounter with a patient is billed
- Understanding medical billing workbook terminology

This project includes a general theoretical overview of medical billing in Ontario.

What Is Medical Billing? Why Do You Bill?

Medical billing is a process that provides payment to physicians for services rendered. Every encounter with a physician results in billing. As a medical biller, it is essential to be accurate and timely with the submission of claims as this is the physician's main source of income.

Following is a chart illustrating the process of medical billing, which will be explored, explained, and developed throughout this workbook:

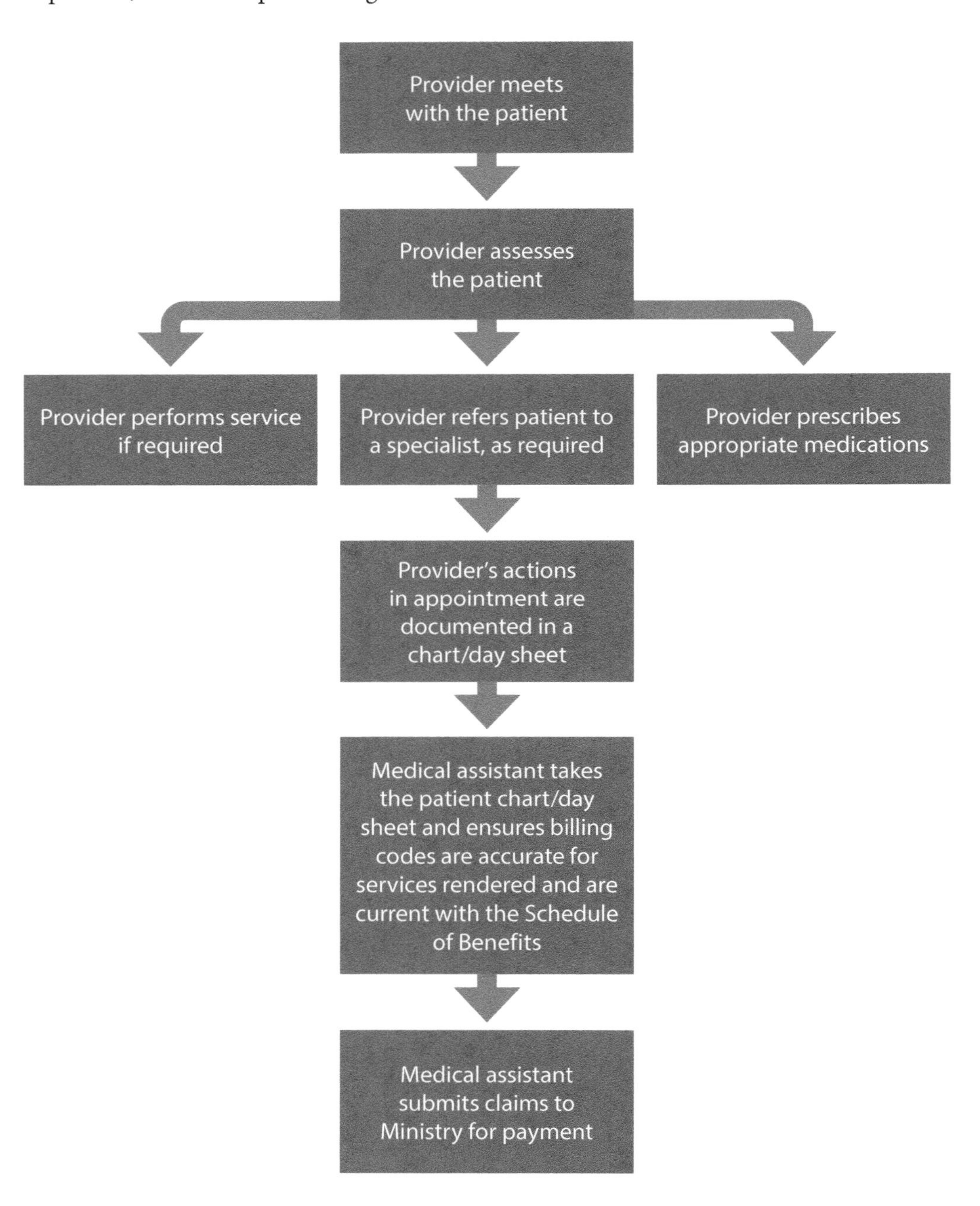

Health Care Legislation

Health care legislation is created federally and provincially to protect the patient, the patient's family, the community as a whole, and the medical specialists administering health care to the community. This legislation includes protections such as right to safe and fair service for anyone requiring medical assistance and privacy of information within any health care facility.

Medical billing records are protected under health care legislation and anyone working in the medical administrative field must be aware of this legislation in order to conduct themselves accordingly. Medical billing records are legal medical records reflecting services performed by physicians. This legislation provides the legal foundation and framework for medical health care, including medical billing.

The primary legislation relating to medical billing in Ontario includes the following:

Canada Health Act (CHA)

The *Canada Health Act* sets the standards for health care in Canada. It outlines the criteria by which provinces and territories receive transfer payments for health insurance programs; it also outlines the penalties imposed should the provinces not comply with the Act.

The Act defines services as medically required services rendered by medical practitioners. A service includes the physician's time and expertise. The physician must maintain appropriate and detailed records of every service rendered.

Health Insurance Act (HIA)

The *Health Insurance Act* for Ontario provides the structure for health care in Ontario. In Ontario, the health care plan is referred to as OHIP (Ontario Health Insurance Plan), and the Ministry of Health and Long-Term Care (MOHLTC) is the provincial government department responsible for health care in Ontario. The Act regulates the insured services, the right to medical insurance, the health card system, and the billing process as a vehicle for claims assessment for payment of insured (medically-necessary) health care services.

Health Insurance Act, RRO 1990, Reg 552

The *Health Insurance Act,* RRO 1990, Reg 552 for Ontario outlines the rules, guidelines, and process of how to apply the *Health Insurance Act*, such as the Schedule of Benefits for physician fees, physician services, health cards, and billing and payment for insured services.

Independent Health Facilities Act (IHFA)

The *Independent Health Facilities Act* for Ontario provides a framework for funding, licensing, and standards of operation of community-based facilities, such as long-term care facilities.

Commitment to the Future of Medicare Act (CFMA)

The *Commitment to the Future of Medicare Act* confirms Ontario's commitment to the principles set out in the *Canada Health Act*: Canadians should be able to access medically-necessary health care based only on need and not on ability to pay. Specifically, the CFMA supports the prohibition of two-tier medicine, extra-billing, queue jumping, and user fees for receipt of, or access to, insured health care services.

The Ministry investigates all extra-billing complaints. The CFMA sets out the process under which the Ministry can investigate a complaint. During an investigation, individuals must provide any information requested by the General Manager (GM) of OHIP. When the GM is satisfied that there has been an unauthorized payment, the Ministry will ask that the patient be reimbursed. If the physician or facility that received the unauthorized payment refuses to reimburse the patient, the Ministry will reimburse the patient and recover the money from the physician or facility, plus an administrative fee for each unauthorized payment received.

Regulated Health Professions Act (RHPA)

The *Regulated Health Professions Act* (RHPA) for Ontario regulates all professional medical colleges in Ontario. It outlines the manner in which the colleges operate in relation to health care professionals and the process for complaints against a health care professional. If fraudulent activity is suspected, it is to be reported to the appropriate professional licensing college.

The colleges regulated by the RHPA are as follows:

- College of Audiologists and Speech-Language Pathologists
- College of Chiropodists of Ontario (including Podiatrists)
- College of Chiropractors of Ontario
- College of Dental Hygienists of Ontario
- Royal College of Dental Surgeons of Ontario
- College of Dental Technologists of Ontario
- College of Denturists of Ontario
- College of Dieticians of Ontario
- College of Massage Therapists of Ontario
- College of Medical Laboratory Technologists of Ontario
- College of Medical Radiation Technologists of Ontario
- College of Midwives of Ontario
- College of Nurses of Ontario
- College of Occupational Therapists of Ontario
- College of Opticians of Ontario
- College of Optometrists of Ontario
- College of Pharmacists of Ontario
- College of Physicians and Surgeons of Ontario
- College of Physiotherapists of Ontario
- College of Psychologists of Ontario
- College of Respiratory Therapists of Ontario

Health Information Protection Act (HIPA)

The Ontario *Health Information Protection Act* was created to protect health information across the health care system. It has two parts: the *Personal Health Information Protection Act* and the *Quality of Care Information Protection Act.*

Personal Health Information Protection Act (PHIPA) – Schedule A

The Ontario *Personal Health Information Protection Act* is Schedule A of the *Health Information Protection Act.* It establishes consistent rules for the collection, use, and disclosure of personal health information possessed by health care providers, referred to as custodians. The Information and Privacy Commissioner of Ontario is responsible for ensuring compliance with the Act. Health cards are protected by privacy rights.

Quality of Care Information Protection Act (QCIPA) – Schedule B

The Ontario *Quality of Care Information Protection Act* is Schedule B of the *Health Information Protection Act.* It promotes the sharing of information and open discussions among health professionals, which can improve patient care and ensure patient safety.

Personal Information Protection and Electronic Documents Act (PIPEDA)

The federal *Personal Information Protection and Electronic Documents Act* ensures that the collection, utilization, and disclosure of personal information received by private organizations for commercial business remains private and protected. Canadians have a right to access their personal information and have the right to be guaranteed their information will not be misused. Formal complaints related to a violation of privacy rights can be filed with the Privacy Commissioner of Canada.

Freedom of Information and Protection of Privacy Act (FIPPA)

The Ontario *Freedom of Information and Protection of Privacy Act* provides a public right of access to information, to ensure the protection of individuals with respect to disclosure of personal information, and to provide individuals with a right of access to their personal information. A formal complaint can be made by an individual to the Information and Privacy Commissioner of Ontario.

Long-Term Care Homes Act (LTCHA)

The *Long-Term Care Homes Act* for Ontario ensures that residents of long-term care facilities receive quality, consistent, and safe care. The LTCHA emphasizes resident-centred respectful care with access to all the services and supports needed for the well-being of the residents of long-term care facilities.

TASK 1

MEDICAL BILLING WORKBOOK – LEGISLATION

It is important to have easy access to medical billing resources. Creating a spreadsheet of these resources will assist you when you are undertaking medical billing.

1. Create a workbook using Microsoft Excel.
2. Save the Microsoft Excel workbook as Medical Billing Workbook.
3. Rename a sheet as **Legislation**.
4. Apply a colour to the tab.
5. In the Legislation sheet, create four columns:
    - Legislation (name of Act or Regulation) (Column A)
    - Abbreviation (Column B)

- Website (active URL) (Column C)
- Purpose (brief purpose of the Act) (Column D)

Following is a sample of the column heads, which are centred:

Legislation	Abbreviation	Website	Purpose
Canada Health Act	CHA	http://laws-lois.justice.gc.ca/eng/acts/c-6/	Canadian health care standards and insurance programs

Following is a sample of the sheet renamed:

6. Add the following:
   - CHA
   - HIA
   - IHFA
   - CFMA
   - RHPA
   - HIPA
   - PHIPA
   - QCIPA
   - PIPEDA
   - FIPPA
   - LTCHA
   - Reg 552
7. Ensure the links are active.
8. Sort alphabetically by website name.

Health Care Regulators and Programs

Provinces and territories are responsible for governing their medical professionals. Following are the primary regulators and programs for Ontario.

Ministry of Health and Long-Term Care (MOHLTC)

The Ontario Ministry of Health and Long-Term Care is responsible for health care in Ontario. The MOHTLC is one of the provincial bodies involved in generating and maintaining the list of medically-necessary insured services for medical billing, as discussed later in this workbook. The Ministry is considered a regulator as well as an insured service provider since medically-necessary claims are submitted to the Ministry for approval prior to payment to the medical service providers.

It is important to remember that services deemed medically-necessary change; it is essential to remain up to date on Ministry changes.

Federation of Health Regulatory Colleges of Ontario (FHRCO)

This regulatory body consists of Ontario's health regulatory colleges, and it was established by the *Regulated Health Professions Act* to ensure safe, competent, and ethical health care. Councils and boards of directors consist of elected professional members and members of the public appointed by the Lieutenant Governor of Ontario. They represent the interests of the health care consumers.

College of Physicians and Surgeons of Ontario (CPSO)

The College of Physicians and Surgeons of Ontario (CPSO) is the governing body that regulates all physicians practising in Ontario. Each physician is licensed to practise by the CPSO, is a registered member, and receives a CPSO number.

Ontario Health Insurance Plan (OHIP)

OHIP is a government-run insurance plan for Ontario residents, which is funded by Ontario taxpayers and federal transfer payments. Ontario residents are entitled to free health coverage for medically-necessary services. The MOHLTC, which is a government department, plays a key role in determining these medically-necessary services.

Ontario Drug Program (ODP)

This Ontario program, regulated through the MOHLTC, assists individuals who have high prescription drug costs relative to their household income, seniors (over 65 years of age), residents of a long-term care facility, individuals in a home care program, recipients of social assistance, and individuals receiving Ontario disability support.

Trillium Drug Program (TDP)

This Ontario program provides a list of approved drugs that are covered under the Ontario Drug Benefit (ODB) program. A physician can apply through the Exceptional Access Program (EAP) for special approval for drugs not on the approved list, in order to financially assist a patient.

Northern Health Travel Grant (NHTG)

Ontario Northern Health Travel Grants are available to those who meet established criteria. Applicants must reside in an approved northern region of the province, must be travelling a certain distance to the nearest medical facility for a service, and must have a referral from a medical specialist before the travel occurs. Applicants are entitled to compensation for mileage and accommodation. The specialist providing the service must complete a section on the application form. The application is made by the patient to the MOHLTC in Sudbury, Ontario, and applications must be received within 12 months from the date of service.

TASK 2

MEDICAL BILLING WORKBOOK – REGULATORS AND PROGRAMS

RESOURCE: Medical Billing Workbook (Created in Task 1)

It is important to have easy access to licensing bodies. Creating a spreadsheet of these resources will assist you when you are undertaking medical billing.

1. Create a Regulators and Programs sheet in your Medical Billing Workbook.
2. Rename the sheet as Regulators and Programs.
3. Apply a colour to the tab.
4. In the Regulators and Programs sheet, create four columns:
   - Regulators and Programs (name) (Column A)
   - Abbreviation (Column B)
   - Website (active URL) (Column C)
   - Purpose (brief purpose of site) (Column D)
5. Add the following:
   - FHRCO
   - CPSO
   - OHIP
   - ODP
   - TDP
   - MOHTLC
   - NHTG
   - Other than OHIP for Ontario, add the remaining provincial and territorial health plans.
6. Ensure the links are active.
7. Sort alphabetically.

Medical Associations

In addition to government regulation, specialists in provinces and territories are governed by their own medical professional associations. Each provincial or territorial association ensures that areas of specialty are represented. The associations provide a variety of information for the members, such as current information related to the medical environment, licensing requirements, codes of conduct, and available resources.

Associations are involved with the government in any changes to current insured services or new procedures that require approval and coding.

The Canadian Medical Association defines a medically-necessary service as one that a qualified physician determines is required to assess, prevent, treat, rehabilitate, or palliate a given health concern of problem.

Professional medical associations include:

- Canadian Medical Association (CMA)
- Canadian Medical Protective Association (CMPA)
- Ontario Medical Association (OMA)
- Canadian Nurses Association (CNA)
- Ontario Nurses' Association (ONA)
- Canadian Dental Association (CDA)
- Ontario Dental Association (ODA)
- Canadian Chiropractic Association (CCA)
- Canadian Physiotherapy Association (CPA)
- Ontario Physiotherapy Association (OPA)
- Registered Massage Therapists' Association of Ontario (RMTAO)
- Canadian Athletic Therapists Association (CATA)

TASK 3

MEDICAL BILLING WORKBOOK – MEDICAL ASSOCIATIONS

RESOURCE: Medical Billing Workbook

1. Create a sheet in your Medical Billing Workbook and rename it as Medical Associations.
2. Apply a colour to the tab.
3. In the Medical Associations sheet, create three columns:
   - Medical Association (name) Column A)
   - Abbreviation (Column B)
   - Website (active URL) (Column C)
4. Add the following:
   - Canadian Medical Association
   - Canadian Medical Protective Association
   - Ontario Medical Association
   - Canadian Nurses Association
   - Ontario Nurses' Association
   - Canadian Dental Association
   - Ontario Dental Association
   - Canadian Chiropractic Association
   - Canadian Physiotherapy Association
   - Ontario Physiotherapy Association
   - Registered Massage Therapists' Association of Ontario
   - Canadian Athletic Therapists Association
5. Ensure the links are active.
6. Sort alphabetically.

Billing Overview

Who can bill for medical services?

The following medical environments can bill:

- Physicians practising in hospitals, clinics, and private practice
- Non-physician practices such as chiropractors, physiotherapists, massage therapists, dentists, and psychologists

Nurses, physician's assistants, and nurse practitioners are paid a salary by the physician; however, services rendered to patients by nurses, physician's assistants, and nurse practitioners can be billed under the physician. All health care providers can refer a patient to a specialist; however, anyone other than a physician must bill under a physician for the referral.

Who can submit claims for billing on behalf of the health care provider?

Billing can be performed by members of the clinical team as follows:

- Physicians
- Nurses and nurse practitioners
- Medical assistants
- Medical billing clerks
- Medical billing specialists, who operate on a contract basis for outsourced medical billing

Who do you bill?

Depending upon the service provided, you would bill:

- Provincial health ministry (MOHLTC in Ontario)
- Third-party insurance companies, for example:
  - University Health Insurance Plan (UHIP)
  - Supplemental insurance companies
  - Public Service Health Care Plan (PSHCP)
- Workplace Safety and Insurance Board (WSIB)
- Patient

Types of billing

You will be encountering a variety of billing methods, which are dependent upon the service provided.

- Insured
  - Insured services are expenses that are deemed medically necessary and are covered by a provincial health plan (OHIP in Ontario), usually with no additional cost to the patient in possession of a valid health card. This payment system is referred to as a fee-for-service system, as the physician is paid a set fee for each insured service provided to an insured client.

- If a patient is from out of province or from a territory, a reciprocal billing process (dollar-for-dollar remuneration) is in place across Canada, with the exception of the province of Quebec.
- Services that are no longer covered as medically necessary are removed from the province's fee schedule and are referred to as deregulated or delisted services.
- It is important that the medical biller stay current with the Ministry changes.

- Private/Third-Party Insurance
  - Private insurance, also known as third-party insurance, may either partially or fully cover certain medical expenses. It is supplementary insurance, with coverage and amounts dependent upon the type of plan.
  - It is important to ensure a patient knows what will not be covered by insurance prior to an appointment. It is the responsibility of the patient to verify coverage with the private insurance carrier.
- Uninsured
  - Uninsured services are expenses that must be covered by the patient and then may be used as an expense for income tax.
  - It is important that a patient knows that the service is not covered by OHIP prior to the appointment.

Insured Billing

Provincial Schedule of Benefits (Schedule or SOB)

Insured billing is governed by the Schedule of Benefits, which is updated periodically by the provincial or territorial government. The Schedule of Benefits determines the medically-necessary services that will be covered by the provincial health plan. In Ontario, the plan is the Ontario Health Insurance Plan (OHIP), administered through the MOHLTC, which is a fee-for-service structure. It applies to physicians who bill privately or through the hospital.

The Schedule is a legal document authorized by the *Health Insurance Act* and is amended only by regulation. Changes to the Schedule are discussed and negotiated with the provincial medical associations and members of the provincial/territorial government. In Ontario, the association is the Ontario Medical Association (OMA).

There are additional services that are covered under insured services:

- Limited Use Drugs – If the physician feels a client should have a drug not on the list of prescriptions covered (Drug Benefit Formulary), the physician can seek approval for funding the drug. This is called a restricted listing drug. The doctor must fill out a form requesting the drug for the client using a Limited Use form.
- Ambulance Service – This is a co-payment, meaning the cost is partly insured and partly paid by the patient.
- Optometry – This is a reduced service because there are restrictions on what is covered as an insured service. An example of a restriction is that coverage is not available for a periodic oculo-visual assessment for patients between ages 20 and 64 years. The medical biller should always consult the MOHLTC Schedule of Benefits for Optometry Services because there are exceptions related to a patient's medical condition, e.g., Type 1 Diabetes.

- Physiotherapy – Ontario offers publicly funded physiotherapy through home care, hospitals, and specialized community clinics (for the vulnerable—those under 19 or over 65, Ontario Works, Ontario Disability Support Program, or those recently released from hospital who need physiotherapy upon discharge). All facilities must be government approved. This provincial government funding is part of a budget process rather than through OHIP at this point in time.

Interim Federal Health (IFH)

Through the federal government department Citizenship and Immigration Canada (CIC), refugees can receive temporary health insurance. Refugees must submit an application to CIC. Once approved, the refugee will receive an 8-digit ID number for health care coverage.

Workplace Safety and Insurance Board (WSIB)

Employers must pay quarterly premiums to WSIB to protect workers in the event of a workplace-related injury. Should an employee be injured on the job, the employer and employee must file reports to WSIB. As well, the attending physician who examined the employee must complete and file a Form 8 report for WSIB.

The hospital or physician will directly bill the MOHTLC and the WSIB will reimburse the Ministry.

TASK 4

MEDICAL BILLING WORKBOOK – INSURED BILLING

RESOURCE: Medical Billing Workbook

1. Create a sheet in your Medical Billing Workbook and rename it as Insured Providers.
2. Apply a colour to the tab.
3. In the Insured Providers sheet, create four columns:
   - Insured Provider (name) (Column A)
   - Abbreviation (where applicable) (Column B)
   - Website (active URL) (Column C)
   - Purpose (brief description of site) (Column D)
4. Add the following:
   - MOHLTC – (same as in Regulator and Program sheet)
   - MOHLTC – Schedule of Benefits
   - MOHTLC – Forms
   - MOHTLC – Programs and Services
   - WSIB
   - IFH
5. Ensure the links are active.
6. Sort alphabetically.

Uninsured Billing

Deregulated services (also known as delisted services) are services that are no longer covered by the province or territory and are considered uninsured services. The *Health Insurance Act*, RRO 1990, Reg 552, for Ontario contains a list of uninsured services. The Ontario Medical Association (OMA) provides a list of recommended fees for uninsured services. Hospital websites and physician offices post lists of uninsured services and related costs offered at their facilities.

In some cases, a deregulated service can be billed if deemed **medically necessary**. For example, for religious, ritual, cultural, or cosmetic reasons, circumcision would not be billable; however, if medically necessary, a circumcision can be billed with approval with the Ministry. The physician must provide an explanation of why the procedure is necessary. Further information is found in the Schedule of Benefits.

Third-Party Billing

Insurance companies act as third-party providers of supplemental insurance to cover the uninsured medical services that are not covered under the Schedule of Benefits. Some of these expenses, however, may not be fully covered by third-party providers, and some expenses may not be covered at all.

Depending upon the service provider, the patient may be expected to pay for the service immediately following the encounter, or the service provider may opt to submit the claim for the service directly to the third-party insurer.

If the patient pays directly, the provider will provide proof of payment in the form of a receipt, and this receipt may be submitted by the patient to the third-party insurer for reimbursement of the cost of the service.

For the purposes of this workbook, we have created an Extended Health Care form with Healthy Life Insurance Co., a fictitious insurance provider.

University Health Insurance Plan (UHIP)

The province will contract, on a term basis, a third-party insurance company to act as a provider for UHIP. The universities must be on a provincial list of accredited institutions registered to participate in the plan. The form can be found on the Internet. For the purposes of this workbook, we have created a UHIP form with Healthy Life Insurance Co., a fictitious insurance provider.

This plan is for foreign university students who are registered with an accredited Canadian university and reside in the province while attending that university. The student must register for the plan and receive a membership number. UHIP will cover the cost of hospital and medical services.

The student would submit a claim form for reimbursement if the provider does not bill directly to OHIP or a third-party insurance provider.

Public Service Health Care Plan (PSHCP)

Members of the federal public service and the Royal Canadian Mounted Police (RCMP) have their own third-party provider, which is the Public Service Health Care Plan (PSHCP). The plan has a claim form for submission of expenses, which can be found on the Internet.

For the purposes of this workbook, we have created a PSHCP form with Healthy Life Insurance Co., a fictitious insurance provider.

Private Billing

When the patient does not have coverage through the provincial health plan or a supplemental insurance plan for the service provided, or if the service is not covered, the patient is considered to be billing privately.

TASK 5

MEDICAL BILLING WORKBOOK – UNINSURED BILLING

RESOURCE: Medical Billing Workbook

1. Create a sheet in your Medical Billing Workbook and rename it as Uninsured Providers.
2. Apply a colour to the tab.
3. In the Uninsured Providers sheet, create four columns:
   - Uninsured Provider (name) (Column A)
   - Abbreviation (Column B)
   - Website (active URL) (Column C)
   - Purpose (brief description of site) (Column D)
4. Add the following:
   - UHIP
   - PSHCP
5. Research three supplemental insurance companies in your area and add them to the list.
6. Ensure the links are active.
7. Sort alphabetically.

Physician records

Medical billing is the physician's responsibility. All insured services must be documented in appropriate records.

Physician records must be kept for 10 years after the last entry or 10 years after the patient would have reached 18 years of age; however, the Canadian Medical Protective Association (CMPA) advises that patient records should be kept up to 15 years, because legal claims may be made up to 15 years after the alleged incident.

How do physicians get paid?

Every provincial and territorial government in Canada makes payments in accordance with the contents of a Schedule of Benefits, commonly referred to as the Schedule.

The Ministry of Health and Long-Term Care (MOHLTC) is the governing body responsible for health care in Ontario. The Ontario Health Insurance Plan (OHIP) is Ontario's medical plan for services in the Schedule of Benefits.

Physicians must be registered with the MOHLTC by completing a Regulated Health Professionals Registration form and possessing an OHIP billing number. Physician

CPSO numbers are not billing numbers. To receive a billing number through the MOHLTC, the physician must hold a valid certificate with the CPSO and must have an Ontario practice address or addresses. Where multiple addresses exist, the physician must provide a primary address to the MOHLTC. Medical practitioners who wish to bill through the provincial or territorial ministry of health must be approved by their provincial or territorial ministry. Once approved, the physician will receive a billing number that must be present on each billing submission.

The billing number consists of three segments:

- The first 4 numbers represent the physician's facility number (medical institution)
- The next 6 numbers represent the physician's unique registration number with the MOHLTC (billing number)
- The last 2 numbers represent the physician's area of specialty (specialty code)
- For example: 0000-543933-07

The provider whose number appears in the claims assumes full responsibility for the service. All insured services must be documented in appropriate records. The *Health Insurance Act* requires that the record must establish that:

- An insured service was provided.
- The service for which the account is submitted is the service that was rendered.
- The service was medically necessary.

It is illegal for physicians to charge extra for insured services. The MOHLTC has the legal right to audit physicians and to send letters to patients to determine if a service was performed as submitted by a physician.

Medical billing is the ultimate responsibility of the physician, and any overpayments must be reimbursed to the Ministry by the physician.

After the claim has been submitted for services rendered, and subsequently approved by the Ministry, payment is made to the physician.

How do you bill each patient's encounter with the physician?

You will be building your medical billing skills as you continue in the workbook, using an Electronic Management Records (EMR) system, if available.

The medical biller must:

- Be familiar with the method (as seen below) the physician is using to record billing codes
- Ensure codes are complete
- Ensure codes are accurate

Depending on the physician's method of practice, medical billing can be done in one of three ways or using all of the following to capture the billing codes:

- Day Sheets
- Patient Records
- Daily Billing Sheets

The medical biller will use these records to:

- Verify the accuracy of codes, if provided
- Obtain codes from physician notes
- Create a claim
- Submit a claim to the MOHTLC

Day Sheets

Day sheets are created through an EMR system. The day sheet is a daily list of patients, appointment times, and reasons for appointments. Throughout the day, the physician may choose to fill in the boxes to the right of the patient notes on the day sheet with billing information such as billing codes, diagnosis codes, and description of the visit. Alternatively, the physician may choose to print the day sheet filling in the information with pen or pencil. This method is used when medical billers are offsite or not connected to the EMR system, or if the physician prefers the manual method. At the end of the day, the day sheet would be available for the medical biller through the EMR or the physician's printed sheet.

Following is a sample of a day sheet:

Day Sheet
10-May-20xx

Alyssa Darby

Start Length	Type	Note	
800 30 **Thomas, Douglas** 03/31/1959 1080331195DT (613) 592-1234 Referred by Dr. , [] Fam Dr. , []	New Consult Consult	this is a meet and greet appointment. Patient is looking for a G.P in his area as he is retiring and does not want to travel a distance.	A
830 30 **Thomas, Cindy** 12/25/1958 1081225195CT (613) 592-1234 Referred by Dr. Thomas, Kyle[592300] Fam Dr. , []	New Consult Consult	*Yearly Check up (Complete Physical Exam) with provider Alyssa Darby*. This is a meet and greet appointment. Her husband has an appointment first today as well. They are looking for a physician close to home for appointments so as not to have to deal with downtown traffic.	
900 30 **Arie, Jules** 06/07/1977 230607197 (867) 761-4689 Referred by Dr. , [] Fam Dr. , []	Prescription Renewal Annual Checkup	Jules would like to get her birth control pills renewed and talk about the patch. she is also having problems with acne, and feels she may need to see a specialist.	

Patient Records

Patient encounter information is recorded either on paper charts or through an EMR system. Many physicians have computers in every examining room to capture the patient's visit, updating the patient record instantly and accurately. An "encounter" is a term used for a patient appointment with a physician.

Physicians may use the physician notes section to record billing codes and/or services performed. Medical billers use the patient records to verify the codes for the services rendered.

Each EMR software program has its own method for inserting procedures and codes.

Following is a sample of a patient record:

NAME: Thomas, Douglas T.	REFERRING MD: --None--
ADDRESS: 108 Second Avenue	
Ottawa, ON K2S 1C5	HEALTH CARD NUMBER: 1080331195DT
HOME PHONE: (613) 592-1234	BIRTHDATE: 1959-Mar-31
WORK PHONE: (000) ___-____	

DIAGNOSIS: Chronic Fatigue

SERVICES
1. Blood Pressure Check
2. Flu Vaccine
3. CBC

BOOK PATIENT FOR THE FOLLOWING:
Please book patient for an EMG and a consultation with a Neurologist.

Physician Notes:

General re-assessment

Daily Billing Sheet

Physicians may choose to create their own record-keeping system. One such method might be a print-off of patient labels for each patient. During the appointment, the physician will place the procedure and the codes beside the label.

Following is a sample of physician notes, which includes billing codes, appointment followups, and tests that need to be requisitioned:

DAILY BILLING SHEET

Dr. Brooke Harte **Date: March 25, 20xx**

Patient	Procedure/Diagnosis/Notes
Douglas T. Laplante Y59-03-31 M 108 Second Avenue, Stittsville, ON K2S 1C5 613-592-1234 1080 331 195 DT	A605 427 Referred by Dr. K. Thomas Book followup in 6/52
Kingsland G. Johnson Y33-06-13 M 8 Sewell Way, Kanata, ON K2G 2X1 613-224-1146 8061 319 333 KJ	A603 428 Book followup 1/12
Lynn S. Kelly Y56-01-14 F 56 Westwood Drive, Nepean, ON K2Z 1X4 613-432-4774 613-732-7447 5601 141 955 LK	A604 402 Book 1/12 Book ECG same day before appt.
Brenda L. Mudda Y60-01-19 F 71 Gagnon Lane, Arnprior, ON K2S 7V3 613-722-2100 613-722-2100 7101 141 960 BM	A606 Referred by Dr. A. Darby Chest Pain – Check code pls. Followup with Family Physician
Chris D. Fry Y80-03-07 M 37 Bunting Lane, Stittsville, ON K2S 0S1 613-234-4123 613-729-1111	A604 426 Followup 2/12 Book Holter Monitor Get OHIP number ********

TASK 6

MEDICAL BILLING WORKBOOK – TERMINOLOGY

RESOURCE: Medical Billing Workbook

1. Create a sheet in your Medical Billing Workbook and rename it as Terminology.
2. Apply a colour to the tab.
3. In the Terminology sheet, create two columns:
   - Term (Column A)
   - Definition (Column B)
4. Add the following:
   - Encounter
   - Day Sheet
   - Patient Record
   - Supplemental Insurance
   - Third-Party Insurance
   - Insured Service
   - Uninsured Service
   - Schedule of Benefits
   - Limited Use Drugs
   - Drug Benefit Formulary
   - Private Billing
   - CPSO Number
   - Billing Number
   - WSIB
   - MOHLTC
   - IFH
   - PSHCP
   - UHIP
5. Sort alphabetically.

Project 2

UNINSURED MEDICAL BILLING

LEARNING OBJECTIVES

- Creating a patient spreadsheet
- Creating an invoice and receipt for uninsured hospital billing
- Creating an invoice and receipt for uninsured physician billing
- Creating an invoice and receipt for third-party billing
- Completing a Workplace Safety and Insurance Board form
- Completing a Universal Health Insurance Plan form
- Completing a Public Service Health Care Plan form
- Understanding medical billing workbook terminology
- Billing Quebec, non-insured, or out-of-country patients using OMA-approved fees
- Understanding block fees

This project introduces medical billing for uninsured services.

Uninsured services are those services not covered by a provincial or territorial health care plan. In Ontario, it is those services not covered by OHIP, and the patient uses a third-party insurance provider for full or partial coverage. The patient is responsible for paying uncovered amounts.

Physicians can charge patients for uninsured services that take the physician's time and resources, such as providing sick notes, providing prescription refills over the telephone, or copying and transferring medical records. This charge is referred to as a block fee. Fees are posted in physician offices so that the patients are aware there will be a cost involved for the service. The Ontario Medical Association also provides a list of uninsured fees.

TASK 1

PATIENTS – STUDENT SPREADSHEET

RESOURCES: Appendix C – Patients – BMC Spreadsheet
Appendix C – Patients – Student Spreadsheet
Appendix I – Patients – BMC Spreadsheet
Appendix I – Patients – Student Spreadsheet

To be able to work with patients throughout the projects, you must create a patient spreadsheet to have your own patients.

Your instructor may prefer you use the BMC spreadsheet; however, you may be responsible for creating your own set of unique patients in order not to conflict with other students.

Note: If you have undertaken this Patient Student Spreadsheet task previously in the *Medical Office Administration: Simulated Projects* workbook, you should transfer your work rather than repeat the task.

Using the student spreadsheet, create 20 new patients using the criteria below:

- Patients 1 to 4 – Family 1 – select the same unique last name, and create an alias (nickname) for Patient 1.
- Patients 5 and 6 – Family 2 – parents of Patient 4 – select the same unique last name.
- Patients 7 to 9 – Family 3 – select the same unique last name.
- Patients 10 and 11 – Family 4 – select the same unique last name, and create an alias for Patient 10.
- Patients 12 to 15 – Family 5 – select the same unique last name, and create an alias for Patient 12.
- Patient 16 – Family 6 – an out-of-province patient
- Patient 17 – Family 7 – an out-of-province patient
- Patient 18 – Family 8 – a Quebec patient – female (RAMQ)
- Patient 19 – Family 9 – a WSIB Ontario patient
- Patient 20 – Family 10 – a foreign student
- Create a unique last name, first name, and middle initial for each of the patients under the appropriate column headings.
- Create the date of birth by choosing a unique month and a day with two digits to add to the year already indicated in the column.
- Create a unique street address that has a 3-digit house number, e.g., 115.
- Use your city and your province except for Patients 16, 17, 18, and 20.
- Create unique postal codes – Ottawa postal codes should start with K, and out-of-province patients should have appropriate area codes for the city chosen.
- Create unique home, work, or cellphone numbers – Ottawa is area code 613.
- OHIP numbers have 10 digits – For our purposes, create unique OHIP numbers except for Patients 16, 17, 18, and 20 – OHIP numbers should begin with the 3-digit street address number (e.g., 108), a 2-digit month of birth (e.g., 03), a 2-digit day of birth (e.g., 31), and the first three numbers of the birth year (e.g., 195 for the year 1958). The OHIP number would be 1080331195. Note: In any EMR system,

invalid health card numbers will appear in red. Please ensure your health card numbers are invalid for the purposes of this workbook.

- The version code for an Ontario patient is the first initials of the patient's first and last name.
- The health card for the Quebec patient (Patient 18 on your spreadsheet) will be as follows:
  - The first four characters are the first three letters of the last name (e.g., JOH) followed by the first letter of the first name (e.g., C).
  - The next four digits are the last two digits of the year of birth (e.g., 58) and the month of birth (e.g., 12). Since the cardholder is a female, the number 50 is added to the year of birth, i.e., 12 + 50 = 62. So 62 would be the last set of digits in the first four numbers.
  - The last four digits are the day of birth and an administrative code used by the Régie (e.g., 2510). Use administrative code 10 for your example.
  - There is no version code for Quebec.
  - The Quebec health card number would be JOHC 5862 2510.
  - Note: If the patient is female, the maiden name will be the last name used on the card.
- For the two out-of-province patients (Patients 16 and 17), create the fictitious information based upon your research in Task 1.
- For Accuro®EMR purposes, create relationships within the families, such as husband, wife, brother, sister, aunt, or common law partner.

TASK 2

UNINSURED HOSPITAL BILLING

RESOURCES: Appendix D – Hope General Invoice Template
Appendix D – Hope General Receipt Template
Appendix E – Hope General Invoice Sample
Appendix E – Hope General Receipt Sample
Appendix I – Hope General Invoice
Appendix I – Hope General Receipt

Not all hospital services are insured; therefore, patients are responsible for payment either in advance of a service or immediately following a service being rendered. Hospitals will provide lists of those services not covered by OHIP.

Following is a list of information required to complete the invoice and receipt:

- Patient 4 required a hospital bed and has requested a private room.
- Patient 4 is billed for four days.
- Hope General Hospital charges $225 for private hospital rooms.
- HST is not charged on hospital services.
- Create a Hope General Hospital invoice for Patient 4.
- Create a Hope General Hospital receipt as Patient 4 paid before discharge, and Patient 4 paid in cash.
- Use today's date on both the invoice and the receipt.

TASK 3

UNINSURED PHYSICIAN BILLING

RESOURCES: Appendix D – BMC Invoice Template
Appendix D – BMC Receipt Template
Appendix E – BMC Invoice Sample
Appendix E – BMC Receipt Sample
Appendix I – BMC Invoice
Appendix I – BMC Receipt

Not all physician services are insured; therefore, patients are responsible for payment either in advance of a service or immediately following a service rendered. Physicians will provide lists of those services not covered by OHIP.

Following is a list of information required to complete the invoice and receipt:

- Patient 11 required a mole removal from the left ear.
- Dr. Cathy Paste provided the service at BMC today at 2:00 p.m.
- The cost of a mole removal was $120.
- HST is applicable.
- Create a BMC invoice for mole removal for Patient 11.
- Create a BMC receipt for Patient 11, assuming the mole removal was completed and the patient paid cash immediately following the procedure.
- Use the today's date on both the invoice and the receipt.

TASK 4

THIRD-PARTY BILLING

RESOURCES: Appendix D – BMC Invoice Template
Appendix D – BMC Receipt Template
Appendix D – Extended Health Care Template
Appendix E – BMC Invoice Sample
Appendix E – BMC Receipt Sample
Appendix E – Extended Health Care Sample
Appendix I – BMC Invoice
Appendix I – BMC Receipt
Appendix I – Extended Health Care Form

Uninsured services can be submitted to third-party insurance providers. For the purposes of this workbook, Healthy Life Insurance Co. is the provider. The third-party insurer may pay up to 100 percent of the service, depending on the insurance company's payment reimbursement schedule. Invoices for services can be sent directly to the third-party insurance provider or can be paid by the patient at the time of the service. If the patient pays for the service, the patient is responsible for submitting a claim for reimbursement of the medical expense. For the purpose of this task, we are assuming the patient is paying the clinic first and subsequently submitting a claim to Healthy Life Insurance Co.

Following is a list of information required to complete the invoice, receipt, and insurance form:

- Patient 7 had massage therapy sessions at BMC on the following dates: May 6, May 13, May 20, and May 27, at a cost of $72 per session. Each appointment was at 1:00 p.m.

- Crystal Fielding, RMT, administered the therapy.
- Create a BMC invoice for Patient 7 for the month of May, listing all treatment dates and costs.
- HST is not applicable.
- Create a BMC receipt for Patient 7 on May 27, covering all of the massages in May. Assume Patient 7 uses Visa to pay for the massages. Patient 7's Visa number is: 4560 1934 4242 6565, Expiry Nov. 20xx.
- Complete a Healthy Life Insurance Co. claim for Patient 7 for the four massage therapy sessions in the month of May.
- Contract number: 050530
- Member ID number: 20124819
- Employer: McLeod Brothers & Associates
- Preferred language: English
- All receipts are Canadian.
- Patient 7 does not have a work-related or motor vehicle-related injury.
- Patient 7 does not have any other supplemental insurance.
- Use today's date.

TASK 5

WSIB FORM 8

RESOURCES: Appendix D – WSIB Form 8 Template
Appendix E – WSIB Form 8 Sample
Appendix I – WSIB Form 8

Any time there is a workplace accident resulting in an injury, the Workplace Safety and Insurance Board must be notified. A WSIB Form 8 must be completed within three days of the accident or an injury involving health care treatment, time away from work, or lost wages. WSIB has a Physician Fee Schedule, which can be found on the WSIB website. Code 8M is used for the submission of a health professional's report in paper format.

- Complete a WSIB Form 8 for Patient 3.
- Assume Dr. Fred Bones, Orthopedic Surgeon, completed Patient 3's examination during the ER visit at Hope General Hospital.
- (A) Patient and Employer Information: Patient 3's information from patient database; Social Insurance Number (SIN): 521 389 210; Language: English; Employer Name: Jones Construction
- (B) Incident Date and Details Section: Kyle was dismounting from workplace scaffolding and slipped to the ground, hurting his right lower leg; Occupation: Labourer; Date of Incident: today's date
- (C) Clinical Information Section: (1) Area of Injury: Lower Leg; (2) Description of Injury/Illness Physical Examination Findings: Pain Rating is 1; Fracture; (3) Not aware of any pre-existing conditions; (4) Diagnosis: Right lower leg fracture
- (D) Treatment Plan:
  - (1) Casting; elevation and no wt. bearing one wk; physio and removal of cast: 6 wks
  - (2) Work Injury/Illness Medications: Acetaminophen as required

- (3) Investigations & Referrals: X-rays; Other – Physiotherapist; Name of Referral or Facility: Raymond Wasylenki, Brooklane Medical Centre; Telephone: 613-224-2308; Appointment Date: 6 wks from today
- (E) Billing Section:
  - Health Professional Designation: Physician
  - Service Code: Already completed
  - WSIB Provider ID: 123790135
  - HST Registration No.: Not required
  - HST Amount Billed: Not applicable
  - Service Code: Already completed
  - Your Invoice No.: HGH0013
  - Service Date: Today's date
  - Health Professional Name: Dr. Fred Bones, Orthopedic Surgeon
  - Address: Brooklane Medical Centre, 33 Brooklane Ave., Ottawa, ON K2B 6M7
  - Telephone: 613-224-2308
  - Fax: 613-224-2300
- (F) Return to Work Information:
  - (1) Have discussed return to work with patient
  - (2) This patient is not able to work because of workplace injury/illness (Explanation: Work return discussed in six-week assessment)
  - (3) Worker's status and functional ability: Able to: Bend/Twist, Use of Upper Extremities, Sit; Unable to: Climb, Kneel, Lift, Operate Heavy Equipment, Operate a Motor Vehicle, Push/Pull, Stand, Use of Public Transportation, Walk
  - (4) Limitations for 14+ days
  - (5) Followup Appointment – Six wks from today

TASK 6 UNIVERSAL HEALTH INSURANCE PLAN (UHIP)

RESOURCES: Appendix D – Healthy Life Insurance Co. UHIP Template
Appendix E – Healthy Life Insurance Co. UHIP Sample
Appendix I – Healthy Life UHIP Insurance Co. Form

Hospital and medical expenses incurred by full-time foreign students, with a permanent Canadian residence, attending university in Canada can be covered by UHIP if the student is registered with an accredited participating university. For the purposes of this task, assume Healthy Life Insurance Co. is the contract holder for UHIP.

Assume Patient 20 is enrolled in UHIP through Flaherty University located in your city. Assume this university is registered with the province as a participating institution in UHIP.

Patient 20 arrived at BMC with an apparent ankle sprain. Dr. Fred Bones, Orthopedic Surgeon, was in the clinic and was available to examine Patient 20, who was diagnosed with a left ankle sprain. Dr. Bones fitted Patient 20 with a walking cast boot; the cost of the boot was $215.00. HST is not charged if a physician provides a prescription for the cast.

Complete the Healthy Life Insurance Co. form for Patient 20 using the following additional information:

- The patient does not have additional health coverage.
- The patient's Member Identification Number is 165229.
- The patient's email address is patient20@gmail.emp.ca.
- The service date is today's date at 3:00 p.m.
- Dr. Bones examined the patient at the clinic.
- The provider ID number for the purposes of this exercise is the physician's billing number.
- As you have not yet familiarized yourself with the Schedule of Benefits (Procedures Codes) and Resource Manual for Physicians (Diagnosis Codes), the codes for billing were provided for you to be able to complete the form (Provincial Billing Procedure Codes): an orthopedic consultation (code A065) for a cost of $83.20, and a diagnostic code of 845 (ankle sprain).
- Payment is to be made directly to the provider.

TASK 7

PUBLIC SERVICE HEALTH CARE PLAN (PSHCP)

RESOURCES: Appendix D – PSHCP Template
Appendix E – PSHCP Sample
Appendix I – PSHCP Form

Uninsured hospital and medical expenses incurred by members of the public service, such as the RCMP and the Department of National Defence (DND), are covered through a third-party biller. For the purposes of this task, Healthy Life Insurance Co. is the contract holder for the PSHCP.

Assume Patient 6 required an uninsurable shingles vaccination (Zostavax) and had the injection administered by Dr. Kyle Thomas, General Practitioner at BMC.

Assume Patient 6 paid $205 for the vaccination at a local pharmacy to have it administered today at BMC. There is no cost to Patient 6 for the injection; however, Patient 6 will be submitting the vaccination cost for reimbursement through a supplemental insurance provider.

Complete the Healthy Life Insurance Co. PSHCP form for Patient 6 using the following additional information:

- The patient does not have additional health coverage other than Healthy Life insurance.
- The service date is today's date at 4:00 p.m.
- This was not a workplace or motor vehicle-related injury.
- All receipts are Canadian.
- The plan is his member plan.
- The certificate number for Patient 6 is 2985736.

TASK 8

MEDICAL BILLING WORKBOOK – TERMINOLOGY

RESOURCE: Medical Billing Workbook

It is essential that a medical billing specialist be familiar with the terminology that is encountered when undertaking medical billing.

1. Add the following terms to Column A in the **Terminology** Sheet of the Medical Billing Workbook.
   - Deregulated (Delisted) Service
   - Fee-for-Service
   - Regulated Medical Service
   - Medically-Necessary Service
   - Hospital Billing
   - EMR
   - Block Fee
   - OMA Billing
2. In Column B, provide a definition in your own words.
3. Sort alphabetically.

Project 3

HEALTH CARDS

LEARNING OBJECTIVES

- Managing provincial/territorial health care coverage
- Completing a spreadsheet on provincial and territorial health cards
- Researching provincial and territorial health card images
- Understanding the Ontario Health Insurance Document Coverage List
- Understanding the Registered Persons Database (RPDB)
- Understanding health card eligibility in Ontario
- Learning about payment of premiums in health cards
- Understanding identification numbers in health cards
- Defining elements of health cards
- Understanding how to update and revise health cards
- Describing the most common forms in the medical office (MOHLTC forms)
- Understanding how a health card is validated
- Describing methods of health card validation
- Understanding real-time health card and batch validation of health cards
- Understanding health card response codes
- Researching medical billing websites

This project provides an understanding of the provincial and territorial health card systems.

Health cards – managing provincial/territorial health care coverage

Patients are required to present a health card before receiving medical services.

Each province or territory has its own application form. When applying for Ontario coverage (OHIP), applicants must provide documents in three categories:

- Proof of Canadian citizenship or immigration status
- Proof of residency
- Supporting documentation for personal identity

In Ontario, applicants must present in person to a ServiceOntario Centre with the required documentation in hand.

Ontario residents may possess a red and white card, which does not have a photograph on it, or the newer green health card, which contains a photograph. Red and white health cards do not have an expiry date and may or may not have a version code.

If a health card is deemed invalid, the patient will be advised when registering for an appointment to have the health card replaced. When validating health cards with the MOHLTC, invalid cards will be flagged and messages sent to the medical office; this will be discussed further in this project.

Upon registration, a card deemed to be lost or stolen should be kept by the medical office assistant and appropriately destroyed. This procedure may vary by facility. In Ontario, any health card fraudulency must be reported to the MOHLTC.

All provinces and territories, with the exception of Quebec, have signed a reciprocal billing agreement. Physicians are paid at their own provincial/territorial rate for services provided, which will be discussed later in this workbook in Project 9, under Claims Submission. Reciprocal billing is voluntary and physicians may opt to receive payment upon rendering services rather than using the reciprocal billing process, therefore making the patient responsible for the cost of services.

Quebec patients pay for their services and make claims through the Quebec Ministry for reimbursement. Some offices may choose to directly bill the Quebec Ministry and accept payment even though the rates are significantly lower than other provinces and territories.

Should a patient not have a health card, payment must be made to the physician, and it is the patient's responsibility to submit the receipt to the Ministry for reimbursement.

TASK 1

PROVINCIAL AND TERRITORIAL HEALTH CARDS

RESOURCE: Appendix I – Provincial and Territorial Health Cards

Canadians regularly travel within the country's provinces and territories. Patients with different health cards may require health care within any medical facility across the country. It is essential that health care workers be familiar with health cards for the provinces and territories.

Note: If you have undertaken this task in the *Medical Office Administration: Simulated Projects* workbook, you will not be required to repeat this task; however, the task should be copied to this assignment.

- Using the document provided in Appendix I, complete the table for provincial and territorial health cards.

TASK 2

PROVINCIAL AND TERRITORIAL HEALTH CARD IMAGES

Note: If you have undertaken this task in the *Medical Office Administration: Simulated Projects* workbook, you will not be required to repeat this task; however, the assignment from the workbook is required to undertake this task.

- Search the Internet for images of health cards from each province and territory.
- Create an MS Word table.
- Each row should contain a cell with a photo of a province's health card image and a cell labelling the province/territory.

TASK 3

ONTARIO HEALTH INSURANCE DOCUMENT COVERAGE LIST

The Ontario Health Insurance Document Coverage List details the identification categories required when applying for an Ontario health card.

- Search for Ontario Central Forms Repository.
- Search for Ontario Health Insurance Document Coverage List.
- Print the Ontario Health Insurance Coverage Document List, which details the three categories of identification required for the Ontario health card application.

Health cards – Registered Persons Database (RPDB)

Information on each registered person is collected on a standardized registration form issued by the Ministry and stored as electronic data on the Registered Persons Database (RPDB). In Ontario, every eligible person who applies for Ontario Health Insurance Plan coverage is assigned a permanent and unique health number, also referred to as a health services number (HSN).

The Registered Persons Database can be accessed only by Ministry-approved organizations and their personnel.

Health cards – eligibility in Ontario

The criteria for an Ontario health card, as regulated by the MOHLTC, are detailed in the Ontario Health Insurance Coverage Document List:

- Canadian citizen (registered at birth or upon citizenship)
- Permanent resident
- Landed immigrant
- Physically present in Ontario for 153 days in a 12-month period
- Physically present in Ontario for at least 153 days of the first 183 days immediately after establishing residency in the province
- Primary place of residence in Ontario

OHIP coverage normally becomes effective three months after the date that residency is established in Ontario. The Ministry encourages new and returning residents to purchase private health insurance in the event of illness during the OHIP waiting period.

When a person relocates to another province or territory, OHIP will provide coverage for a period of three months while the covered person waits for health insurance to be effective in the new province or territory.

All newborns born in Ontario are eligible for OHIP. Temporary health card numbers are provided until the birth certificate can be registered by completing an Ontario Health Coverage Infant Registration form. The form provides a pre-printed health number assigned to the baby. This record is kept until the Ontario permanent health card is received by mail. The temporary and permanent health cards possess the same health card number.

Adopted children are considered new registrants, and an application would be filed for a new health card number. The medical biller must ensure that the health card is valid.

Health cards – payment of premiums

In Ontario, payment for OHIP is income-based. Those with a lower income could be exempt from paying any premiums. The Ontario Health Premium is paid through Ontario's personal income tax system when a person files an annual income tax return.

Health cards – identification numbers

Each health card has a personal identification number on it.

Depending on the province or territory, this number ranges from 7 to 12 digits. In Ontario, each person is assigned a health card number for life; however, updating a card for reasons such as a name change will result in a change in the version code. In Ontario, the version code consists of two letters. Version codes reduce the risk of health card fraud.

A health card is an important personal document that must be treated as private and confidential.

Health cards – elements

Each province or territory will determine the necessary information required on the health card, as well as the application process. The elements included on an Ontario health card are:

- Health card number (HCN)
- Version code (not on all red and white Ontario health cards)
- Date of birth (DOB)
- Sex
- Expiry date/renewal date (not on red and white Ontario health cards)
- Photo identification (with signature) – not on red and white health cards. When a health card is issued in a long-term care facility, where a patient cannot physically access a ServiceOntario location, the photo is replaced with a trillium symbol.

After the expiry date, the health card is invalid and must be renewed. The renewal is the cardholder's responsibility.

It is illegal to ask someone to show a health card for identification purposes (e.g., cashing a cheque, applying for a credit card, or proof of age).

Health cards – updating and revising cards

Health cards must be updated under the following circumstances:

- Name change
- Address change
- Gender change
- Damaged card
- Lost card
- Stolen card
- Expired card

Ministry forms

The most common forms used in medical offices for medical billing purposes are:

- Registration for Ontario Health Coverage
- Health Card Re-Registration
- Health Card Renewal
- Change of Address
- Change of Information
- Out-of-Province, Out-of-Country Claim Submission

TASK 4

MOHLTC CHANGE OF ADDRESS FORM

Patient 10 has just moved and is required to notify the MOHLTC of a change of address.

1. Go to the MOHLTC website (Central Forms Repository) and locate the Change of Address Notification Form.
2. Complete the Change of Address Form using the fictitious information below:

   New address: 208 McElroy Drive, Kanata, ON K2L 3A4

   Move date: One month from today

   Home telephone: 613-123-4567

   Business telephone: 613-246-8101
3. Patient 10's spouse is also changing address.
4. Complete the PDF form.

Validation of health cards

Health card validation (HCV) allows a heath care provider to access the Ministry's Registered Person Database (RPDB) to determine the status of a health number and health card version code when presented at the point of service.

In a hospital setting, patients with an invalid card can be turned away and rescheduled if the reason for presenting to the hospital is not urgent. In the hospital Emergency Department, a patient is seen but must sign a Release of Health Card

Information form. Invalid cards are one of the most common reasons for claims rejection.

A person's health number and version code is considered personal health information under the *Personal Health Information Protection Act* (PHIPA).

TASK 5

RELEASE OF HEALTH CARD INFORMATION FORM

Patient 10 is booked for surgery and arrives at Brooklane Medical Centre for a pre-admission appointment. Patient 10 arrives without a health card. The appointment will not proceed without the patient signing a Release of Health Card Information.

- Search on the MOHLTC website (Ontario Central Forms Repository) for the Health Number Release Form.
- Complete the form using Patient 10's details.
- Use information from Task 2.
- The physician's name is Dr. Paul Blue, Cardiologist, Brooklane Medical Centre.
- Section 2 will be filled out as the Facility, not the Provider.
- The facility number for BMC is 3003.
- The date of service is today's date.

Methods of Health Card Validation (HCV)

There are currently two methods of access for Health Card Validation:

- Real-time validation: HCV Web Service, Interactive Voice Response, and Health Card Reader Software Application
- Batch validation: Overnight Batch Eligibility Checking (OBEC)

Real-time validation of health cards

There are three types of real-time (immediate) validation of health cards. To use these services, the health care provider must be a registered user. The MOHLTC does not send or receive emails or facsimiles for confidentiality reasons. The Ministry will provide the message "Valid Health Card" if there are no errors, and should there by an error with the card, whether it be version code or out of date, to name a few, an explanation and error code will be provided.

The three types of real-time validation are:

- Interactive Voice Response (IVR) – Service available 24/7 using a touch-tone phone to call a toll-free number. A provider MUST apply for IVR participation. The IVR system cannot be used with a cellular phone because the confidential data transmitted may be intercepted by others.
- Health Card Reader (HCR)/Point-of-Service (POS) Device – a range of devices, called magnetic card readers or point-of-service devices, are available for health card validation. These devices can be used alone or incorporated into the office's software program. This method of access for health card validation is not available to new vendors and is best suited for high-volume users.

- Health Card Validation (HCV) Web Service: The Ministry verifies card numbers via the Electronic Business Service (EBS), which is an Internet-enabled service that can be accessed from any computer using third-party software. The HCV Web Service provides a more secure service to validate the eligibility of a patient's health card in real time against Ministry databases. The HCV Web Service is available 24/7 with the exception of weekly scheduled system maintenance.

TASK 6

INTERACTIVE VOICE RESPONSE (IVR)

Complete an Application for IVR Participation by locating the application on the MOHLTC website (Ontario Central Forms Repository).

Use the following information:

- Complete on behalf of Dr. Paul Blue, Cardiologist, at the Brooklane Medical Centre.
- The MOHLTC registration number is Dr. Blue's billing number.
- Where a date is required, use today's date.

Batch validation of health cards – Overnight Batch Eligibility Checking (OBEC)

OBEC is used to validate a health number and version code before a health service is provided, reducing the potential for claims rejections. The health numbers and version codes are inputted and batched into formatted files to be electronically submitted to the Ministry. Eligibility is verified against the Ministry's database based on the date the file is submitted. A response file is returned to the user the next business day.

OBEC uses the Medical Claims Electronic Data Transfer (MC EDT) service and the current Electronic Data Transfer (EDT) service for the electronic transmission of batches of files from the medical service provider's EMR system to the Ministry's mainframe computer.

Health care providers validate health card eligibility for pre-scheduled appointments for referred patients, for out-of-town patients, and for patients who have had claims rejected in the past. Pre-validating with OBEC emphasizes any discrepancies with patients either before or during their office visit, to identify where direct billing may be necessary.

Response codes

An HCV response code is generated by the Ministry's mainframe as part of the HCV process. The HCV response code provides the status of a health card.

In the event of suspected fraud, the health care provider must contact the Ministry Fraud Line.

TASK 7

WEBSITES

RESOURCE: Medical Billing Workbook

It is essential that a medical billing specialist be familiar with websites that are encountered when undertaking medical billing. Add the following websites to your Medical Billing Workbook within the sheets indicated in brackets.

- ServiceOntario (Insured)
- OHIP Health Card Validation Reference Manual (Insured)
- Ontario Central Forms Repository (Insured)
- MOHLTC Registered Persons Database (RPDB) (Insured)
- Ontario Health Card Validation Reference Manual (Insured)
- Interactive Voice Response Form (Insured)
- Interactive Voice Response Manual (Insured)
- MOHTLC Fraud Line (Regulators)

TASK 8

TERMINOLOGY

RESOURCE: Medical Billing Workbook

1. Add the following terminology to the Medical Billing Workbook **Terminology** sheet:
   - HSN
   - HCN
   - RPDB
   - Version Code
   - Validation
   - Real-Time Validation
   - IVR
   - Batch Validation
   - OBEC
   - Response Codes
2. Sort alphabetically.

Project 4

CODES

LEARNING OBJECTIVES

- Understanding the types of codes and their purposes
- Understanding and defining specialty codes
- Understanding procedure codes (prefixes, numeric component, suffixes)
- Understanding premium codes
- Understanding diagnosis codes
- Understanding diagnostic and therapeutic procedure codes
- Understanding and defining provincial/territorial codes
- Understanding facility number, master numbers, and group numbers
- Researching medical terminology and billing codes

This project discusses the codes involved in medical billing. It is essential to understand the types of codes and their purpose to accomplish the role of medical biller.

Codes

Medical billing is based upon the submission of codes to the Ministry. The accuracy and completeness of the submission ensures the physician is reimbursed accordingly. It is a very complex process and familiarization with the Schedule of Benefits and Physicians Resource Manual is essential. The Ministry also provides assistance should you have questions. **It is better to ask than to submit a claim erroneously.**

A code is an identification number (consisting of letters, numbers, or a combination of letters and numbers). There are a variety of codes used in the submission of claims to the Ministry, and the medical biller must be familiar with the types of codes and their purposes.

Medical billing uses Ministry-approved codes to bill for **medically-necessary** physician services. If there are errors in these codes, the claim will be rejected by the Ministry, and explanations will be provided for the claim to be revised and resubmitted for payment.

Following are the codes used in medical billing:

Specialty Codes

Every physician practises in a specialty area; therefore, a physician is a specialist and the Specialty Codes identify the area of specialty. Following are examples of Specialty Codes:

- Family Practice, General Practice 00
- Anaesthesia 01
- Dermatology 02
- General Surgery 03
- Neurosurgery 04
- Community Medicine 05

Each area of specialty has its own specialty code. Consultations and visits by patients to specialists are listed in the Schedule of Benefits by the area of specialty and Specialty Code. Generally, the Specialty Code is part of the Procedure Code for consultations and assessments. For example, the code for a consultation by a family practice physician is A005. The 00 is the Specialty Code. Emergency Medicine is the exception; an Emergency Department consultation falls under the Specialty Code for Community Medicine, and the code is H055A, even though the Specialty Code for Emergency Medicine is 12. Procedure Codes for services are specific to the area of specialty, which will be explained next.

Claims can be rejected if the Procedure Code for the service rendered does not match a service that would be provided within that particular specialty. For example, an optometrist cannot bill for an orthopedic procedure. The Ministry would reject the claim. Medical billers check codes for accuracy prior to submission to the Ministry.

TASK 1

SPECIALTY CODES

RESOURCES: Medical Billing Workbook
MOHTLC Schedule of Benefits

It is essential for medical billing purposes to have access to and understand all the specialty areas of physicians and the Specialty Codes assigned to each specialty area.

1. Rename a sheet in the Medical Billing workbook as **Specialty Codes**.
2. Apply a colour to the tab.
3. Create two columns:
   - Specialty Code (Column A)
   - Area of Specialty (Column B)
4. Using the Internet, locate the MOHLTC Schedule of Benefits' List of Specialty Codes to complete the sheet.
5. Sort numerically by code number.

Procedure Codes

A Procedure Code is the billing code for the service performed by the registered physician or health care professional on an insured patient. Procedure Codes are the codes used for claim submission to the Ministry, and are published in the Schedule of Benefits by the MOHLTC.

A Procedure Code is alphanumeric, and reflects the treatment performed by the health care professional and determines the fee to be paid by the health care plan. Note that Procedure Codes are often referred to as Service Codes. For the purposes of this workbook, we have opted to refer to billing codes as Procedure Codes, which matches the terminology of Accuro®EMR.

In Ontario, a Procedure Code consists of five alphanumeric characters – a prefix (one character), a numeric component (three characters), and a suffix (one character).

When a Procedure Code is no longer deemed medically necessary, it becomes a deregulated or delisted code. It is essential that the medical biller stay current by reading the Ministry InfoBulletins.

Prefixes

A prefix is a letter that appears first in the Procedure Code. It denotes the type of assessment, where the assessment occurred, or the speciality of the provider.

There are four different prefixes used in the **Consultations and Visits** section of the Schedule of Benefits: A, C, W, and H, which are used in the following five health care environments.

1. **General Listing** – consultation or assessment except if the service has been provided at an acute care hospital, long-term care facility, emergency department, or rehabilitation unit. Use an **A** prefix.
2. **Acute Care Hospital** – non-emergency in-patient services. Use a **C** prefix.

3. **Long-Term Care Institution** – non-emergency in-patient services. Use a **W** prefix.
4. **Emergency Department** – services rendered by a physician on duty. Use an **H** prefix.
5. **Rehabilitation Unit** – services rendered by a specialist in Physical Medicine. Use an **H** prefix.

There are other prefixes in the Schedule of Benefits that you will encounter as you familiarize yourself with the contents.

TASK 2

PREFIXES

RESOURCES: Medical Billing Workbook
MOHLTC Schedule of Benefits

1. Rename a sheet in the Medical Billing Workbook as **Prefixes.**
2. Add a colour to the tab.
3. Create two columns:
   - Prefix (Column A)
   - Description (Column B)
4. Add the following codes in Column A:
   - A
   - B
   - C
   - D
   - E
   - F
   - G
   - H
   - J
   - K
   - L
   - M
   - N
   - P
   - Q
   - R
   - S
   - U
   - W
   - X
   - Z
5. Using the MOHLTC Schedule of Benefits, describe each prefix in the Prefixes sheet as you encounter definitions throughout the workbook. Note: There is more than one description in some cases for the use of the prefix; record the various descriptions as you encounter them.

Numeric component

The numeric component, following the prefix, identifies the service provided to the patient by the health care professional; it usually consists of three unique numbers. An example of a numeric component would be XX5 (consultation).

Assessments and consultations relate to the initial visit by the patient. The Schedule of Benefits details in the General Preamble the definition of each. Note: Each specialty has its own type of assessments and not all are the same for each specialty. **Always refer to each specialty area for the appropriate consultation and assessment codes.**

A consultation is generally the initial encounter with a patient to gather a complete medical history. A consultation with a specialist requires a written referral from the original referring physician. For a specialist to bill for a consultation, a written referral by the referring physician must be provided to the specialist and be available upon request by the Ministry.

An assessment, whether specific or general, is performed by the physician to determine a diagnosis in order to determine a treatment plan. An assessment requires a full medical history of the patient, in addition to an examination.

Following is a list of the most common consultations and assessments that are contained within the scenarios in Project 7:

Consultation

- Service is provided upon written request from a referring physician who requests the opinion of another physician competent to provide advice
- For Family Medicine and the Emergency Department, consultations do not require referrals
- Physician must perform a general or specific assessment, which involves a complete medical history and an examination
- Ends in the number 5

  Examples:

  - A005 – Family Practice Consultation
  - C615 – Hematology In-Patient Consultation
  - W075 – Geriatric Long-Term In-Patient Consultation

Repeat Consultation

- Additional consultation rendered by the same physician regarding the same problem
- Ends in the number 6

  Examples:

  - A616 – Hematology Repeat Consultation
  - C186 – Neurology In-Patient Repeat Consultation
  - W186 – Neurology Long-Term Care In-Patient Repeat Consultation

Limited Consultation

- Requires less time than a full consultation (e.g., a plantar wart does not take as long as an infectious disease assessment)
- Ends in the number 5

  Examples:

  - A255 – Endocrinology and Metabolism Limited Consultation
  - C655 – Hematology In-Patient Limited Consultation

Emergency Department Physician Consultation

- Does not require a referral
- Begins with an H
- Ends in the number 5

  Example:

  - H055 – Emergency Department Consultation

Special Surgical Consultation

- Surgeon provides a consultation prior to surgery lasting at least 50 minutes per surgery
- Ends in the number 5

  Examples:
  - A935 – Neurosurgery Special Surgical Consultation
  - C935 – Orthopedic In-Patient Special Surgical Consultation

Special Palliative Care Consultation

- Requested for specialized management for palliative care
- Minimum of 50 minutes with patient or patient's representative in consultation
- Service includes a psycho-social assessment, comprehensive review of pharmacotherapy, counselling, and consideration of community services required
- Start and stop times must be recorded
- If the consultation exceeds 50 minutes, other premium codes can be utilized (e.g., K023)
- Ends in the number 5

  Example:
  - A945 – Family Practice Special Palliative Care Consultation

General Assessment

- Family practice service, which includes a full history and an examination
- Ends in the number 3

  Example:
  - A003 – Family Practice General Assessment

General Reassessment

- Does not include a patient's history as this is part of the initial General Assessment
- For Family Practice
- Ends in the number 4

  Example:
  - A004 – Family Practice General Reassessment

Periodic Health Visit (Annual Checkup)

- Takes place after second birthday
- Limited to one per year by any one physician
- Codes are different for Family Practice physicians and Pediatric physicians
- Begins with K

  Examples:
  - K017 – child for Family Practice
  - K267 – child for Pediatrics

Specific Assessment and Medical-Specific Assessment

- Rendered by specialists
- Require a full history and detailed examination to make a diagnosis

- Ends in the number 3

  Examples:
  - A203 – Obs/Gynie Specific Assessment
  - C063 – Orthopedics Specific Assessment
  - A263 – Medical-Specific Assessment
  - C603 – Cardiology Medical-Specific Assessment

Specific Re-Assessment and Medical-Specific Re-Assessment

- Rendered by specialists
- Require a full history and examination of one or more systems
- Limited to two per patient per physician per year except for hospital admissions
- Ends in the number 4

  Examples:
  - A154 – Endocrinology Medical-Specific Re-Assessment
  - C464 – Infectious Disease Medical Specific Re-Assessment
  - C094 – Cardiac Surgery Specific Re-Assessment

Comprehensive Consultation

- Some specialty areas have comprehensive consultations specific to the specialty
- Ensure you refer to each specialty area until you are familiar with the codes

  Examples:
  - A775 – Comprehensive Geriatric Medical Consultation
  - C460 – Comprehensive Infectious Disease Consultation

Complex Medical Specific Re-Assessment

- Re-assessment of a patient due to the seriousness of the patient's condition
- Limited to four per patient per physician per year
- Ends in the number 1

  Examples:
  - A611 – Hematology Complex Medical Re-Assessment
  - C181 – Neurology Complex Medical Re-Assessment

Partial Assessment

- History of the complaint and the necessary examination and advice
- Ends in the number 4

  Example:
  - A024 – Dermatology Partial Assessment

Non-Emergency Acute Care Hospital In-Patient Services

- Consultations and assessment rendered to admitted patients on a non-emergency basis
- Begins with C

  Example:
  - C185 – Neurology In-Patient Consultation

Suffixes

A suffix is the last letter in a Procedure Code. It identifies who provided the service.

The suffix can be:

- A for physician performing the procedure
- B for physician assisting at the surgery
- C for physician administering the anesthetic

TASK 3

SUFFIXES

RESOURCES: Medical Billing Workbook
MOHLTC Schedule of Benefits

1. Rename a sheet in the Medical Billing Workbook as **Suffixes**.
2. Add a colour to the tab.
3. Create two columns:
   - Suffix Code (Column A)
   - Description (Column B)
4. Add the following codes in Column A.
   - A
   - B
   - C
5. Using the MOHLTC Schedule of Benefits, complete the sheet.

Sample Procedure Code

An example of a complete Procedure Code number is A005A:

A Physician's office/hospital out-patient clinic

005 Consultation for family practice physicians

A Service provided by physician

Common practice is not to include the suffix (A), as it is the default in the EMR system (A005). The suffix would only be included in the EMR system if the service was performed by someone other than the physician configured within the software. The medical biller should ensure that the correct physician is the default in the system when creating a claim. The default can be changed in the system through dropdown menus.

Diagnosis Codes

Diagnosis Codes represent the reason for the patient encounter, e.g., migraines, and the subsequent physician diagnosis. The specialist treats the patient based upon the diagnosis.

Diagnosis Codes for physicians usually consist of three numbers. The Resource Manual for Physicians contains a list of most commonly used Diagnosis Codes. Some Diagnosis Codes consist of four number characters, such as in the physiotherapy specialty; however, we have opted to focus on the specialties with three numbers.

When undertaking medical billing and preparing a claim, there must be a Diagnosis Code for every Procedure Code; the Procedure Code always precedes the Diagnosis Code. When there is a Premium Code, the Premium Code also precedes the Diagnosis Code.

These codes accompany the Procedure Codes in an EMR system. In an EMR, the medical biller can key the words for the diagnosis into the diagnosis field, and the EMR will provide a list of the diagnoses alphabetically. The medical biller can select the appropriate diagnosis to populate the field with the code.

When searching the Resource Manual for Physicians to locate a Diagnosis Code, it is essential that the medical biller be familiar with medical terminology and body systems to locate the correct diagnosis. Some codes are not found alphabetically, but rather under the body system section. Also, some diagnoses may be in layman's terms, and the medical biller must know the medical term to locate the code. The use of the Internet in some instances may be necessary for the translation.

Following is a sample of a claim detail page in an EMR system:

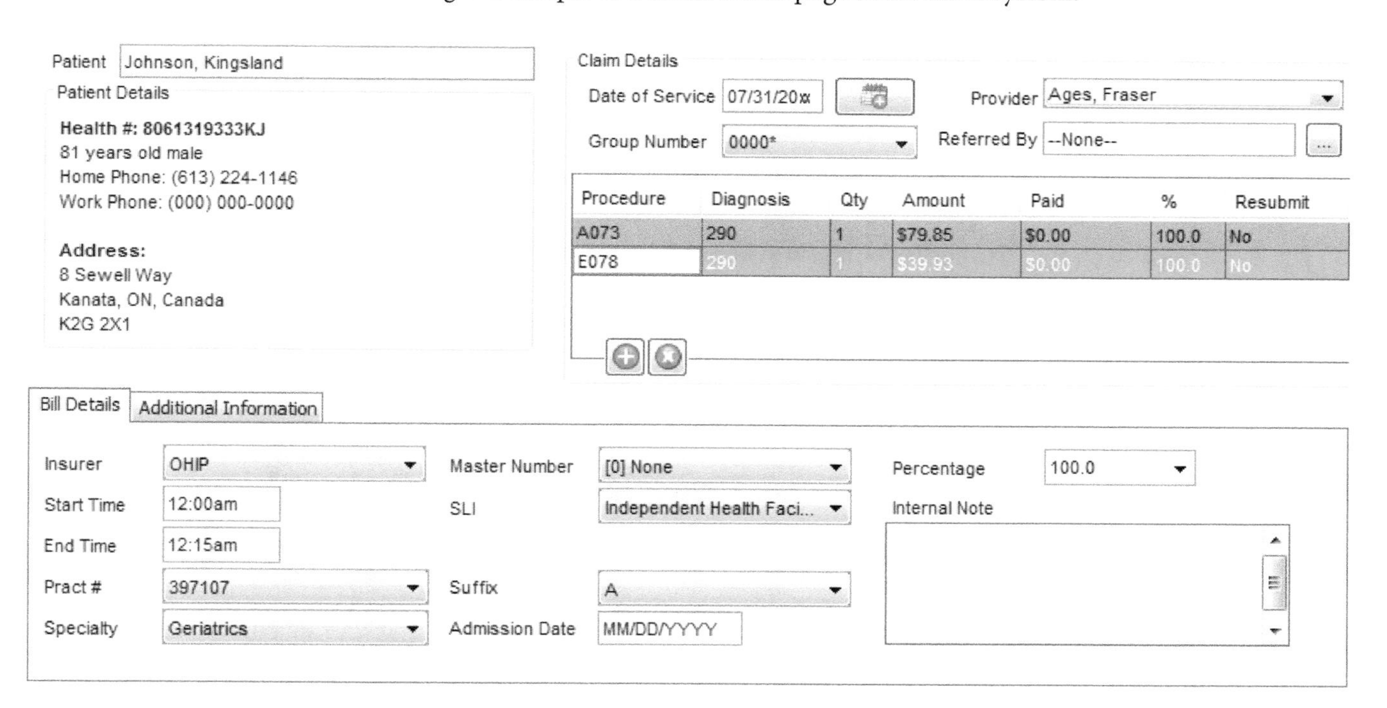

Patient: Johnson, Kingsland

Patient Details

Health #: 8061319333KJ
81 years old male
Home Phone: (613) 224-1146
Work Phone: (000) 000-0000

Address:
8 Sewell Way
Kanata, ON, Canada
K2G 2X1

Claim Details

Date of Service: 07/31/20xx
Provider: Ages, Fraser
Group Number: 0000*
Referred By: --None--

Procedure	Diagnosis	Qty	Amount	Paid	%	Resubmit
A073	290	1	$79.85	$0.00	100.0	No
E078	290	1	$39.93	$0.00	100.0	No

Bill Details | Additional Information

Insurer: OHIP
Start Time: 12:00am
End Time: 12:15am
Pract #: 397107
Specialty: Geriatrics
Master Number: [0] None
SLI: Independent Health Faci...
Suffix: A
Admission Date: MM/DD/YYYY
Percentage: 100.0
Internal Note

Premium Codes

A Premium Code is a payment to a physician for services provided under special circumstances. Premium Codes must be submitted following a Procedure Code. A Premium Code follows a Procedure Code and precedes a Diagnosis Code since they are correlated. Premiums are paid based upon the Schedule of Benefits fee for service obtained from the Procedure Code.

Premium Codes may be based upon time units, complexity of illness, or a percentage of a visit.

Premium Codes are often used in care of very young patients, the elderly, after-hours home visits and office visits, after-hours labour and delivery, chronic conditions, and other emergency situations where additional care by the physician is undertaken and, in some instances, office hours have to be cancelled, which is referred to as sacrifice of hours. A home visit is one deemed medically necessary by the physician.

Always refer to the Schedule of Benefits' General Preamble for explanations and tables of premiums.

An EMR system will automatically calculate the percentage of the premium based upon the Procedure Code fee.

Some examples of Premium Codes and their explanations are:

- E409 – Physician administering care to a patient between the hours of 17:00 and 24:00 or daytime and evenings on Saturdays, Sundays, and holidays – 50 percent premium
- E410 – Physician administering to a patient between the hours of 00:00 and 07:00 – 75 percent premium
- E078 – Physician administering to a patient with a chronic illness such as emphysema

Following is a list of the most commonly used premiums:

Special Visit Premiums

Special Visit Premium Codes contain prefixes that denote where the special visit took place, the time of the visit, and the number of patients involved. These are flat rate fees for travel time, the first patient seen, or additional persons seen. Consult the Schedule of Benefits' General Preamble for the criteria.

- Has a travel component – premium for travelling from one location to another to see a patient (does not apply when travelling from one department of a hospital to another department)
  - Travel Premium to the Emergency Department has a K prefix.
  - Travel Premium to a Hospital Out-Patient Department has a U prefix.
  - Travel Premium to a Hospital In-Patient Department has a C prefix.
  - Travel Premium to a Long-Term Care Facility has a W prefix.
  - Travel Premium to the Emergency Department by an Emergency Department physician has an H prefix.
  - Travel Premium to the patient's home has a B prefix.
  - Travel Premium to a physician's office has an A prefix.
  - Travel Premium to a non-professional setting has a Q prefix.
  - Obstetrical Delivery Premium with sacrifice of office hours has a C prefix.

- Have a person seen component – premium for first person seen after the travel – for the second person seen, there is no travel premium.
  - First Person Seen Premium to the Emergency Department has a K prefix, to a maximum of 10 persons seen.
  - First Person Seen Premium to a Hospital Out-Patient Department has a U prefix, to a maximum of 10 persons seen.
  - First Person Seen Premium to a Hospital In-Patient Department has a C prefix, to a maximum of 10 persons seen.
  - First Person Seen Premium to a Long-Term Care Facility has a W prefix, to a maximum of 10 persons seen.
  - First Person Seen Premium to the Emergency Department by an Emergency Department physician has an H prefix, to a maximum of 5 persons seen.
  - First Person Seen Premium to the patient's home has a B prefix, to a maximum of 10 persons seen.
  - First Person Seen Premium to a physician's office has an A prefix, to a maximum of 1 person seen.
  - First Person Seen Premium to a non-professional setting has a Q prefix, to a maximum of 1 person seen.
  - Obstetrical Delivery Premium with sacrifice of office hours has a time period maximum of 1 person seen.
  - Refer to the General Preamble Special Visit Premium Tables for other types of special visits.

Time Premiums

Time Premiums correlate to Special Visit Premiums. The Schedule of Benefits' General Preamble outlines the criteria such as:

- Premiums are paid for times of the day or days of the week that are after hours.

Chronic Disease Assessment Premium

A chronic disease is a condition or disease that has been diagnosed as long-lasting. The Schedule of Benefits lists chronic diseases that have been approved for premium payments. Diseases that have not been diagnosed as chronic by the MOHLTC cannot be billed. The chronic disease premium is disallowed when the diagnosis by the physician has not been established.

Premium Codes for chronic illnesses can only be applied to assessments. Premium Codes for chronic illnesses cannot be applied to assessments rendered by physicians of patients in hospitals, long-term care facilities, or the Emergency Department.

- A premium is payable in addition to the amount payable for an assessment when the assessment is:
  - Medical-specific assessment
  - Medical-specific re-assessment
  - Complex medical-specific assessment
  - Complex medical-specific re-assessment
  - Partial assessment
- The Chronic Disease Premium is not allowed when the diagnosis by the physician has not been established.

Admission Assessment Premium for the Most Responsible Physician (MRP)

The Most Responsible Physician is the physician involved in the primary care of an in-patient.

When a patient is seen in the Emergency Department, the Emergency Department physician determines which service the patient should be seen under. The on-call physician for that service provides a consultation. The on-call physician may admit the patient based upon the diagnosis and the level of care required, and the on-call physician becomes the MRP once the patient has been admitted.

- If the MRP admits the patient:
  - The premium is 30 percent.
  - There is one MRP per patient per admission.
  - The Premium Code is E082 for Emergency Most Responsible Physician (MRP) Admission Assessment in a Hospital Emergency Department.
  - Non-Emergency Admission Assessments may have an A or C Prefix.

Subsequent Visits by the MRP

The MRP is entitled to a premium for visits to the in-patient for two days following admission.

- Day following admission – C122
- Second day following admission – C123
- C122 and C123 are limited to one of each per hospital admission.

Discharge from Hospital by the MRP

The physician is entitled to a premium for discharging an in-patient.

- Day of discharge – C124
- Cannot be paid for C122 or C123 on same day as C124
- Not eligible if patient discharged within 48 hours of admission to hospital

Emergency Department

Physicians who work within the Emergency Department are not entitled to premiums because patient encounters are part of their regular shift responsibilities. Physicians are entitled to bill for Emergency Department consultations and assessments but not for travel or first person seen premiums.

- H prefix
- On-call physician or on regular shift

Time Units

Time Units are based on minutes. Each block of time is considered a unit, e.g., 20 minutes may be 1 unit. Minutes per block vary depending upon the service. See the General Preamble in the Schedule of Benefits. Time Units are used when:

- Providing counselling and other forms of mental health therapy
- Performing procedures during the same encounter as the therapy unless the procedure is listed separated in the Schedule of Benefits as an amount payable

- Making arrangements for related assessment, procedures, or therapy
- Making arrangements for followup care
- Interviewing
- Providing supplies, equipment, and personnel

Age-Based Fee Premiums

Physicians can bill for Age Premiums when administering consultations to patients up to 16 years of age. The premiums are percentage based. Refer to the General Preamble of the Schedule of Benefits for detailed information.

Premiums are payable, and following are some of the services:

- Consultation, limited consultation, or repeat consultation by a specialist
- Surgical procedures listed in Parts K to Z in the Schedule of Benefits

Age premiums are also payable for patients 65 years of age and older, and following are some of the services:

- General assessments
- House call assessments
- Periodic health visits

Again, always refer to the Schedule of Benefits, particularly for services that are not encountered frequently.

TASK 4

SPECIAL VISIT PREMIUM CODES

RESOURCES: Medical Billing Workbook
MOHLTC Schedule of Benefits

1. Rename a sheet in the Medical Billing Workbook as **Special Visit Premium Codes**.
2. Add a colour to the tab.
3. Create two new columns:
   - Prefix (Column A)
   - Description (Column B)
4. Add the following codes in Column A.
   - A
   - B
   - C
   - E
   - H
   - K
   - Q
   - U
   - W
5. Using the MOHLTC Schedule of Benefits, complete the sheet.

Diagnostic and Therapeutic Procedure codes

A Diagnostic Procedure is a test or procedure undertaken in further treatment of the patient. A Diagnostic Procedure can encompass ultrasounds, X-rays, minor and major surgeries, sleep studies, and laboratory investigations.

A Therapeutic Procedure is a service that contributes to the treatment and management of a disease or condition, such as an X-ray or an excision. These codes are also listed in the Schedule of Benefits, Diagnostic and Therapeutic Procedures, and can only be billed if the specialist is part of an Independent Health Facility (IHF).

These procedures may contain two components: technical and professional. A technical component includes preparing a patient for a test, arranging followup care, updating the records based on test results, and providing any documentation required to physicians. A professional component includes supervising and monitoring a test, performing clinical procedures that are not separately billed, and interpreting results. The technical and professional components are billed separately.

Physicians working for an IHF, registered with the MOHLTC, can bill for these services. For the purposes of this workbook, BMC is an IHF.

The Schedule of Benefits contains an itemized list of Diagnostic and Therapeutic Procedures, and they are usually billed in combination with a consultation or assessment.

Provincial/territorial codes for reciprocal medical billing

It is essential for medical billing purposes to have access to provincial and territorial billing codes to undertake reciprocal medical billing. Each province and territory is assigned a two-letter code. For instance, Ontario is ON. These codes are found in the MOHLTC Resource Manual for Physicians.

In Ontario, when a patient from another province or territory is seen by a physician in Ontario, the patient's home province or territory will be billed under the patient's provincial or territorial medical plan for the service. This is known as reciprocal medical billing (RMB). Quebec is the only province not involved in reciprocal medical billing.

The medical billing process is the same as someone living in the province; however, the medical plan responsible for payment of the billing will bill the patient's province or territory to receive the funds. The patient from out of province must present a valid health card; otherwise, the service will be billed directly to the patient. If billed directly, the out-of-province patient can seek reimbursement from the home province.

For example, in Ontario, when a patient from Manitoba sees a physician in Ontario, the physician bills the patient through OHIP, and the physician is paid directly by the Ministry. The Ministry then collects the payment back from Manitoba Health. The claim is generated and processed within the facility's EMR system.

TASK 5

PROVINCIAL AND TERRITORIAL CODES FOR RECIPROCAL BILLING

RESOURCES: Medical Billing Workbook
MOHLTC Resource Manual for Physicians

1. Rename a sheet in the Medical Billing workbook as **Provincial and Territorial Codes**.
2. Apply a colour to the tab.

3. Create two columns.
   - Province/Territory (Column A)
   - Abbreviation (two-letter abbreviation) (Column B)
4. Using the Internet, locate the MOHLTC Resource Manual for Physicians and complete the workbook sheet.
5. Sort alphabetically.

Facility numbers, master numbers, and group numbers

Every medical facility is assigned a unique facility number and a master number(s) by the province or territory. Each of these numbers consists of a four-digit number.

All medical facilities are classified according to the service provided, e.g., AT is an acute care treatment hospital, MH is a mental health unit, and TH is telehealth. The MOHLTC publishes the Master Numbering System, which identifies each facility's classification (type), master number, and facility number.

The facility number indicates the medical facility where the service was rendered. Physicians may practise at more than one facility. Each facility has one facility number. Examples of facility numbers would be 0777 (Queensway Carleton Hospital, Ottawa) and 0958 (The Ottawa Hospital). For a complete list, refer to the MOHLTC Master Numbering System document.

Medical facilities may have more than one master number, depending upon the type of service provided. An acute care hospital may have a mental health centre, for instance, and each would have its own master number based upon the classification. When there is more than one service being offered within a facility, there is one facility number, but more than one master number. An example would be the Queensway Carleton Hospital in Ottawa, which is classified as follows:

- Acute care treatment hospital (1681)
- Ambulatory care (3970)
- Mental health (4543)
- General rehabilitation hospital (4584)

When creating an EMR system, the group number (if applicable) and the master number are inserted into the system under the Provider section when you are configuring the physician into the system. The medical biller must ensure that the correct facility number and master number are selected when creating a medical claim for submission to the Ministry.

Brooklane Medical Centre is an Independent Facility (IF) and Hope General Hospital is an Acute Care Treatment Hospital (AT), Ambulatory Care (AM), Mental Health Unit (MH), and Private Radiological Facility (PR), to name a few.

Group numbers are used when physicians wish to bill under a group rather than individually. The MOHTLC will issue a group number and pay for claims directly to the group's bank account. Each physician is responsible for the claims submitted, and the group is responsible for the disbursement of the payment from the MOHLTC. The Ministry does not oversee this aspect.

TASK 6

FACILITY NUMBERS, MASTER NUMBERS, AND GROUP NUMBERS

RESOURCE: Medical Billing Workbook

1. Rename a sheet in the Medical Billing Workbook as **Facility, Master, and Group Numbers**.
2. Add a colour to the tab.
3. Create two new columns:
   - Website (Column A)
   - Description (Column B)
4. Add the following websites in Column A.
   - MOHLTC Master Numbering System
   - Ontario Medical Association – OHIP Billing Number and Group Number
5. Sort alphabetically.

TASK 7

TERMINOLOGY

RESOURCE: Medical Billing Workbook

It is essential that a medical billing specialist be familiar with the terminology that is encountered when undertaking medical billing.

1. Add the following terms to the Terminology sheet in Column A:
   - Prefix
   - Suffix
   - Procedure Code
   - Specialty Code
   - Facility Number
   - Master Number
   - Group Number
   - Classification (Type)
   - Premium Code
   - Schedule of Benefits
   - Resource Manual for Physicians
   - Reciprocal Billing
   - Independent Health Care Facility
   - Diagnosis Code
   - Diagnostic Code
   - Therapeutic Code
   - Provincial/Territorial Codes

- Time Units
- Time Premiums
- Age Premiums
- Special Visit
- Subsequent Visits by the MRP
- Discharge from Hospital
- Admission to Hospital
- Admission Assessment
- Most Responsible Physician
- Chronic Disease
- First Person Seen
- First Visit by Primary Care Physician After Hospital Discharge
- In-Patient
- Non-Emergency Acute Care Hospital In-Patient Services
- Partial Assessment/Partial Reassessment
- Consultation
- Assessment/Reassessment
- Complex Medical Specific Assessment/Reassessment
- Comprehensive Consultation
- Specific Assessment/Reassessment
- Medically Specific Assessment/Reassessment
- Period Health Visit
- Special Palliative Care Consultation
- Special Surgical Consultation
- Emergency Department Physician Consultation
- Limited Consultation

2. In Column B, provide a definition in your own words.
3. Sort alphabetically.

Project 5
SCHEDULE OF BENEFITS AND RESOURCE MANUAL FOR PHYSICIANS

LEARNING OBJECTIVES

- Understanding the MOHLTC Schedule of Benefits
- Understanding the MOHLTC Resource Manual for Physicians

This project explores the two primary resources for medical billing—the MOHLTC Schedule of Benefits and the MOHLTC Resource Manual for Physicians.

It is essential that medical billers be familiar with how to navigate these two resources effectively and efficiently.

Schedule of Benefits

Each province and territory has its own Schedule of Benefits; it is often referred to as a Fee Schedule or the Schedule. The Schedule is approved by the government—the MOHLTC—and provides a framework for medical billing of insured services.

It is essential to have a strong knowledge of the Schedule of Benefits to work efficiently and effectively when billing. The Schedule of Benefits for Ontario is available online or it can be downloaded as a PDF.

The Schedule of Benefits is used primarily for locating Procedure Codes.

The Schedule of Benefits contains the following major sections:

- General Preamble
- Consultations and Visits
- Diagnostic Imaging (nuclear medicine, radiology, ultrasound, and pulmonary function)
- Diagnostic and Therapeutic Procedures
- Obstetrics
- Surgical Preamble
- Surgical Procedures
- Numeric Index of Codes

The General Preamble includes:

- General definitions
- General payment rules
- Assessments and consultations
- Premiums

The Schedule of Benefits does not contain:

- Uninsured services
- Facility numbers
- Diagnostic codes

The MOHLTC posts InfoBulletins periodically, outlining changes to the Schedule of Benefits. It is the responsibility of the medical biller to check the Ministry website frequently for updates. Some EMR systems, such as Accuro®EMR, have frequent technical updates, which are provided electronically.

TASK 1

MOHLTC SCHEDULE OF BENEFITS FAMILIARIZATION

RESOURCES: MOHTLC Schedule of Benefits
Appendix J – MOHLTC Schedule of Benefits Familiarization
Appendix I – MOHLTC Schedule of Benefits Familiarization

Using the MOHLTC Schedule of Benefits, answer questions related to the schedule by completing the table found in Appendix J.

Resource Manual for Physicians

The MOHLTC publishes a resource manual to aid physicians with medical coding. The Resource Manual for Physicians is available online or it can be downloaded as a PDF.

The Resource Manual for Physicians is used primarily for locating Diagnosis Codes and referencing the claims process for submission and reconciliation.

The Resource Manual for Physicians contains the following major sections:

- Physician Registration
- Physician Payment
- Payment Integrity
- Claims Submission
- Registration for OHIP Coverage
- General Information

TASK 2

MOHLTC RESOURCE MANUAL FOR PHYSICIANS FAMILIARIZATION

RESOURCES: MOHLTC Resource Manual for Physicians
Appendix J – MOHLTC Resource Manual for Physicians Familiarization
Appendix I – MOHLTC Resource Manual for Physicians Familiarization

Using the MOHLTC Resource Manual for Physicians, answer questions related to the schedule by completing the table found in Appendix J.

Project 6

CREATING CLAIMS

LEARNING OBJECTIVES

- Defining the basic billing cycle
- Understanding a claim
- Understanding timeframes for submitting medical claims
- Learning the frequency of medical billing and submission of claims
- Creating a new bill
- Deciphering codes
- Understanding procedure and diagnosis codes in Accuro®EMR
- Learning the information required to create a new bill in Accuro®EMR
- Learning how to do a manual review in Accuro®EMR
- Understanding independent consideration (IC)
- Defining shadow billing

Creating patient claims is the primary function of a medical biller. This is the process by which a physician is reimbursed for services rendered.

Basic Billing Cycle

The following is an illustration of the billing cycle in Ontario:

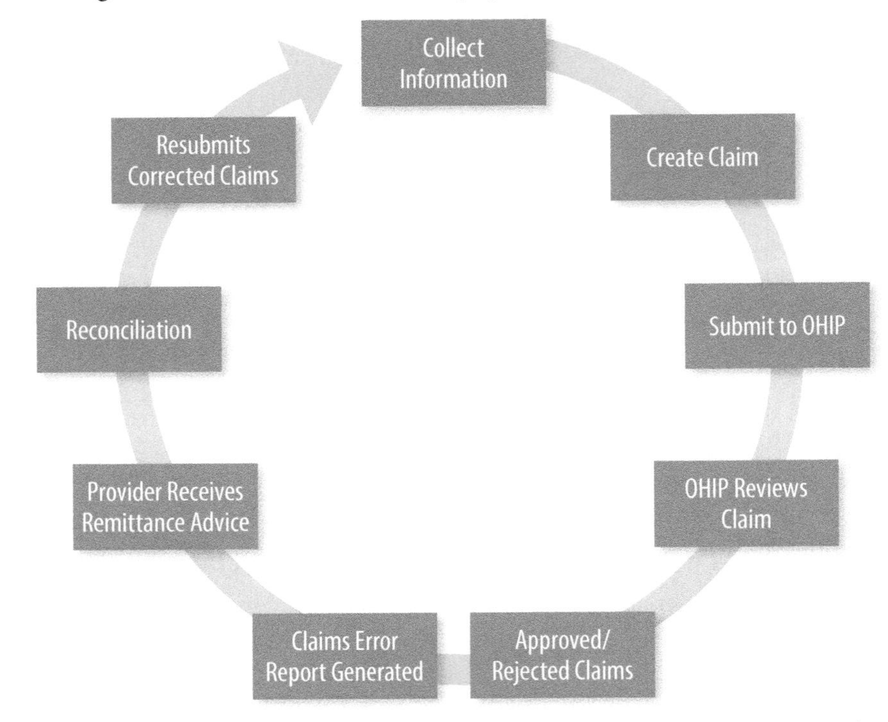

- Medical biller collects information obtained from day sheet, patient record, and/or physician notes.
- Medical biller creates claims and assigns codes.
- Medical biller submits claims to OHIP with submission being through MC EDT software.
- MOHTLC reviews claims in accordance with OHIP guidelines.
- OHIP approves or rejects claims.
- Claims Error Report is generated. Any claims errors are placed in a report and returned to the physician because they do not meet OHIP's guidelines for fee payment; claims may be partially or fully rejected.
- Provider receives Remittance Advice Report with payment. The Remittance Advice may contain codes that indicate if a service has been reduced or disallowed.
- Medical biller reconciles claims based on the Remittance Advice Report.
- Medical biller corrects any errors or deletes erroneous claims.
- Medical biller resubmits corrected claims for payment.

What Is a Medical Claim?

A claim is a submission to the MOHLTC for reimbursement of a medical service by a registered medical specialist (registered with the MOHLTC). Physicians are paid for the services they provide, and it is essential that the medical biller capture the codes for each service rendered.

Timeframes for Submitting Medical Claims

The timeframe for submission of claims to MOHLTC is from the 19th of one month to the 18th of the next month. Claims are considered "stale dated" if they are not received within six months of the encounter; the MOHTLC will reject these claims, and no payment will be made to the physician.

A physician may submit a letter to the Ministry for special consideration of stale-dated claims.

Frequency of Medical Billing and Submission of Claims

Medical billers may bill daily, weekly, or monthly. This is dependent upon the physician's office procedures. The Ministry recommends that claims be submitted as early as possible in the billing period for an early review to occur so that errors can be corrected by the medical billers. This allows time in the period for reconciliation and resubmission of claims.

Creating a New Bill (Claim)

The medical biller reviews the day sheets, patient records, and/or the physician notes and assigns codes for the services provided by the physician using the Schedule of Benefits, the Resource Manual for Physicians, and/or the EMR system, which has its own database of codes.

The medical biller should ask these questions:

Who?
What?
When?
Where?
Why?

Who Which physician and which patient?

What What service did the physician provide or procedure did the physician perform? (Procedure Code)

When Date of service?

Where Location of service?

Why What was the reason the patient was seen? (Diagnosis Code)

Case 1:

A young man goes to see his family physician in his private office with chest pain on a Monday afternoon at 3:00 p.m.

Who Family Physician

What General Assessment

When Monday @ 3:00 p.m.

Where Office Visit

Why Chest Pain – Diagnosis

Billing code for Case 1:

The Procedure Code is A003A (A = Physician's Office; 00 = Family Practice Specialty; 3 = General Assessment; A = service performed by Physician), and the Diagnosis Code is 785.

Case 2:

A female presents herself on a Saturday morning at the Emergency Department of Hope General Hospital as a result of a serious burn from a spilled coffee while driving.

Who Emergency Department Physician

What Consultation

When Saturday morning

Where Hospital Emergency Department (ER)

Why Thermal Burn – Diagnosis

Determining Diagnosis Codes can be complicated. If in doubt, ask the physician or call the MOHLTC for verification.

Billing code for Case 2:

The Procedure Code is H055A (H = Emergency Department; 05 = Community Medicine Specialty; 5 = Consultation; A = service performed by Physician), and the Diagnosis Code is 949.

Case 3:

A pregnant woman goes to see her obstetrician for her regular monthly visit at BMC on a Friday after 5:00 p.m.

Who Obstetrician

What Specific Assessment by a Specialist

When Friday after 5:00 p.m. (Office hours 9:00 a.m. to 6:00 p.m.)

Where Office

Why Uncomplicated Pregnancy – Diagnosis

Billing code for Case 3:

The Procedure Code is A203A (A = Physician's Office; 20 = Obstetrics Specialty; 3 = Specific Assessment; A = service performed by Physician), and the Diagnosis Code is 650.

Practice – Codes

RESOURCES: MOHLTC Schedule of Benefits
MOHLTC Resource Manual for Physicians

Review the following cases and determine the Procedure and Diagnosis Codes. Where applicable determine the Premium Codes. Practise your own skills prior to reviewing the answers.

Practice 1

Mr. Douglas Thomas saw Dr. B. Harte, Cardiologist, in her office last Wednesday at 3:00 p.m. for a medical-specific assessment. Mr. Thomas was diagnosed with a new finding of hypertensive heart disease.

Procedure: Diagnosis:

Practice 2

Mrs. Cindy Thomas was seen by Dr. A. Darby, General Practitioner, for a consultation related to congestive heart failure.

Procedure: Diagnosis:

Dr. Darby referred Cindy Thomas to the Hope General Emergency Department where Dr. B. Harte, Cardiologist, provided a consultation (Physician on-call that evening).

The time was 6:30 p.m. on a Sunday. Dr. Harte made a special trip to the hospital Emergency Department to see this first patient that evening. Dr. Harte saw Mrs. Thomas for a consultation and later diagnosed her with congestive heart failure. Subsequently, Mrs. Thomas was admitted to Hope General Hospital that night by Dr. Harte as the Most Responsible Physician (MRP) who performed an admission assessment.

Practice 1 Answer

Procedure: A603A Diagnosis: 402

Practice 2 Answer

Procedure:	A005A	Diagnosis: 428
Procedure:	A605A	Diagnosis: 428
Premium 1:	K963 (travel)	Diagnosis: 428
Premium 2:	K998 (first person seen)	Diagnosis: 428
Premium 3:	E082 (admission by MRP)	Diagnosis: 428
Premium 4:	No premium for chronic disease – an in-patient	

Accuro®EMR Screen Capture

The following screen capture highlights the fields displayed in Accuro when creating a claim.

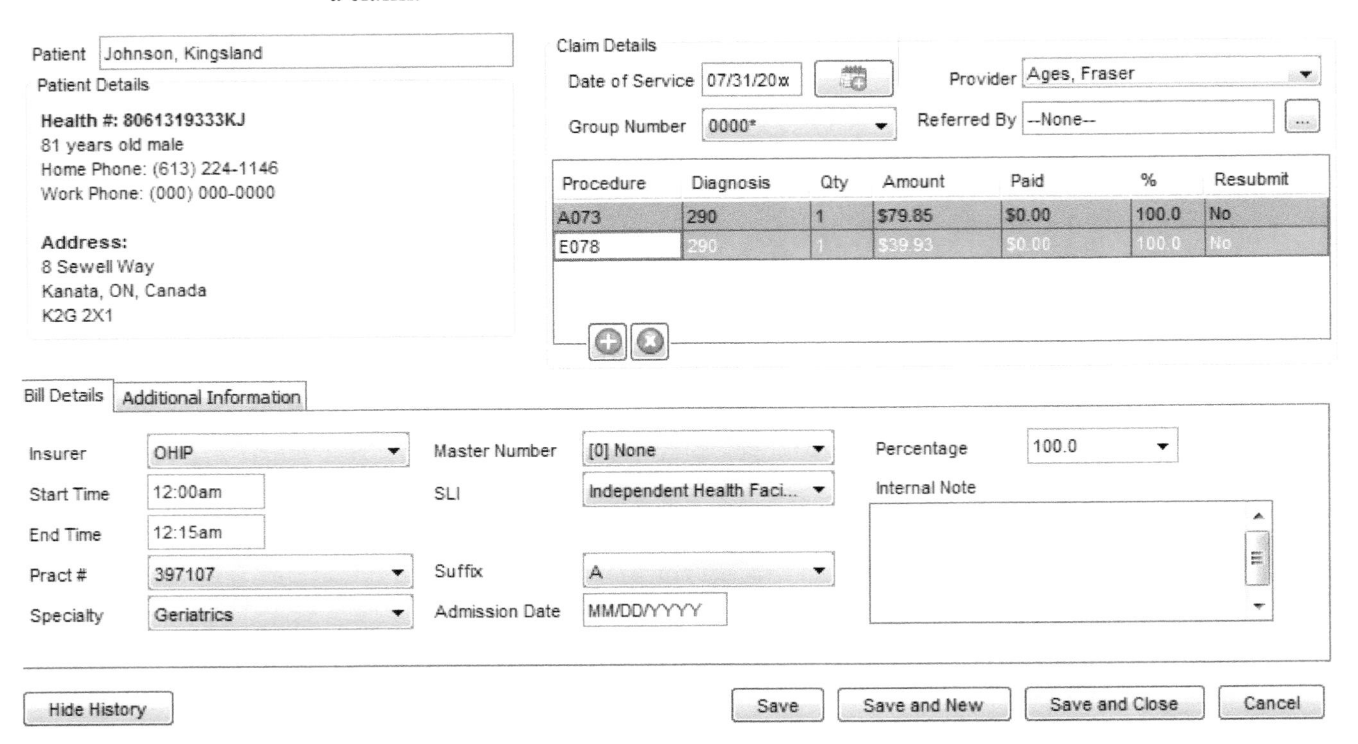

Following are descriptions of the fields:

- Patient
  - Patient name and demographics
- Date of Service
  - Date of encounter/patient appointment
- Provider
  - Name of specialist
- Group Number
  - Used when a group of physicians are billing under one facility rather than independently
  - It is not a billing number; individual physicians are responsible for all claims and payments made using their individual billing numbers.
  - The Ministry provides a group number for direct payment to the group's bank account.
  - The Ministry does not oversee to whom the monies are disbursed among the physicians affiliated with a group.
  - Examples of where a group is used: independent health facilities, family health groups, alternate payment programs such as emergency department alternate funding arrangements, and academic health science centres

- Referred By
  - Provider referring to specialist for a consultation or second opinion
  - The referring physician's individual MOHLTC provider number is entered when setting up the referring provider.
- Procedure
  - Code from Schedule of Benefits, based upon what the physician did to earn payment from the patient.
- Diagnosis
  - From Resource Manual for Physicians, based upon how the physician diagnosed the patient
- Premium:
  - From the Schedule of Benefits
  - Premium Codes are billed directly under the Procedure Code in an EMR system, since a premium is directly associated with the procedure. If the Premium Code is based on a percentage (e.g., E078), the EMR software calculates the premium appropriately. Each Procedure Code and associated Premium Code will be accompanied by a Diagnosis Code.
- Insurer – Choices:
  - HCP (Health Care Plan): OHIP
  - RMB (Reciprocal Medical Billing): claims to any other province than Ontario; these claims go to OHIP, which will in turn bill the home province of the patient and pay the provider, except in the case of Quebec
  - WSIB (Workplace Safety Insurance Board)
  - Third party
- Start Time
  - Time appointment began
- End Time
  - Time appointment ended
- Practice Number (Pract #)
  - Physician's billing number provided by the MOHLTC
- Specialty
  - Area of specialty
- Master Number
  - Number assigned by Ministry where the billing is occurring in a facility based upon the classification of the service
  - Unique four-digit identifying code
- Service Location Indicator (SLI)
  - Where the service occurred, such as at the IHF, in-patient, hospital Emergency Department, or Rehabilitation Centre
- Suffix
  - A for physician
- Admission Date
  - Applicable when patient is being admitted to a hospital or other medical institution
  - Date admitted to hospital or other facility

- Percentage
  - Percentage payable to provider
  - Usually 100 percent to the provider except for premiums, which are based upon a percentage of the procedure

Manual Review

Once the bills have been created, the Manual Review field is used to flag or identify claims that deviate in some way from programmed billing criteria and require an explanation of the circumstances.

Within an EMR system, when the manual review box is checked, it notifies the Ministry upon submission that a claim must be reviewed manually.

Any claim marked for Manual Review must have supporting documentation and be sent at the same time as the claims submission.

An example might be when a physician has submitted two hospital visits on the same patient on the same day. An explanation must accompany the billing submission, e.g., in the case of two hospital visits, it could be that the physician saw the patient just after midnight and then again in the afternoon.

Claims that are not submitted within six months of the date of service are deemed stale dated. If the Ministry has not finalized a review and the six months is approaching, the medical biller should resubmit the claim to obtain a new date.

Following is a sample of a manual review request. The checkbox is selected for this claim to be manually reviewed by the Ministry:

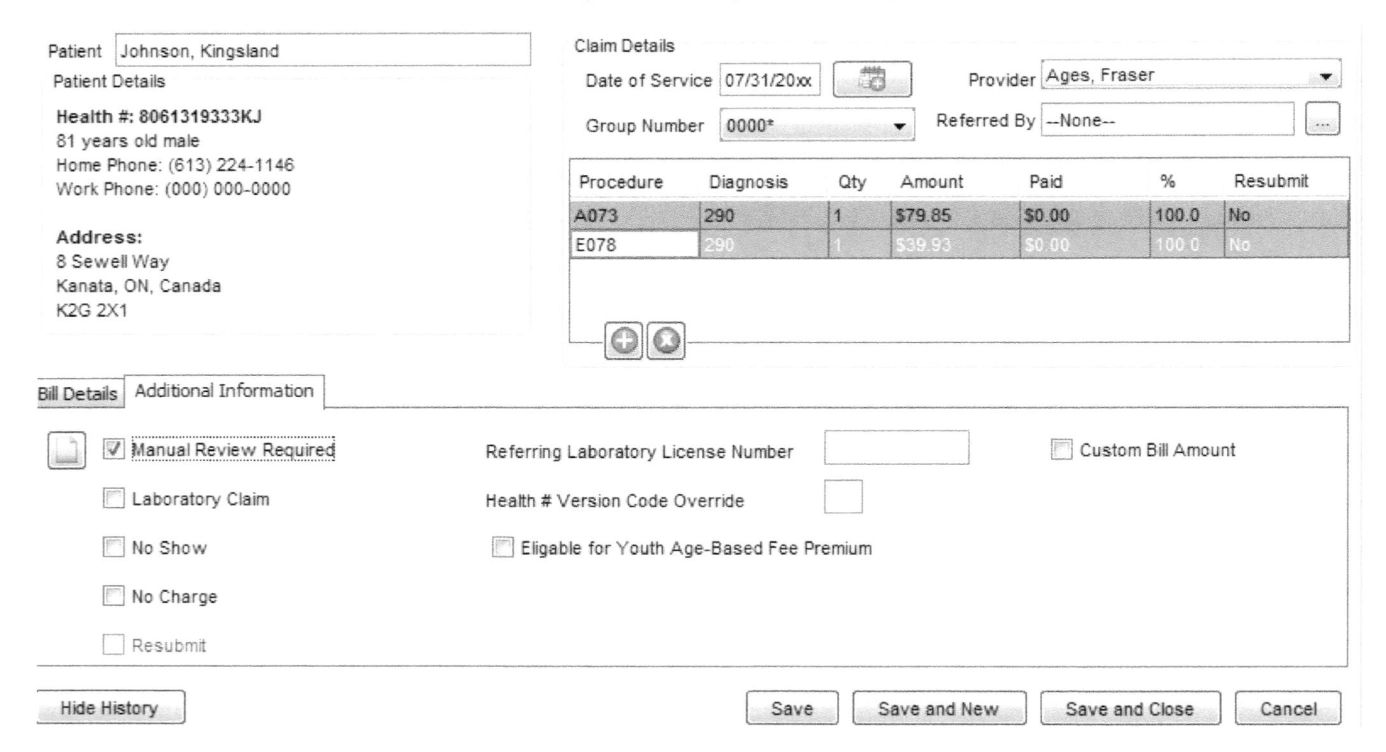

Pre-Checking Errors Prior to Submission

The green checkmark in the bottom right corner of the screen below is used to prompt the system to review the claims before they are submitted to the Ministry in order to pre-check for errors.

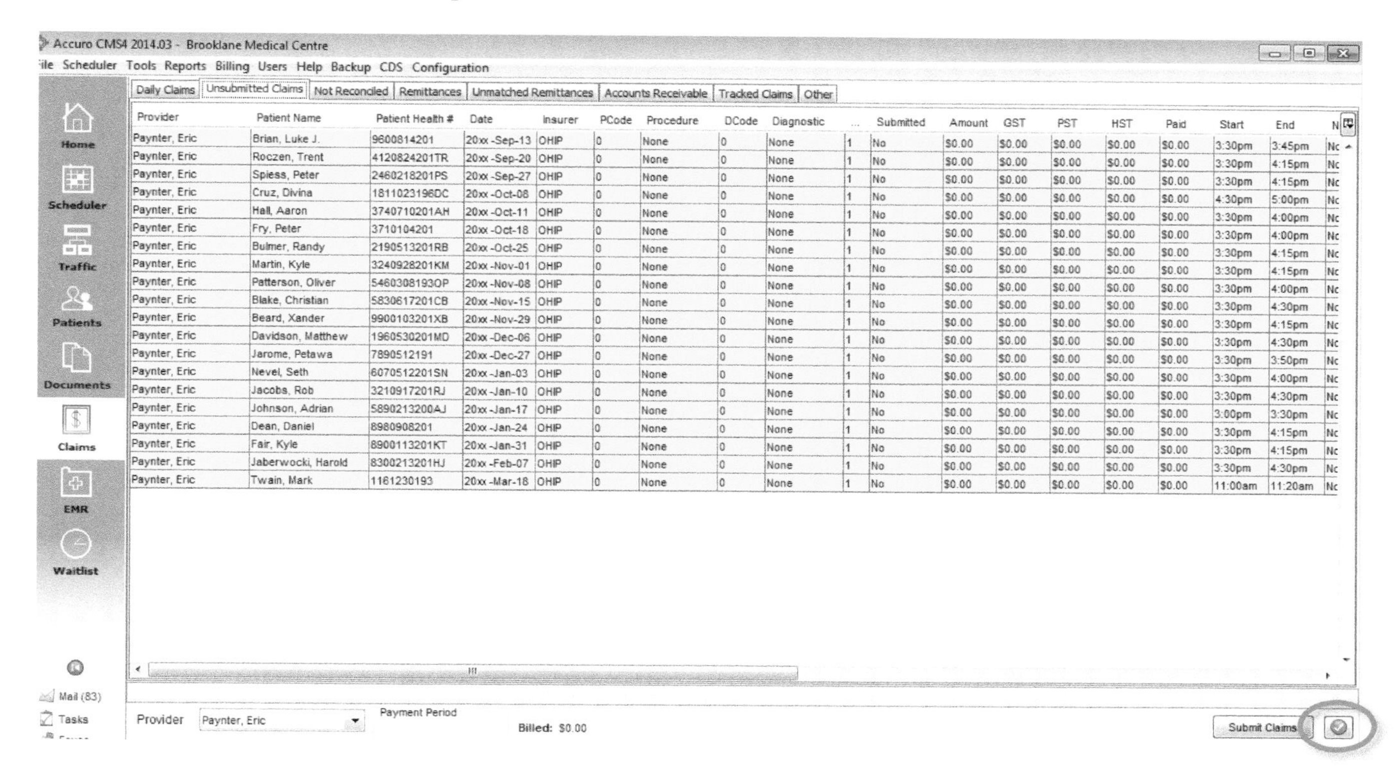

Provider	Patient Name	Patient Health #	Date	Insurer	PCode	Procedure	DCode	Diagnostic	...	Submitted	Amount	GST	PST	HST	Paid	Start	End	N
Paynter, Eric	Brian, Luke J.	9600814201	20xx-Sep-13	OHIP	0	None	0	None	1	No	$0.00	$0.00	$0.00	$0.00	$0.00	3:30pm	3:45pm	Nc
Paynter, Eric	Roczen, Trent	4120824201TR	20xx-Sep-20	OHIP	0	None	0	None	1	No	$0.00	$0.00	$0.00	$0.00	$0.00	3:30pm	4:15pm	Nc
Paynter, Eric	Spiess, Peter	2460218201PS	20xx-Sep-27	OHIP	0	None	0	None	1	No	$0.00	$0.00	$0.00	$0.00	$0.00	3:30pm	4:15pm	Nc
Paynter, Eric	Cruz, Divina	1811023196DC	20xx-Oct-08	OHIP	0	None	0	None	1	No	$0.00	$0.00	$0.00	$0.00	$0.00	4:30pm	5:00pm	Nc
Paynter, Eric	Hall, Aaron	3740710201AH	20xx-Oct-11	OHIP	0	None	0	None	1	No	$0.00	$0.00	$0.00	$0.00	$0.00	3:30pm	4:00pm	Nc
Paynter, Eric	Fry, Peter	3710104201	20xx-Oct-18	OHIP	0	None	0	None	1	No	$0.00	$0.00	$0.00	$0.00	$0.00	3:30pm	4:00pm	Nc
Paynter, Eric	Bulmer, Randy	2190513201RB	20xx-Oct-25	OHIP	0	None	0	None	1	No	$0.00	$0.00	$0.00	$0.00	$0.00	3:30pm	4:15pm	Nc
Paynter, Eric	Martin, Kyle	3240928201KM	20xx-Nov-01	OHIP	0	None	0	None	1	No	$0.00	$0.00	$0.00	$0.00	$0.00	3:30pm	4:15pm	Nc
Paynter, Eric	Patterson, Oliver	5460308193OP	20xx-Nov-08	OHIP	0	None	0	None	1	No	$0.00	$0.00	$0.00	$0.00	$0.00	3:30pm	4:00pm	Nc
Paynter, Eric	Blake, Christian	5830617201CB	20xx-Nov-15	OHIP	0	None	0	None	1	No	$0.00	$0.00	$0.00	$0.00	$0.00	3:30pm	4:30pm	Nc
Paynter, Eric	Beard, Xander	9900103201XB	20xx-Nov-29	OHIP	0	None	0	None	1	No	$0.00	$0.00	$0.00	$0.00	$0.00	3:30pm	4:15pm	Nc
Paynter, Eric	Davidson, Matthew	1960530201MD	20xx-Dec-06	OHIP	0	None	0	None	1	No	$0.00	$0.00	$0.00	$0.00	$0.00	3:30pm	4:30pm	Nc
Paynter, Eric	Jarome, Petawa	7890512191	20xx-Dec-27	OHIP	0	None	0	None	1	No	$0.00	$0.00	$0.00	$0.00	$0.00	3:30pm	3:50pm	Nc
Paynter, Eric	Nevel, Seth	6070512201SN	20xx-Jan-03	OHIP	0	None	0	None	1	No	$0.00	$0.00	$0.00	$0.00	$0.00	3:30pm	4:00pm	Nc
Paynter, Eric	Jacobs, Rob	3210917201RJ	20xx-Jan-10	OHIP	0	None	0	None	1	No	$0.00	$0.00	$0.00	$0.00	$0.00	3:30pm	4:30pm	Nc
Paynter, Eric	Johnson, Adrian	5890213200AJ	20xx-Jan-17	OHIP	0	None	0	None	1	No	$0.00	$0.00	$0.00	$0.00	$0.00	3:00pm	3:30pm	Nc
Paynter, Eric	Dean, Daniel	8980908201	20xx-Jan-24	OHIP	0	None	0	None	1	No	$0.00	$0.00	$0.00	$0.00	$0.00	3:30pm	4:15pm	Nc
Paynter, Eric	Fair, Kyle	8900113201KT	20xx-Jan-31	OHIP	0	None	0	None	1	No	$0.00	$0.00	$0.00	$0.00	$0.00	3:30pm	4:15pm	Nc
Paynter, Eric	Jaberwocki, Harold	8300213201HJ	20xx-Feb-07	OHIP	0	None	0	None	1	No	$0.00	$0.00	$0.00	$0.00	$0.00	3:30pm	4:30pm	Nc
Paynter, Eric	Twain, Mark	1161230193	20xx-Mar-18	OHIP	0	None	0	None	1	No	$0.00	$0.00	$0.00	$0.00	$0.00	11:00am	11:20am	Nc

Following is a sample of what messages might appear as a result of this prompt. At this point, you can print the screen and revise the claims as required prior to submission to the Ministry.

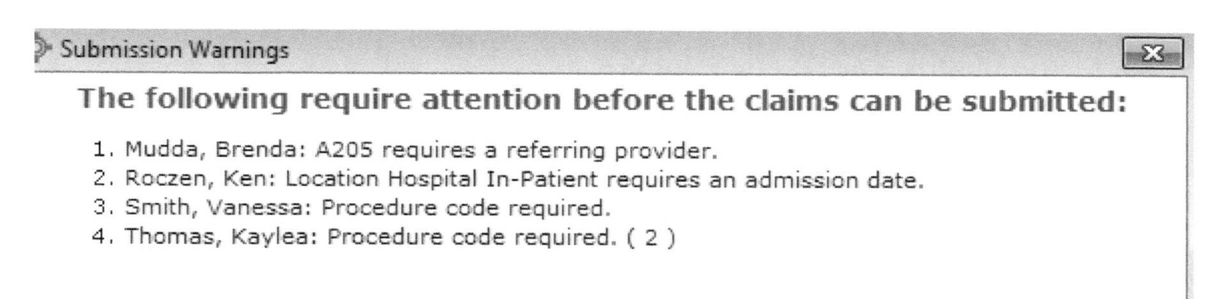

Independent Consideration

Independent consideration (IC) is used when a physician would like the Ministry to determine if a service not provided in the Schedule of Benefits is eligible for payment. The request is sent by letter with supporting reports to the Ministry.

Shadow Billing

Shadow billing is a format used in practices that have entered into primary care reform agreements with the Ministry (Alternate Funding Program – AFP).

The billing process is completed as fees for service; however, the amount agreed upon is what is received by the physician regardless of the total amount billed. The physicians are paid a yearly amount for each patient registered based upon a set of criteria per patient and remuneration based upon the Schedule of Benefits fees for services.

Project 7

GENERATING CLAIMS FROM SCENARIOS

LEARNING OBJECTIVES

- Understanding diagnosis codes and diagnoses for medical specialty areas
- Generating claims for new bills based on scenarios from different specialties using the Accuro®EMR system

For each of the specialty areas contained within this workbook, you will be adding diagnosis codes and diagnoses to an MS Excel medical billing code workbook and creating patient claims in Accuro®EMR based upon the scenarios provided, which enable you to practise using the most common medical billing codes.

In some instances, advanced procedure codes and premium codes were omitted in the scenarios, particularly where surgery is involved.

The areas of specialty are:

- Family Medicine
- Urology
- Hematology
- Mental Health
- Dermatology
- Neurology and Neurosurgery
- Orthopedics
- Gastroenterology
- General Surgery
- Cardiology
- Obstetrics and Gynecology
- Endocrinology and Metabolism
- Geriatrics
- Pediatrics
- Otolaryngology
- Infectious Disease
- Plastic Surgery
- Rheumatology
- Miscellaneous

Task 1 is repetitive throughout each specialty area. You will be creating a Medical Diagnosis Codes Workbook to capture common Diagnosis Codes by specialty area. These codes will be sorted and displayed both alphabetically and numerically.

If you are not using an EMR system, do not complete the search by Diagnosis Code.

Knowledge of medical terminology and body systems is a key factor when searching for diagnoses. It is helpful to search by the root word or key word within the diagnosis. The Resource Manual for Physicians has two sections—alphabetical and body system.

TASK 1

BILLING CLAIMS – DIAGNOSIS CODES

RESOURCES: Medical Billing Codes Workbook
Resource Manual for Physicians
Billing Scenarios

1. Rename a sheet as **Diagnosis Codes**.
2. Apply a colour to the tab.
3. In the Diagnosis Codes worksheet, create two columns:
   - Diagnosis Code (Column A)
   - Diagnosis (Column B)
4. Sort numerically by Diagnosis Code.
5. Copy Columns A and B to Sheet 4.
6. Rename Sheet 4 as Diagnosis Codes Alphabetically.
7. Sort alphabetically.

TASK 2

GENERATING CLAIMS FROM SCENARIOS

RESOURCES: Appendix C – BMC Student Patient Database
Appendix F – Accuro®EMR Instructions
Appendix G – Accuro®EMR Instructions for Medical Billing
Appendix I – Billing Scenario Template
MOHLTC Resource Manual for Physicians
MOHLTC Schedule of Benefits

Using your EMR system (Accuro®EMR), create claims for new bills for each of the scenarios using the student BMC patient database created in Project 1.

Note: MOHLTC no longer supports manual billing. Health care providers must submit claims through an EMR system.

The following tasks are divided into scenarios (Scenario 1's are basic, Scenario 2's are intermediate, and Scenario 3's are advanced billing exercises).

Use the Schedule of Benefits, Resource Manual for Physicians, and/or your EMR system to determine the necessary information essential to creating new bills (claims).

The chart below has been provided electronically only if you are not using an EMR system.

Your instructor will provide the necessary guidance for creating the bills in terms of the calendar timeframes each student will be using; in an EMR system, it may be necessary for each student to have a different timeframe in order not to overlap with other students.

If you do not have an EMR system in your classroom, the following template has been provided to capture the information.

Specialty	Scenario	Procedure	Diagnosis	Premium	Units

When identifying premiums, list the applicable Premium Code. **If the scenario does not warrant a Premium Code, provide an explanation of why this scenario cannot be billed as a Premium Code.**

Family Medicine

Common Medical Diagnoses and Diagnosis Codes:

Diagnosis	Code
Strep Throat	
Wax in Ear	
Influenza	
Diabetes (including complications)	
Asthma	
Pneumonia	
Shortness of Breath	
Foreign Body in Eye	
Cough	
Allergy – Rhinitis	
	917
	428
	989
	919
	949
	691
	040
	595
	009
	897

Scenario 1:

Patient 10 complains of burning and blood streaks upon urination. Patient 10 made a general assessment appointment to see Dr. K. Thomas, General Practitioner, at BMC on Thursday at 4:00 p.m. The nurse asked Patient 10 to provide a urine sample upon arrival, and a dipstick analysis was performed. The result was white blood cells and was positive for blood. Dr. Thomas diagnosed a urine infection.

Procedure: Diagnosis:

Scenario 2:

Patient 8 is coming into BMC on Friday at 10:30 a.m. for a periodic health visit to see Dr. K. Thomas, General Practitioner. Patient 8 always plans a yearly appointment close to flu season so that the influenza vaccine can be administered at the same time.

Procedure: Diagnosis:

Procedure: Diagnosis:

Scenario 3:

Patient 6 has been diagnosed with Stage 4 small cell carcinoma. The patient is scheduled to see Dr. A. Darby, General Practitioner, on Tuesday at 9:00 a.m. for a 50-minute special palliative-care consultation. The family accompanied the patient to the appointment for an interview to receive necessary instructions for patient care. The appointment lasted 90 minutes.

Procedure: Diagnosis:

Premium: Diagnosis:

Units:

Urology

Common Medical Diagnoses and Diagnosis Codes:

Diagnosis	Code
Incontinence of Urine	
Neoplasm – Benign – Kidney	
Neoplasm – Malignant Testis	
Pyelonephritis – Acute or Chronic	
Seminal Vesiculitis	
Sexual Deviations	
Sexual Dysfunction	
Spermatocele	
Sterilization Advice	
Sterility	
	585
	591
	593
	598
	581
	592
	233
	604
	580
	599

Scenario 1:

Patient 11 was once again experiencing excruciating low back pain. Dr. A. Darby, General Practitioner, provided a partial assessment on Thursday at 1:00 p.m.

Procedure: Diagnosis:

Scenario 2:

Patient 1 has been seeing Dr. H. Manley, Urologist, for chronic prostatitis over the last year. Patient 1 comes to Dr. Manley for a repeat consultation and has an appointment on Wednesday at 3:00 p.m.

Procedure: Diagnosis:

Premium: Diagnosis:

Dr. Manley has decided surgery is required and has booked Patient 1 for a perineal prostatectomy one month from today; however, will have a surgical consultation next week on Tuesday at 10:00 a.m., and Dr. Manley will be performing the surgery. Assume he has now performed the surgery.

Procedure: Diagnosis:

Procedure: Diagnosis:

Premium: Diagnosis:

Scenario 3:

Patient 12 has been seeing Dr. K. Thomas, General Practitioner, on and off this past year at the clinic for sterilization advice. Patient 12 booked a specific assessment at 3:30 p.m. on Monday at BMC to discuss Patient 12's decision regarding the sterilization. Patient 12 has four children and feels the family is complete.

Procedure: Diagnosis:

Dr. Thomas referred Patient 12 to Dr. H. Manley, Urologist, for a special surgical consultation to discuss the vasectomy.

Procedure: Diagnosis:

Dr. Manley performed the bilateral vasectomy the following Tuesday.

Procedure: Diagnosis:

Hematology

Common Medical Diagnoses and Diagnosis Codes:

Diagnosis	Code
Iron Deficiency Anemia	
Pernicious Anemia	
Thalassemia	
Sickle Cell Anemia	
Acquired Hemolytic Anemia	
Aplastic Anemia	
Other Anemias	
Coagulation Defects	
Hypogammaglobulinemia	
Spleen Disease	
	287
	287
	288
	288
	288
	282
	038
	451
	204
	286

Scenario 1:

Patient 16 was referred to Dr. L. Black, Hematologist and General Medicine, at BMC by Dr. K. Johnston, General Practitioner, for a consultation. The patient complains of weight loss, fatigue, and increased pallor. Blood work was done by Dr. Johnston a week before the Thursday appointment at 2:30 p.m. Blood work indicated an iron deficiency, and Dr. Black concurred with the diagnosis.

Procedure: Diagnosis:

Scenario 2:

Dr. L. Black, Hematologist and General Medicine, examined Patient 1 for a medical-specific assessment. The siblings of this patient have a history of hemophilia. This is a chronic condition for Patient 1. Patient 1 was aware of the possibility of this diagnosis, so an appointment was made during regular hours.

Procedure: Diagnosis:

Premium: Diagnosis:

Scenario 3:

Patient 15 (3 years of age) was playing with neighbouring children and fell and scraped a knee. The mother could not stop the bleeding over a period of time. The mother brought Patient 15 to see Dr. K. Thomas, General Practitioner, for a medical-specific assessment, and Dr. Thomas requisitioned blood work, questioning a coagulation defect. Dr. Thomas referred Patient 15 to Dr. L. Black, BMC's Hematologist.

Procedure: Diagnosis:

Premium: Diagnosis:

Dr. Black met with Patient 15 the next day at 11:00 a.m. for a consultation. Patient 15 was sent for further blood work, which included a PT and PTT.

Procedure: Diagnosis:

A followup medical-specific reassessment for Patient 15 was made for two weeks later on a Monday afternoon at 3:00 p.m. The diagnosis provided was Factor II Deficiency.

Procedure: Diagnosis:

Premium: Diagnosis:

Mental Health

Common Medical Diagnoses and Diagnosis Codes:

Diagnosis	Code
Alcoholic Psychosis	
Alcoholism	
Anorexia Nervosa	
Anxiety Neurosis	
Paranoid States	
Tobacco Abuse	
Sexual Deviations	
Mental Deficiency	
Child Abuse, Child Neglect	
Drug Psychosis	
	299
	290
	296
	295
	307
	307
	301
	905
	901
	291

Scenario 1:

Patient 5 has been diagnosed as a disturbed patient with alcoholic psychosis. Patient 5 is having a consultation with Dr. R. Headley, Psychiatrist, at BMC, on Tuesday at 2:00 p.m.

Procedure: Diagnosis:

Scenario 2:

Patient 16 has been experiencing bouts of depression – non-reactive over the past number of years. As a result of this depression, Dr. A. Darby, General Practitioner, referred Patient 16 to Dr. R. Headley, Psychiatrist, for a consultation. Dr. Headley saw the patient at BMC on Friday at 10:00 a.m.

Procedure: Diagnosis:

Six months later, Dr. Darby requested a repeat consultation at BMC with Patient 16 for further examination. It was discovered that Patient 16 suffers from obsessive-compulsive neurosis.

Procedure: Diagnosis:

Scenario 3:

Patient 20 is enrolled in a difficult and time-consuming degree program. Patient 20 visited a friend who recently had surgery and stole the pain medication that was prescribed. Patient 20 was distraught and took all the pills at once in a suicide attempt before calling 911. The patient arrived by ambulance on a Saturday evening at 11:00 p.m. The ER physician called the on-call psychiatrist, Dr. R. Headley, for a consultation. He had to travel from home to Hope General Hospital, as this was his first patient.

Procedure: Diagnosis:

Premium 1: Diagnosis:

Premium 2: Diagnosis:

Dermatology

Common Medical Diagnoses and Diagnosis Codes:

Diagnosis	Code
Acne Rosacea	
Warts – All Types	
Allergy – Drugs and Medication	
Alopecia	
Athlete's Foot	
Bed Sore	
Boil	
Neoplasm – Malignant Skin	
Scleroderma – Localized	
Sweating – Excessive	
	691
	691
	691
	690
	695
	684
	700
	680
	216
	210

Scenario 1:

Patient 15 was referred to Dr. F. Skinner, Dermatologist, at BMC by Dr. K. Johnston, General Practitioner, at the clinic at 10:15 a.m. on Tuesday for a repeat consultation. Patient 15 experiences allergic reactions to certain food groups. The resulting diagnosis was hives.

Procedure: Diagnosis:

Scenario 2:

Dr. A. Darby, General Practitioner, is seeing Patient 2 for a specific assessment of a foot problem. The appointment is at BMC next Thursday at 4:00 p.m. Patient 2 noticed dryness and peeling between the toes. Dr. Darby was unsure if it was psoriasis or something else.

Procedure: Diagnosis:

Dr. A. Darby referred Patient 2 to Dr. F. Skinner, Dermatologist, for a consultation at BMC the following Friday at 3:00 p.m. Dr. Skinner diagnosed Patient 2 with Athlete's Foot and prescribed a powder to help treat the problem, along with foot-care instructions.

Procedure: Diagnosis:

Scenario 3:

Patient 10 was walking to the car and slipped and fell on an icy sidewalk. Patient 10 was taken to Hope General Hospital's Emergency Department. Patient 10 was admitted to the hospital by the Orthopedic Surgeon, Dr. F. Bones, for a fractured right femur. Dr. Bones was already in the hospital when the patient arrived. Patient 10 was found to be 16 weeks pregnant. Dr. Bones noticed a full-body rash and, subsequently, ordered a dermatology consultation.

Procedure: Diagnosis:

Premium: Diagnosis:

Dr. Bones consulted Dermatologist Dr. F. Skinner who visited Patient 10 at 3:00 p.m. at Hope General Hospital after admission (during normal business hours) for a non-emergency in-patient consultation. Patient 10 was diagnosed with Pruritic Urticarial Papules (PUPPS).

Procedure: Diagnosis:

Patient 10 had a subsequent visit by Dr. Skinner, Dermatologist, related to a rash one week after the patient was admitted to Hope General Hospital.

Procedure: Diagnosis:

Neurology and Neurosurgery

Common Medical Diagnoses and Diagnosis Codes:

Diagnosis	Code
Trigeminal Neuralgia	
Bell's Palsy	
Myasthenia Gravis	
Muscular Dystrophy	
Scoliosis	
Convulsions	
Headache	
Lumbar Strain	
Muscle Pain	
Raynaud's Disease	
	323
	320
	330
	332
	340
	343
	345
	349
	036
	722

Scenario 1:

Patient 10 is a patient of Dr. S. Neuverly, Neurologist, as a result of a Bell's Palsy diagnosis from a previous pregnancy. Dr. Neuverly saw his patient at the clinic on Thursday at 10:00 a.m. for a medical-specific re-assessment.

Procedure: Diagnosis:

Scenario 2:

Patient 2 is experiencing numbness and tingling on her right hand from computer work.

Dr. K. Johnston, General Practitioner, felt a neurology consultation was necessary and booked Patient 2 to see Dr. S. Neuverly, Neurologist, on Thursday at 4:15 p.m. at the clinic. Patient 4 was diagnosed with carpal tunnel syndrome.

Procedure: Diagnosis:

Dr. Neuverly booked Patient 2 for day surgery in two months. A surgical consultation was not required. An electrophysiological assessment was performed pre-op with the physician present.

Procedure: Diagnosis:

The next day, Dr. Neuverly performed a carpal tunnel release and Patient 2 was sent home.

Procedure: Diagnosis:

Scenario 3:

Patient 12 was having muscle spasms, tension headaches, and muscle pain from a suspected diagnosis of Parkinson's disease, which is a chronic condition. Dr. K. Thomas, General Practitioner, referred Patient 12 to Dr. S. Neuverly, Neurologist, for a consultation at BMC on Friday at 1:00 p.m. The consultation lasted 1.5 hours.

Procedure: Diagnosis:

One week after the initial consultation, Patient 12 was feeling very unwell. Dr. Neuverly was on-call at Hope General Hospital and asked Patient 12 to come into the Emergency Department. Patient 12 was seen by the Emergency physician. The Emergency physician paged and consulted Dr. Neuverly, who provided a limited consultation after travelling to the hospital on a Sunday at 10:00 p.m. Dr. Neuverly admitted Patient 12 to the hospital. Dr. Neuverly was the Most Responsible Physician (MRP).

Procedure: Diagnosis:

Premium 1: Diagnosis:

Premium 2: Diagnosis:

Premium 3: Diagnosis:

Patient 12 was seen one more time by Dr. Neuverly on the day discharge, a day later.

Procedure: Diagnosis:

Premium: Diagnosis:

Orthopedics

Common Medical Diagnoses and Diagnosis Codes:

Diagnosis	Code
Coccyx Trauma	
Knee Sprain	
Upper Limb Amputation – Traumatic	
Club Foot	
Flat Foot	
Gout	
Recurrent Dislocation	
Other Dislocation	
Lower Limb Amputation	
Arthritis – Osteo	
	812
	813
	816
	823
	821
	824
	831
	832
	834
	845

Scenario 1:

Patient 8 was referred to Dr. F. Bones, Orthopedic Surgeon, at BMC for bunions on the right foot for a consultation on Thursday at 3:30 p.m.

Procedure: Diagnosis:

Scenario 2:

Patient 1 was in a motor vehicle accident and taken to Hope General Hospital by ambulance where Patient 1 was seen in consultation by Dr. Bones, Orthopedic Surgeon, in the Emergency Department. Dr. Bones was already in the hospital and was the Most Responsible Physician (MRP) and admitted Patient 1 due to Patient 1's age and broken ribs.

Procedure: Diagnosis:

Premium: Diagnosis:

Dr. Bones saw Patient 1 for the next two days in hospital as the MRP.

Procedure: Diagnosis:

Premium: Diagnosis:

Procedure: Diagnosis:

Premium: Diagnosis:

Scenario 3:

While skating on the Rideau Canal in Ottawa, Patient 15 fell and broke the left arm. Patient 15 was referred to Dr. F. Bones, Orthopedic Surgeon, by Dr. K. Thomas, General Practitioner, for an initial consultation at BMC on Monday at 10:30 a.m.

Procedure: Diagnosis:

Dr. Bones saw Patient 15 that morning for a specific assessment at 11:30 a.m. Dr. Bones did an X-ray of the left arm with three views of the left ulna (forearm). The result was a fracture of the ulna. Dr. Bones applied a cast.

Procedure: Diagnosis:

Procedure: Diagnosis:

Procedure: Diagnosis:

Premium: Diagnosis:

Gastroenterology

Common Medical Diagnoses and Diagnosis Codes:

Diagnosis	Code
Gastric Ulcer Without or With Hemorrhage or Perforation	
Duodenal Ulcer	
Stomal Ulcer	
Gastrojejunal Ulcer	
Rectal Bleeding	
Malabsorption Syndrome	
Irritable Colon	
Acute Appendicitis	
Crohn's Disease	
Impaction of Intestine	
	556
	536
	560
	579
	787
	565
	787
	535
	536
	573

Scenario 1:

Patient 8 was booked at BMC on Friday at 9:00 a.m. for a limited consultation with Dr. W. Gas, Gastroenterologist, related to celiac disease. Patient 8 required a definitive diagnosis from Dr. Gas.

Procedure: Diagnosis:

Scenario 2:

Patient 3 was seen in Hope General Hospital's Emergency Department. Patient 3 appeared to be dehydrated. Dr. W. Gas, Gastroenterologist, was called in from home on Sunday at 4:00 p.m. Patient 3 was sent home with instructions to follow up with Dr. Gas with regard to the possibility of malabsorption syndrome.

Procedure: Diagnosis:

Premium 1: Diagnosis:

Premium 2: Diagnosis:

Scenario 3:

Patient 7 had constipation and made an appointment with Dr. K. Thomas, General Practitioner, at BMC for a general reassessment on Friday at 10:30 a.m.

Procedure: Diagnosis:

Dr. Thomas referred Patient 7 to Dr. W. Gas, Gastroenterologist, at the clinic on Monday at 2:30 p.m. Dr. Gas ordered and performed a double contrast X-ray on Patient 7's esophagus, stomach, and duodenum and a barium enema. The digestive tract was visualized, and a more precise diagnosis was found.

Procedure: Diagnosis:

Procedure: Diagnosis:

Procedure: Diagnosis:

Patient 7 had a repeat consultation with Dr. Gas one week later on a Friday at 9:15 a.m. at BMC. The final diagnosis was irritable colon, and Patient 7 was given educational material to help cope with this condition.

Procedure: Diagnosis:

General Surgery

Common Medical Diagnoses and Diagnosis Codes:

Diagnosis	Code
Inguinal Hernia Without Obstruction	
Ingrown Toe Nail	
Laceration to Lower Limb	
Diverticulitis	
Disease of Pancreas	
Intestinal Obstruction	
Femoral Hernia Without Obstruction	
Peritonitis With or Without Abscess	
Open Wound Upper Limb	
Hemorrhoids	
	565
	879
	611
	569
	879
	226
	215
	552
	574
	618

Scenario 1:

Patient 7 has experienced further issues with an inguinal hernia. Patient 7 is has an appointment today at the clinic at 11:30 a.m. with Dr. B. Cutter, General Surgeon, for a special surgical consultation.

Procedure: Diagnosis:

Scenario 2:

Patient 16 is at a convalescent home following surgery on a spinal decompression with instrumentation. Dr. Cutter provided a general surgery consultation as Patient 16 was experiencing complications and possible infection to the wound site. Dr. Cutter determined that debridement to the wound into the ligament and tendon was necessary. Dr. Cutter debrided the area, added two additional sutures to promote healing, and redressed the area.

Procedure: Diagnosis:

Procedure: Diagnosis:

Premium: Diagnosis:

Scenario 3:

Patient 11 was experiencing abdominal problems and feared appendicitis. Patient 11 was given a general assessment appointment at BMC with Dr. A. Darby, General Practitioner, on Friday at 3:00 p.m.

Procedure: Diagnosis:

Dr. Darby referred Patient 11 to Dr. B. Cutter, General Surgeon, at BMC for suspected appendicitis.

Dr. Cutter provided a consultation at BMC where he decided an appendectomy was necessary.

Procedure: Diagnosis:

Dr. Cutter performed the appendectomy the following morning at 9:00 a.m. at Hope General Hospital.

Procedure: Diagnosis:

Cardiology

Common Medical Diagnoses and Diagnosis Codes:

Diagnosis	Code
Angina Pectoris	
Angina, Common Ludwig's	
Angina, Vincent's	
Arteriosclerotic Heart Diseases Without Symptoms	
Arteriosclerosis	
Atrial Fibrillation, Flutter	
Bradycardia	
Cardiac Arrest	
Mitral Insufficiency or Stenosis	
Rheumatic Heart Disease – Other	
	746
	428
	426
	413
	410
	402
	429
	394
	530
	391

Scenario 1:

Dr. B. Harte, Cardiologist, saw Patient 4 at BMC on Tuesday at 2:30 p.m., having been referred by Dr. A. Darby, General Practitioner, for a medical-specific assessment with regard to Patient 4's chronic hypertensive heart disease.

Procedure: Diagnosis:

Premium: Diagnosis:

Scenario 2:

Dr. A. Darby, General Practitioner, made a house call to Patient 8 on Monday at 8:00 a.m. for a patient with a disability who required a house call assessment. Dr. Darby examined Patient 8 and noticed an enlarged chest area around the heart and was concerned of heart disease.

Procedure: Diagnosis:

Premium 1: Diagnosis:

Premium 2: Diagnosis:

Scenario 3:

Dr. A. Darby, General Practitioner, saw Patient 14 at BMC for a consultation for suspicion of Endocarditis.

Procedure: Diagnosis:

Dr. Darby referred Patient 14 to Dr. B. Harte, Cardiologist, for a consultation for suspicion of Endocarditis. The appointment with Dr. Harte was today at 2:00 p.m.

Procedure: Diagnosis:

Patient 14 met with Dr. Harte one week later at BMC at 3:00 p.m. and confirmed the suspected diagnosis of Endocarditis. Following the consultation, Dr. Harte performed an electrocardiogram (12-lead) with the clinic's machine and interpreted the results.

Procedure: Diagnosis:

Procedure: Diagnosis:

Procedure: Diagnosis:

Obstetrics and Gynecology

Common Medical Diagnoses and Diagnosis Codes:

Diagnosis	Code
Bleeding – Post Menopausal	
Candidiasis	
Breast Carcinoma	
Cervical Dysplasia	
Condyloma	
Dysmenorrhea	
Endometriosis	
Ovarian Dysfunction, Failure	
Pelvic Inflammatory Disease	
Prolapse, Uterine	
	895
	634
	767
	646
	762
	636
	765
	675
	651
	660

Scenario 1:

Patient 4 was in menopause and has been referred to Dr. B. Boom, Obstetrician and Gynecologist, by Dr. K. Thomas, General Practitioner, Tuesday at 4:00 p.m. at BMC for a consultation.

Procedure: Diagnosis:

Scenario 2:

Patient 9 had a pregnancy followup appointment at BMC for a partial assessment Monday at 11:00 a.m. with Dr. B. Boom, Obstetrician and Gynecologist. Patient 9 was having problems urinating and suspected a urinary tract infection.

Procedure: Diagnosis:

This was Patient 9's third infection during pregnancy and Dr. Boom referred Patient 9 to Dr. H. Manley, Urologist, at the clinic for a consultation.

Procedure: Diagnosis:

Scenario 3:

Patient 13 needed advice on terminating a pregnancy due to it being an unwanted pregnancy. Patient 13 thought she was 16 weeks pregnant. Patient 13 was referred to Dr. B. Boom, Obstetrician and Gynecologist, by Dr. A. Darby, General Practitioner, at the clinic on Tuesday at 9:15 a.m. at BMC for a consultation.

Dr. Boom administered a pap smear at the same time as the consultation as the patient had not had a pap smear in over a year. Dr. Boom performed an ultrasound, which concluded that the patient had already had a complete abortion naturally.

Procedure: Diagnosis:

Procedure: Diagnosis:

Patient 13 was given a repeat consultation appointment at BMC in three weeks on a Wednesday at 9:00 a.m. to discuss methods of birth control and the possibility of an IUD insertion.

Procedure: Diagnosis:

Procedure: Diagnosis:

Premium: Diagnosis:

Endocrinology and Metabolism

Common Medical Diagnoses and Diagnosis Codes:

Diagnosis	Code
Non-Toxic Nodular Goiter	
Hyperthyroidism, Thyrotoxicosis, Exophthalmic Goiter	
Hypothyroid – Congenital	
Immunity Disorders	
Thyroiditis	
Pre-Diabetes	
Diabetes Mellitus, Including Complications	
Vitamin and Other Nutritional Deficiencies	
Obesity	
Testicular Dysfunction	
	270
	263
	272
	277
	253
	240
	252
	255
	256
	244

Scenario 1:

Patient 7 has been diagnosed with diabetes mellitus. Patient 7 has been referred to Dr. E. Paynter, Endocrinologist and Metabolism, by Dr. K. Thomas, General Practitioner, both of BMC, for a comprehensive endocrinology consultation. Patient 7 spent 90 minutes yesterday (Tuesday), commencing at 9:15 a.m., with Dr. Paynter, due to her chronic disease.

Procedure: Diagnosis:

Premium: Diagnosis:

Scenario 2:

Patient 11 was hospitalized for chronic kidney stones. While in Hope General Hospital, the Most Responsible Physician, Dr. E. Paynter, Endocrinologist, ordered complete blood work and the results determined that Patient 11 required a complex endocrine neoplastic disease assessment.

Procedure: Diagnosis:

Dr. Paynter was called out on Saturday at 2:00 p.m. from home for an in-patient consultation at Hope General Hospital.

Procedure: Diagnosis:

Premium 1: Diagnosis:

Premium 2: Diagnosis:

Scenario 3:

Patient 9 collapsed on a baseball field after neglecting to properly hydrate. Patient 9 was brought to Hope General Hospital Emergency Department where the ER physician ran a number of tests and performed an Emergency Department Consultation.

Procedure: Diagnosis:

Dr. E. Paynter, Endocrinologist, was called from within Hope General Hospital for a consultation in the Emergency Department. Dr. Paynter admitted Patient 9 to Hope General Hospital at 9:00 p.m. on Saturday evening for further testing and monitoring.

Procedure: Diagnosis:

Premium 1: Diagnosis:

Premium 2: Diagnosis:

After reviewing the results, Dr. Paynter determined that Patient 9 was suffering from dangerously low blood sugar. Dr. Paynter saw Patient 9 three days in a row while Patient 9 was in Hope General Hospital. Dr. Paynter was the Most Responsible Physician (MRP). Patient 9 was discharged and asked to follow up with Dr. Paynter monthly for the next three months.

Procedure: Diagnosis:

Premium: Diagnosis:

Procedure: Diagnosis:

Premium: Diagnosis:

Procedure: Diagnosis:

Premium: Diagnosis:

Geriatrics

Common Medical Diagnoses and Diagnosis Codes:

Diagnosis	Code
Bronchitis – Acute	
Bronchitis – Allergic	
Bronchitis – Chronic	
Bruises	
Cataract – Congenital	
Cerebral Degenerations	
Cerebral Hemorrhage	
Cerebro-Vascular Accidents – Acute	
Corneal Ulcer	
Emphysema	
	496
	548
	571
	440
	173
	373
	373
	369
	780
	365

Scenario 1:

Patient 6 was referred to Dr. F. Ages, Geriatrician, by Dr. A. Darby, General Practitioner, for medical-specific re-assessment today at the clinic at 3:00 p.m. Patient 6 has chronic bronchitis.

Procedure: Diagnosis:

Premium: Diagnosis:

Scenario 2:

Patient 5 was admitted to BMC on Sunday by another physician, who transferred the patient to the care of Dr. F. Ages, Geriatrician, the Most Responsible Physician. Patient 5 was seen by Dr. Ages on Monday at 2:00 p.m. (day after admission), and Tuesday (second day after admission) for a stroke. Subsequently, Patient 5 was transferred to a rehabilitation hospital. Before the transfer took place, Dr. Ages met with Patient 5's family for an interview that lasted 78 minutes.

Procedure: Diagnosis:

Premium: Diagnosis:

Procedure: Diagnosis:

Premium: Diagnosis:

Procedure: Diagnosis:

Units:

Scenario 3:

Patient 6 reported to Hope General Hospital Emergency Department on Monday at 8:00 p.m., and Patient 6 was seen by the ER physician for a suspected drug overdose.

Procedure: Diagnosis:

Patient 6 required a comprehensive geriatric consultation in the Emergency Department at Hope General Hospital. Dr. F. Ages, Geriatrician, was called from home to assess Patient 6. It was determined that Patient 6 had to be admitted to the hospital for a few days due to prescription drug overdose due to a miscalculation in medication. Dr. Ages admitted Patient 6.

Procedure: Diagnosis:

Premium 1: Diagnosis:

Premium 2: Diagnosis:

Premium 3: Diagnosis:

Dr. Ages is now the MRP. The first-day visitation and second-day visitation were progress checks. Patient 6 was discharged on Day 3.

Procedure: Diagnosis:

Premium: Diagnosis:

Procedure: Diagnosis:

Premium: Diagnosis:

Procedure: Diagnosis:

Premium: Diagnosis:

Pediatrics

Common Medical Diagnoses and Diagnosis Codes:

Diagnosis	Code
Acne	
Autism	
Battered Child	
Behaviour Disorders of Childhood and Adolescence	
Croup	
Bites, Non-Venomous	
Lice, Head or Body	
Common Cold	
Hives	
Mumps	
	903
	916
	464
	466
	486
	009
	034
	056
	608
	243

Scenario 1:

Patient 15 was seen by Dr. S. Childs, Pediatrician, at BMC on Wednesday at 1:30 p.m. for a consultation because the patient was having problems breathing and had a high fever and a cough. Patient 15 was diagnosed with pneumonia.

Procedure: Diagnosis:

Scenario 2:

Patient 14 saw Dr. S. Childs, Pediatrician, on Thursday at BMC at 10:00 a.m. for a consultation. Patient 14 was born premature and was seen by Dr. Childs for acute diarrhea.

Procedure: Diagnosis:

Scenario 3:

Patient 17 was seen by Dr. S. Childs, Pediatrician, on Monday at the clinic at 3:30 p.m. Patient 17 is suffering from acne and was seen for a consultation.

Assume Patient 17 is 16 years old for this scenario.

Procedure: Diagnosis:

Premium: Diagnosis:

Otolaryngology

Common Medical Diagnoses and Diagnosis Codes:

Diagnosis	Code
Halitosis	
Meniere's Disease	
Nasal Polyp	
Nasopharyingitis, Acute	
Otitis Externa	
Conditions of Tonsilitis, Acute	
Performation of Tympanic Membrane	
Rhinitis, Allergic	
Disease of Salivary Gland	
Labyrinthitis	
	474
	474
	530
	389
	351
	381
	383
	381
	477
	112

Scenario 1:

Patient 5 met with Dr. J. Herring, ENT, at BMC, on Tuesday at 10:00 a.m. for a special surgical consultation to discuss the possibility of having a cochlear implant due to deafness.

Procedure: Diagnosis:

Scenario 2:

Patient 14 is consistently complaining of ear aches and made an appointment for Thursday at 3:30 p.m. at the clinic with Dr. K. Johnston, General Practitioner, for a general assessment.

Procedure: Diagnosis:

Dr. Johnston, General Practitioner, referred Patient 14 to Dr. J. Herring, ENT, at BMC for Friday at 4:00 p.m. Dr. Herring flushed the wax from Patient 14's ear.

Procedure: Diagnosis:

Scenario 3:

Dr. F. Ages, Geriatrician, is the staff physician at Sunnyside Long-Term Care Facility, and has referred Patient 5 to Dr. J. Herring, ENT. Patient 5 has a nodule or polyp on the external area of the left ear. Dr. Herring saw Patient 5 for a consultation in the long-term care facility. Dr. Herring performed an excision of the polyp under local anesthetic.

Procedure: Diagnosis:

Premium: Diagnosis:

Infectious Diseases

Common Medical Diagnoses and Diagnosis Codes:

Diagnosis	Code
Salmonella Infection	
Herpes Simplex, Cold Sore	
TB Test	
Malaria	
Herpes Zoster	
Viral Gastro-Enteritis	
Fungus	
Food Poisoning	
Encephalomyelitis	
Scabies	
	052
	682
	030
	684
	730
	097
	132
	042
	127
	070

Scenario 1:

Patient 13 was referred by Dr. A. Darby, General Practitioner, to Dr. C. Voyage, Infectious Disease and Tropical Medicine, at BMC for chronic fatigue. The consultation was Wednesday at 9:30 a.m.

Procedure: Diagnosis:

Scenario 2:

Patient 3 returned from travelling internationally. Patient 3 noticed abscesses on both legs and felt the abscesses were growing. Dr. K. Thomas, General Practitioner, referred Patient 3 to Dr. C. Voyage, Infectious Disease and Tropical Medicine, for a comprehensive consultation today at 10:00 a.m. at BMC. Patient 3 was diagnosed with a parasitic disease. Dr. Voyage performed a biopsy on one of the three lumps on Patient 3's leg. Two sutures were used to close the incision.

Procedure:	Diagnosis:
Procedure:	Diagnosis:
Premium:	Diagnosis:

Scenario 3:

Patient 9 was seen in Hope General Hospital's Emergency Department Saturday at 5:00 a.m. by the ER physician. Patient 9 was suffering from a questionable viral disorder accompanied by a severe body rash.

Procedure:	Diagnosis:

The ER physician ordered an infectious disease consultation Saturday morning at 6:00 a.m. Dr. C. Voyage, Infectious Disease and Tropical Medicine, came from home to the Emergency Department at Hope General Hospital, reviewed Patient 9's history, and conducted a comprehensive infectious disease consultation, which lasted 90 minutes.

Dr. Voyage diagnosed Patient 9 with Hansen's Disease.

Procedure:	Diagnosis:
Premium 1:	Diagnosis:
Premium 2:	Diagnosis:

Plastic Surgery

Common Medical Diagnoses and Diagnosis Codes:

Diagnosis	Code
Sebaceous Cyst	
Breast Cyst	
Corns	
Carcinoma In Situ – Skin	
Carpal Tunnel Syndrome	
Canker Sore	
Lacrimal Duct Calculus	
Bullet Wound – Internal Injury	
Basal Cell Carcinoma	
Skin and Subcutaneous Abscess	
	994
	616
	228
	727
	373
	749
	470
	749
	446
	701

Scenario 1:

Patient 14 was seen for possible frostbite on the toes from skating outdoors the day before. Patient 14 was seen at BMC on Monday at 1:00 p.m. by Dr. K. Thomas, General Practitioner, who referred the patient to Dr. C. Paste, Plastic Surgeon, for a consultation. Patient 14 was diagnosed with frostbite and was given instructions on care.

Procedure: Diagnosis:

Scenario 2:

Patient 12 was noticing problems with sitting for periods of time due to a lump on the buttocks. Dr. A. Darby, General Practitioner, met the patient on Monday at 10:00 a.m. for a consultation. Dr. Darby felt it was a pilonidal cyst.

Procedure: Diagnosis:

Dr. Darby referred Patient 12 to Dr. C. Paste, Plastic Surgeon, for next Wednesday at 9:00 a.m. for a consultation. Dr. Paste diagnosed Patient 12 with a pilonidal cyst that required a simple excision and skin shift.

Procedure: Diagnosis:

Procedure: Diagnosis:

Scenario 3:

Patient 4 was having problems with numbness and tingling on the right hand as well as lack of strength. Dr. K. Thomas, General Practitioner, referred Patient 4 to Dr. C. Paste, Plastic Surgeon; an appointment is scheduled for next Monday at 3:00 p.m. for a surgical consultation. Dr. Paste diagnosed Patient 4 with carpal tunnel syndrome.

Procedure: Diagnosis:

Patient 4 was booked for a carpal tunnel release for next Thursday at Hope General Hospital.

Procedure: Diagnosis:

Rheumatology

Common Medical Diagnoses and Diagnosis Codes:

Diagnosis	Code
Lupus Erythematosus	
Pyogenic Arthritis	
Rheumatoid Arthritis	
Osteoarthritis	
Traumatic Arthritis	
Stills Disease	
Fibromyalgia	
Sciatica	
Muscular Rheumatism	
Leg Cramps	
	720
	724
	728
	756
	732
	781
	781
	785
	795
	735

Scenario 1:

Patient 6 was seen for followup at BMC by Dr. S. Aches, Rheumatologist, on Friday at 2:00 p.m. for a medical-specific assessment of Stills Disease.

Procedure: Diagnosis:

Scenario 2:

Patient 5 is suffering from arthritis due to a possible cartilage tear in the right ankle. Dr. A. Darby, General Practitioner, referred Patient 5 to Dr. S. Aches, Rheumatologist, for a comprehensive consultation at the clinic on Friday at 11:15 a.m. It was determined that Patient 5 had a cartilage tear.

Procedure: Diagnosis:

Dr. Aches performed a 4-view X-ray (at BMC) of Patient 5's ankle.

Procedure: Diagnosis:

Patient 5 was then referred to Dr. F. Bones, Orthopedics, for a special surgical consultation at BMC.

Procedure: Diagnosis:

Scenario 3:

Patient 6 was seen in Hope General Hospital's Emergency Department where a rheumatology consultation was ordered on the suspicion of ankylosing spondylitis. Dr. S. Aches, Rheumatologist, had to travel from BMC, during office hours where an appointment had to be cancelled, on Wednesday at 3:00 p.m. for a consultation.

Procedure: Diagnosis:

Premium 1: Diagnosis:

Premium 2: Diagnosis:

Patient 6 spent five days in the hospital and Patient 6 was seen on the day following admission, the second day after admission, and on the day of discharge. Dr. Aches was the Most Responsible Physician.

Procedure: Diagnosis:

Premium: Diagnosis:

Procedure: Diagnosis:

Premium: Diagnosis:

Procedure: Diagnosis:

Premium: Diagnosis:

Quebec Billing

RESOURCES: Quebec Application for Reimbursement Form
Receipt Template
Ontario Medical Association Site

Patient 18 was referred to Dr. B. Harte, Cardiologist, for a consultation from his family doctor in Northern Quebec, Dr. C. Louis. The appointment was in the clinic on a Tuesday at 4:30 p.m. Patient 18 has a history of Endocarditis. Patient 18 has been working in Ottawa, Ontario for two months with ABC Technologies Inc. and is in need of a specialist. Dr. Harte agreed to see Patient 18. Patient 18 has agreed to the fee from the Schedule of Benefits of Ontario and will be paying by Visa.

Procedure: Diagnosis:

- Complete a Quebec application for reimbursement form. Patient 18 came to Ontario one month prior to the appointment and will be returning to Quebec one month after the appointment date. Preferred language is English. The relationship to the application is "self."
- Physicians are eligible to charge the OMA fees, which are the Schedule of Benefits fees plus a surcharge. Refer to the OMA Fee Schedule and the Physician's Guide.
- Provide a receipt for the Visa payment for the amount allowed for the consultation in the Schedule of Benefits and applying the OMA formula of 1.97 percent.

Project 8

CREATING CLAIMS FROM DAY SHEETS, PATIENT RECORDS, AND PHYSICIAN NOTES

LEARNING OBJECTIVES

- Understanding how to interpret day sheets, patient records, and daily billing sheets in order to accurately retrieve the billing codes to create a new claim

Using day sheets, patient records, and daily billing sheets, the medical biller will be able to transfer the information into medical codes in order to create new claims.

Medical billers have access to patient records in a variety of formats. For the purposes of this workbook, we have selected day sheets generated through an EMR system, patient records, and daily billing sheets.

TASK 1

DAY SHEETS

RESOURCES: MOHLTC Schedule of Benefits
MOHLTC Resource Manual for Physicians

Create and complete the following Day Sheet table:

Patient	Procedure	Diagnosis	Premium
Kenneth Kelly			
Brenda Mudda			
Jules Arie			

Using the information from Dr. Skinner's Day Sheet (Dermatology) below, complete the table for patients Cindy Thomas and Jules Arie based on the information provided. Note: All cells may not be populated.

Day Sheet
07-May-20xx

Frank Skinner

Start	Length		Type	Note	
1200	20	**Kelly, Kenneth** 07/04/1954 5607041954KK (613) 432-4771 Referred by Dr. Darby, Alyssa[587600] Fam Dr. Darby, Alyssa[587600]	New Consult Specialist New Consult	Patient referred by Dr Darby for possible Psoriasis and treatment.	
1220	10	**Mudda, Brenda** 06/11/1960 7110611196 (000) ___-____ Referred by Dr. Thomas, Kyle[592300] Fam Dr. Thomas, Kyle[592300]	Follow-Up Follow up	Brenda is coming for a repeat consultation related to her chronic Rosacea	
1300	10	**Arie, Jules** 06/07/1977 230607197 (867) 761-4689 Referred by Dr. , [] Fam Dr. Johnston, Kaylea[423800]	Follow-Up Follow up	Note: bill as specific assessment for Shingles (10 minute appointment) Patient know to Dr Skinner, seen 2 months ago.	

Booked Appointments 3

TASK 2

PATIENT RECORDS

RESOURCES: MOHLTC Schedule of Benefits
MOHLTC Resource Manual for Physicians

Using Dr. Darby's Patient Record below for Douglas Thomas, create and complete the following Patient Record table. (Note: All cells may not be populated.)

Patient	Procedures	Diagnoses	Premium
Douglas Thomas			

NAME:	Thomas, Douglas T.	REFERRING MD: --None--
ADDRESS:	108 Second Avenue	
	Ottawa, ON K2S 1C5	HEALTH CARD NUMBER: 1080331195DT
HOME PHONE: (613) 592-1234		BIRTHDATE: 1959-Mar-31
WORK PHONE: (000) ___-____		

DIAGNOSIS: Chronic Fatigue

SERVICES
4. Blood Pressure Check
5. Flu Vaccine
6. CBC

BOOK PATIENT FOR THE FOLLOWING:
Please book patient for a Neurology Consultation

Physician Notes:

General re-assessment

TASK 3

DAILY BILLING SHEET

RESOURCES: MOHLTC Schedule of Benefits
MOHLTC Resource Manual for Physicians

Using Dr. Harte's Daily Billing Sheet below, create and complete the following table:

Patient	Name the Procedure	Name the Diagnosis
Kingsland Johnson		
Lynn Kelly		
Brenda Mudda		
Chris Fry		

DAILY BILLING SHEET

Dr. Brooke Harte **Date: March 25, 20xx**

Patient	Procedure/Diagnosis/Notes
Kingsland G. Johnson Y33-06-13 M 8 Sewell Way, Kanata, ON K2G 2X1 613-224-1146 8061 319 333 KJ	A603 428 Book followup 1/12
Lynn S. Kelly Y56-01-14 F 56 Westwood Drive, Nepean, ON K2Z 1X4 613-432-4774 613-732-7447 5601 141 955 LK	A604 402 Book 1/12 Book ECG same day before appt.
Brenda L. Mudda Y60-01-19 F 71 Gagnon Lane, Arnprior, ON K2S 7V3 613-722-2100 613-722-2100 7101 141 960 BM	A606 Referred by Dr. A. Darby Chest Pain – Check code pls. Followup with Family Physician
Chris D. Fry Y80-03-07 M 37 Bunting Lane, Stittsville, ON K2S 0S1 613-234-4123 613-729-1111	A604 426 Followup up 2/12 Book Holter Monitor Get OHIP number ********

Project 9

CLAIMS SUBMISSION

LEARNING OBJECTIVES

- Reviewing claims submission process checklist
- Understanding how medical claims are submitted

This project discusses the claims submission process for medical claims that are submitted to the MOHLTC.

Claims Submission Process Checklist

Once a claim has been generated in the EMR system, it must be checked for accuracy. Prior to submission of a claim, the following requirements must be met:

- Provider must have a valid billing number.
- Service claimed is authorized by provincial guidelines (Schedule of Benefits).
- Fee claimed is the one determined by the Fee Schedule.
- Patient has a valid health card.
- Claim is submitted in a technically correct manner (MC EDT approved).
- Claim is submitted within a preauthorized designated timeframe (six months).
- Claim is accurate and complete.

How Are Medical Claims Submitted?

Medical claims are submitted through Medical Claims Electronic Data Transfer (MC EDT) software. When a medical specialist registers with the MOHLTC, the specialist must select a Ministry-approved software system. The Ministry no longer accepts paper submissions. For the purposes of this workbook, we are using Accuro®EMR.

Once the medical codes have been entered into the system in patient records, claims are made to the Ministry by submitting each claim individually or in a batch submission (many patient claims together). Whoever is responsible for billing must ensure the accuracy and completeness of the codes.

See Appendix H for instructions on submission using Ontario's MC EDT.

Project 10

MINISTRY FEEDBACK

LEARNING OBJECTIVES

- Understanding the types of feedback from the MOHLTC upon submitting claims

This project discusses the MOHLTC feedback for any claims submissions.

Feedback from the Ministry

Once the MOHTLC has received and reviewed the claims submission, the MOHLTC issues various reports that will advise of the status of all claims submitted.

These reports are:

File Reject Message

- This report is sent immediately or within a few hours if the Ministry rejects an entire claims file.
- This message would only be received if the entire submission was rejected due to technical difficulties.
- Rejected claims must be resubmitted to be processed for payment.

Batch Edit Report

- This report notifies of the acceptance and processing of claims batches.
- Notification is sent within 24 hours of the Ministry receiving the claims submission.
- If a claims submission is uploaded on a weekend, holiday, or month end, the Batch Edit Report is sent on the next claims processing day.
- The Batch Edit Report begins with the letter B.

1. Claim Created: February 10, 20xx, 10:15 a.m.
2. BF592300.199
3. Dr. K. Thomas
4. Range: 2001 to 2020
5. Total Claims Submitted: 53 Records: 143
6. BF295599.19955
7. Total Amount Claimed: $1,689.00

1. Date and time claim received by Ministry
2. B = February, physician billing number, Ministry file number
3. Physician's name
4. Files submitted
5. Total Claims Submitted is the number of individual claims. Records is the total of all procedure codes billed within the claims. For example, if you bill Patient 1 with A001 and G005, it would be one claim with two records.
6. Ministry file number again
7. Amount of payout for claims submitted

Claims Error Report

- A Claims Error Report is sent to the physician by the Ministry listing all of the rejected claims and provides an error code and/or explanation for each rejection and instructions, if necessary, to reconcile the error.
- When the Error Codes are returned to the physician, the medical biller will then reconcile by correcting the errors and/or deleting an erroneous claim and resubmitting the claim as soon as possible in order for the payment to be made to the physician for services rendered.
- This report lists the rejected claims and provides an error code for each rejection or underpayment.
- Rejected claims may have more than one error code assigned.
- Notification is sent within 24 to 48 hours of claim submission.
- Claims rejected to an Error Report are automatically deleted from the payment stream.
- Claims with errors must be corrected and resubmitted to be processed for payment. The Ministry permits resubmission of corrected claims.
- Error Codes appear on the right side of the list.
- The Error Report begins with the letter E.
- An Error Code is a three-character alphanumeric code. The first character is a letter and denotes the type of rejection. For example:
  - V – Validity error
  - A – Assessment error
  - E – Eligibility error
  - R – Reciprocal Medical Billing (RMB) specific error
- Some samples of Error Codes are:
  - VH1 – Invalid health number
  - A3E – No such service code of date of service
  - AD9 – Premium not allowed alone
  - EF3 – Insured services are excluded from IHF billings
  - R01 – Missing HSN
- A listing of Error Codes can be found in the MOHLTC Resource Manual for Physicians under the Claims Submission section.
- Error Report Messages are the explanation of any billing submissions that are not reimbursed by the Ministry. They consist of two characters – some are two numbers and some are one letter and one number.
- Some examples of Error Report Messages are:
  - 30 – Service is not a benefit of OHIP
  - 56 – Claim under review
  - 57 – A payment that is an adjustment on an earlier account
  - DA – Allowed as repeat procedure – initial procedure previously claimed
  - D9 – Not allowed to a hospital department
  - E5 – Service date not within an eligible period
  - H7 – Allowed as chronic care
  - MD – Daily maximum exceeded

- A listing of Error Report Messages can be found in the MOHLTC Resource Manual for Physicians under the Claims Submission section.
- Claims that are not reconciled are returned to the EMR system under the Not Reconciled Tab, showing the explanation codes and their descriptions.
- Following is a sample of a Claims Error Report:

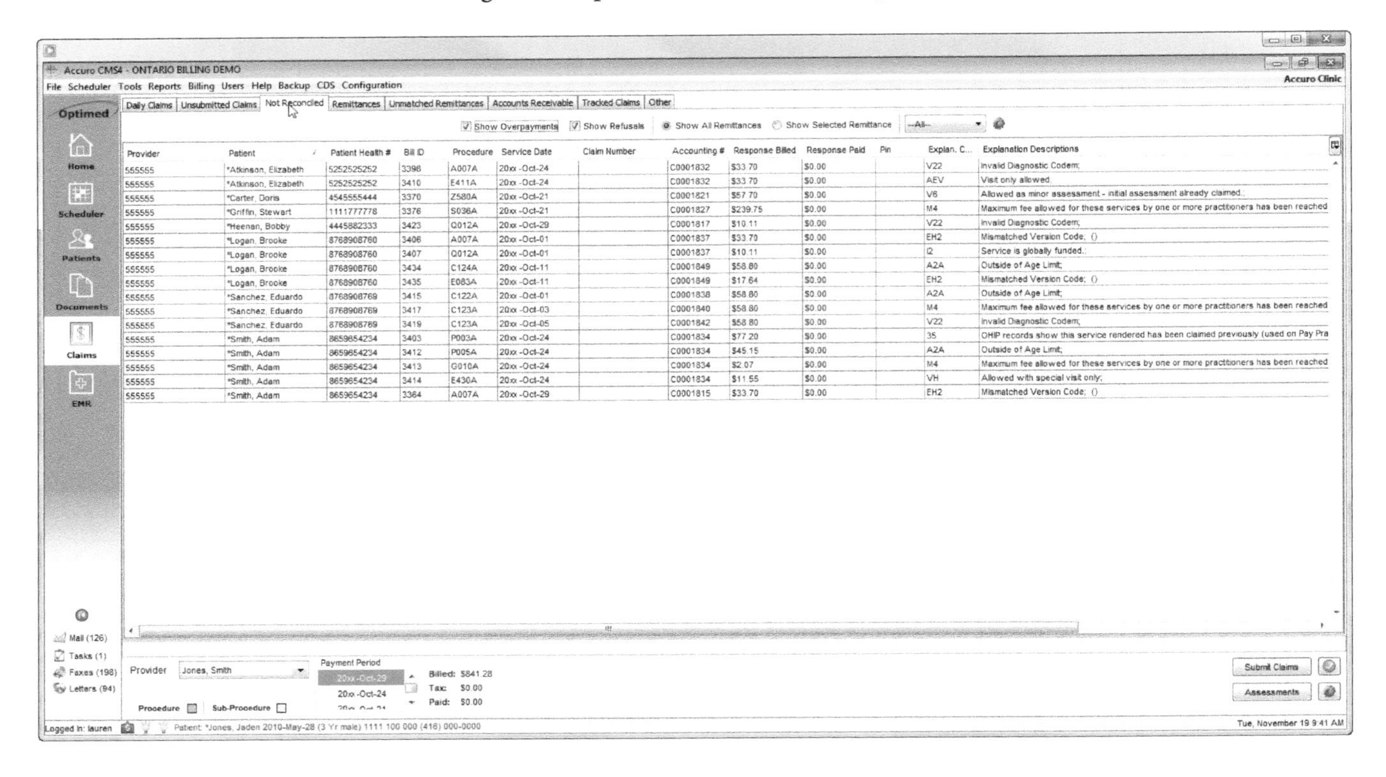

Provider	Patient	Patient Health #	Bill ID	Procedure	Service Date	Claim Number	Accounting #	Response Billed	Response Paid	Pin	Explan. C...	Explanation Descriptions
555555	*Atkinson, Elizabeth	5252525252	3398	A007A	20xx -Oct-24		C0001832	$33.70	$0.00		V22	Invalid Diagnostic Codem;
555555	*Atkinson, Elizabeth	5252525252	3410	E411A	20xx -Oct-24		C0001832	$33.70	$0.00		AEV	Visit only allowed.
555555	*Carter, Doris	4545555444	3370	Z580A	20xx -Oct-21		C0001821	$57.70	$0.00		V6	Allowed as minor assessment - initial assessment already claimed.;
555555	*Griffin, Stewart	1111777778	3376	S036A	20xx -Oct-21		C0001827	$239.75	$0.00		M4	Maximum fee allowed for these services by one or more practitioners has been reached
555555	*Heenan, Bobby	4445882333	3423	Q012A	20xx -Oct-29		C0001817	$10.11	$0.00		V22	Invalid Diagnostic Codem;
555555	*Logan, Brooke	8768908760	3406	A007A	20xx -Oct-01		C0001837	$33.70	$0.00		EH2	Mismatched Version Code; ()
555555	*Logan, Brooke	8768908760	3407	Q012A	20xx -Oct-01		C0001837	$10.11	$0.00		I2	Service is globally funded.;
555555	*Logan, Brooke	8768908760	3434	C124A	20xx -Oct-11		C0001849	$58.80	$0.00		A2A	Outside of Age Limit;
555555	*Logan, Brooke	8768908760	3435	E083A	20xx -Oct-11		C0001849	$17.64	$0.00		EH2	Mismatched Version Code; ()
555555	*Sanchez, Eduardo	8768908769	3415	C122A	20xx -Oct-01		C0001838	$58.80	$0.00		A2A	Outside of Age Limit;
555555	*Sanchez, Eduardo	8768908769	3417	C123A	20xx -Oct-03		C0001840	$58.80	$0.00		M4	Maximum fee allowed for these services by one or more practitioners has been reached
555555	*Sanchez, Eduardo	8768908769	3419	C123A	20xx -Oct-05		C0001842	$58.80	$0.00		V22	Invalid Diagnostic Codem;
555555	*Smith, Adam	8659654234	3403	P003A	20xx -Oct-24		C0001834	$77.20	$0.00		35	OHIP records show this service rendered has been claimed previously (used on Pay Pra
555555	*Smith, Adam	8659654234	3412	P005A	20xx -Oct-24		C0001834	$45.15	$0.00		A2A	Outside of Age Limit;
555555	*Smith, Adam	8659654234	3413	G010A	20xx -Oct-24		C0001834	$2.07	$0.00		M4	Maximum fee allowed for these services by one or more practitioners has been reached
555555	*Smith, Adam	8659654234	3414	E430A	20xx -Oct-24		C0001834	$11.55	$0.00		VH	Allowed with special visit only;
555555	*Smith, Adam	8659654234	3364	A007A	20xx -Oct-29		C0001815	$33.70	$0.00		EH2	Mismatched Version Code; ()

Remittance Advice Report

- A Remittance Advice Report (RA) is a monthly statement of approved claims.
- It is received within the EMR system under Remittances.
- It is issued at the same time as the payment.
- The Remittance Advice Report may contain codes that indicate if a service has been reduced or disallowed. These codes are known as explanatory codes.
- Physicians receive a Remittance Advice Report between the 5th and 7th of each month.
- The Remittances are returned to the EMR system under the Remittance tab.
- Following is a sample of a Remittance Advice Report:

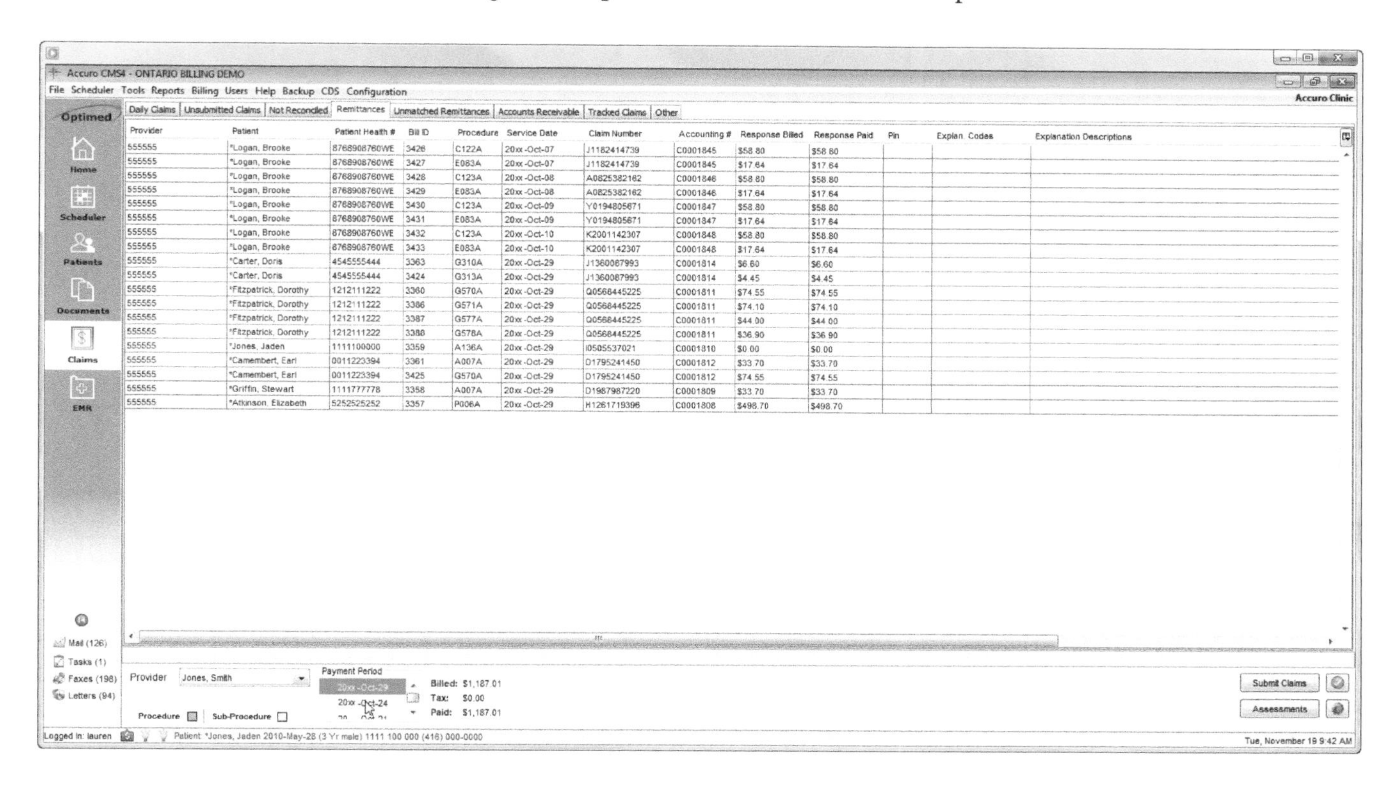

Provider	Patient	Patient Health #	Bill ID	Procedure	Service Date	Claim Number	Accounting #	Response Billed	Response Paid	Pin	Explan. Codes	Explanation Descriptions
555555	*Logan, Brooke	8768908760WE	3426	C122A	20xx-Oct-07	J1182414739	C0001845	$58.80	$58.80			
555555	*Logan, Brooke	8768908760WE	3427	E083A	20xx-Oct-07	J1182414739	C0001845	$17.64	$17.64			
555555	*Logan, Brooke	8768908760WE	3428	C123A	20xx-Oct-08	A0825382162	C0001846	$58.80	$58.80			
555555	*Logan, Brooke	8768908760WE	3429	E083A	20xx-Oct-08	A0825382162	C0001846	$17.64	$17.64			
555555	*Logan, Brooke	8768908760WE	3430	C123A	20xx-Oct-09	Y0194805671	C0001847	$58.80	$58.80			
555555	*Logan, Brooke	8768908760WE	3431	E083A	20xx-Oct-09	Y0194805671	C0001847	$17.64	$17.64			
555555	*Logan, Brooke	8768908760WE	3432	C123A	20xx-Oct-10	K2001142307	C0001848	$58.80	$58.80			
555555	*Logan, Brooke	8768908760WE	3433	E083A	20xx-Oct-10	K2001142307	C0001848	$17.64	$17.64			
555555	*Carter, Doris	4545555444	3363	G310A	20xx-Oct-29	J1360087993	C0001814	$6.60	$6.60			
555555	*Carter, Doris	4545555444	3424	G313A	20xx-Oct-29	J1360087993	C0001814	$4.45	$4.45			
555555	*Fitzpatrick, Dorothy	1212111222	3360	G570A	20xx-Oct-29	Q0568445225	C0001811	$74.55	$74.55			
555555	*Fitzpatrick, Dorothy	1212111222	3386	G571A	20xx-Oct-29	Q0568445225	C0001811	$74.10	$74.10			
555555	*Fitzpatrick, Dorothy	1212111222	3387	G577A	20xx-Oct-29	Q0568445225	C0001811	$44.00	$44.00			
555555	*Fitzpatrick, Dorothy	1212111222	3388	G578A	20xx-Oct-29	Q0568445225	C0001811	$36.90	$36.90			
555555	*Jones, Jaden	1111100000	3359	A136A	20xx-Oct-29	I0505537021	C0001810	$0.00	$0.00			
555555	*Camembert, Earl	0011223394	3361	A007A	20xx-Oct-29	D1795241450	C0001812	$33.70	$33.70			
555555	*Camembert, Earl	0011223394	3425	G570A	20xx-Oct-29	D1795241450	C0001812	$74.55	$74.55			
555555	*Griffin, Stewart	1111777778	3358	A007A	20xx-Oct-29	D1987987220	C0001809	$33.70	$33.70			
555555	*Atkinson, Elizabeth	5252525252	3357	P006A	20xx-Oct-29	H1261719396	C0001808	$498.70	$498.70			

Project 11

RECONCILIATION AND RESUBMISSION

LEARNING OBJECTIVES

- Understanding reconciliation of claims returns from the MOHLTC and how to resubmit

After the Ministry provides feedback through the Claims Error Report, the medical biller will then make the necessary changes to the original submissions. This may require modifying codes, deleting codes, or deleting entire claims.

Making these revisions is known as reconciliation.

The Ministry may have paid the physician in full, in partial payment, or no payment at all. Until the claims are submitted completely and accurately, full payment to the physician is not made.

Methods of Reconciliation by the medical biller are as follows:

- Adjusting Claims
  - If an error occurs in the Claims Submission, the Ministry can issue a partial payment for the portion of the claim allowable.
  - The medical biller will reconcile the claim by investigating the error, correcting the error, and submitting an amended claim.
- Deleting Claims
  - If an error occurs in the Claims Submission and is listed on the Remittance Advice Report, the claim can be deleted from the system and from the Claims Submission History.
  - Deleting a claim is referred to as "writing off a claim."
- Inquiring About Claims
  - If the physician and medical biller feel the Claims Submission was correct, and disagree with the Ministry as to why the claim was not paid, a Remittance Advice Inquiry can be sent to the Ministry for review using the Ministry's form.
  - Inquiries regarding overpayments or underpayments on the Remittance Advice Report should be submitted within one month and no later than six months from date of service. Inquiries should be submitted on a Remittance Advice Inquiry Ministry Form.

Once the reconciliation has occurred, files are once again submitted to MOHTLC for review and payment, which normally occurs in the next monthly billing physician payout.

TASK 1

MEDICAL BILLING WORKBOOK – TERMINOLOGY

RESOURCE: Medical Billing Workbook

It is essential that a medical billing specialist be familiar with the terminology that is encountered when undertaking medical billing.

1. In the Terminology sheet, add the following terms to Column A.
   - File Reject Message
   - Batch Edit Report
   - Claims Error Report
   - Remittance Advice
   - Remittance Advice Inquiry
   - MC EDT
   - Submission
   - Reconciliation
   - Stale Dated
   - Manual Review
   - Shadow Billing
   - Independent Consideration
   - Error Codes
   - Explanation Codes
2. Sort alphabetically.

TASK 2

ERROR CODES AND RECONCILIATION

RESOURCE: MOHLTC Resource Manual for Physicians
Appendix I – Error Code Template

Assume you received the following Error Codes from the Ministry. Using the following table, provide the description of the Error Code and describe what you would do to reconcile each claim.

Error Code Explanation	Error Code	Reconciliation Action
	VJ7	
	A34	
	AC1	
	R02	
	R01	
	V10	
	V13	
	V16	
	AD9	
	A4D	

TASK 3

ERROR REPORT MESSAGES AND RECONCILIATION

RESOURCE: MOHLTC Resource Manual for Physicians
Appendix I – Error Report Messages Template

Assume you received the following explanation codes from the Ministry. Using the following table, provide the description of the explanation code and describe what you would do to reconcile each claim.

Error Report Messages Explanation	Error Report Messages Code	Reconciliation Action
	12	
	21	
	27	
	30	
	E5	
	MY	
	32	
	EV	
	V7	
	VS	

Summary

The keys to success in medical billing are:

1. Familiarization with the Schedule of Benefits
2. Familiarization with the Resource Manual for Physicians
3. Understanding the medical billing terminology
4. Understanding the billing cycle
5. Understanding how to validate health cards
6. Accuracy in locating codes
7. Accuracy in submitting claims
8. Learning how to use an EMR system
9. Learning how to connect to the Ministry through the Medical Claims Electronic Data Transfer (MC EDT) software
10. Ability to reconcile claims based upon Ministry feedback

Congratulations – You now have the basics of medical billing in Ontario!

Appendix A

Organization Chart

ORGANIZATION CHART

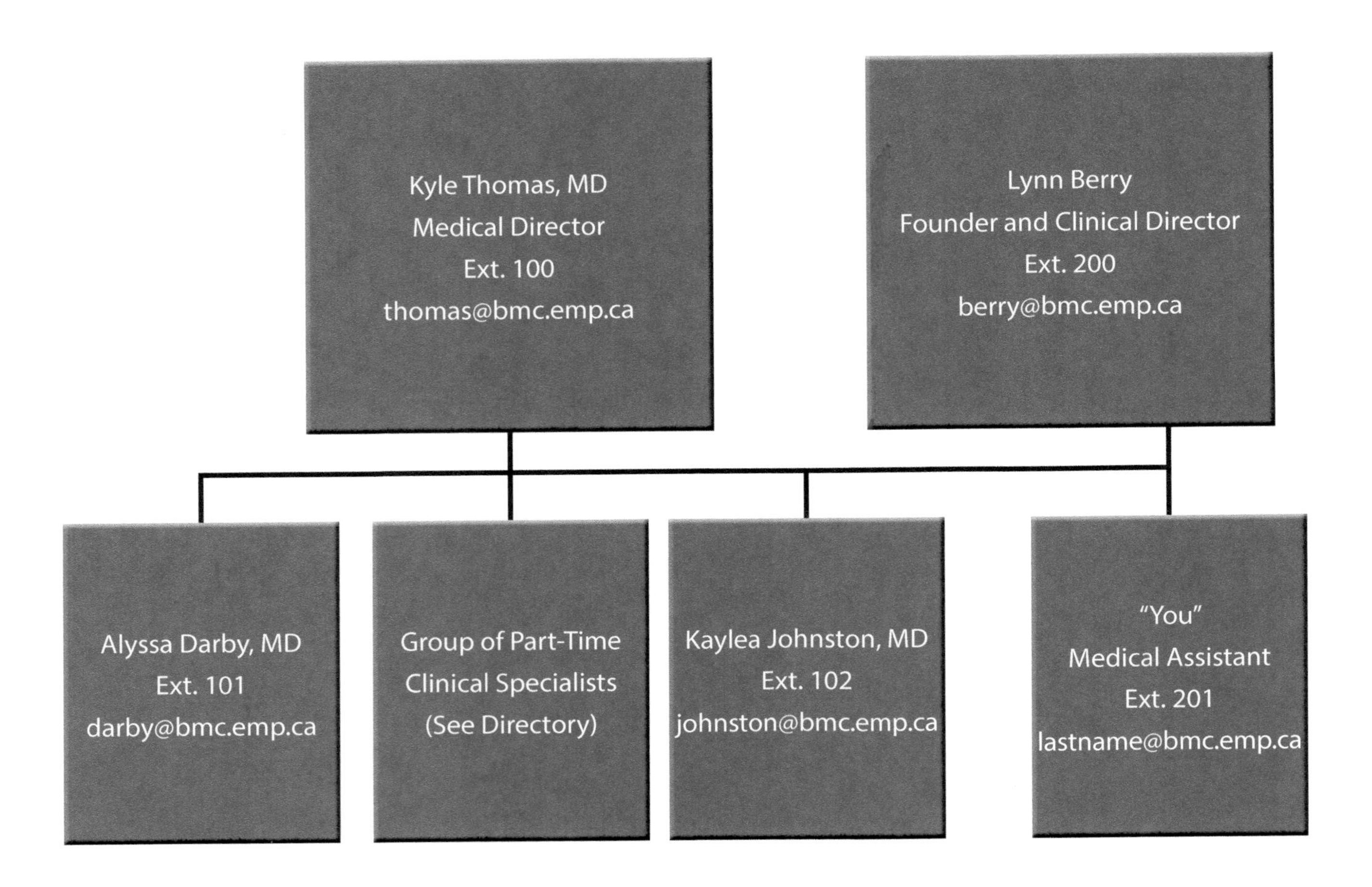

Appendix B

Clinical Specialists

CLINICAL SPECIALISTS

CLINICAL SPECIALISTS

Specialist	Specialty	Billing Number	CPSO Number	Ext.	Email
Aches, Stephen	Rheumatologist	982222	24103	133	aches@bmc.emp.ca
Ages, Fraser	Geriatrician	397107	19854	103	ages@bmc.emp.ca
Black, Lori	Hematologist	543261	26605	104	black@bmc.emp.ca
Blue, Paul	Cardiologist	533260	46579	105	blue@bmc.emp.ca
Bones, Fred	Orthopedic Surgeon	789106	95137	106	bones@bmc.emp.ca
Boom, Brian	Obstetrician and Gynecologist	233220	25841	107	boom@bmc.emp.ca
Butternut, William	Allergist	684662	12587	108	butternut@bmc.emp.ca
Childs, Samuel	Pediatrician	316426	44897	109	childs@bmc.emp.ca
Circuit, Sean	Vascular Surgeon	654317	13467	110	circuit@bmc.emp.ca
Cutter, Bob	General Surgeon	111203	25897	111	cutter@bmc.emp.ca
Darby, Alyssa	General Practitioner	587600	51511	101	darby@bmc.emp.ca
Fielding, Crystal	Massage Therapist	N/A	N/A	112	fielding@bmc.emp.ca
Gas, William	Gastroenterologist	553211	35911	132	gas@bmc.emp.ca
Googly, Albert	Ophthalmologist	321523	58529	113	googly@bmc.emp.ca
Harte, Brooke	Cardiologist	123460	14793	114	harte@bmc.emp.ca
Headley, Rich	Psychiatrist	897419	49438	115	headley@bmc.emp.ca
Herring, James	Otolaryngologist	553324	36985	116	herring@bmc.emp.ca
Innis, Cheryl	Internal and Occupational Medicine Specialist	364113	78916	117	innis@bmc.emp.ca
Jarvis, Wayne	Cardiologist	258960	36984	118	jarvis@bmc.emp.ca
Johnston, Kaylea	General Practitioner	423800	60191	102	johnston@bmc.emp.ca
Kelly, Erica	Chiropractor	N/A	N/A	119	kelly@bmc.emp.ca
Manley, Heather	Urologist	310235	15935	120	manley@bmc.emp.ca
Neuverly, Stephen	Neurologist	297118	46792	121	neuverly@bmc.emp.ca
Nightingale, Emma	Nurse Practitioner	N/A	N/A	122	nightingale@bmc.emp.ca
Oldfields, Brian	Geriatrician	325407	49138	123	oldfields@bmc.emp.ca
Paste, Cathy	Plastic Surgeon	445808	32145	124	paste@bmc.emp.ca
Paynter, Eric	Endocrinologist	546815	65478	125	paynter@bmc.emp.ca
Raymond, Xavier	Radiologist	978433	50662	126	raymond@bmc.emp.ca
Redden, Sy	Cardiologist	352960	58470	127	redden@bmc.emp.ca
Roots, Tee	Dentist	N/A	N/A	128	roots@bmc.emp.ca
Skinner, Frank	Dermatologist	888402	98754	129	skinner@bmc.emp.ca
Thomas, Kyle	General Practitioner	592300	31388	100	thomas@bmc.emp.ca
Voyage, Cyr	Infectious Disease and Tropical Medicine Specialist	543246	35791	130	voyage@bmc.emp.ca
Wasylenki, Raymond	Physiotherapist	N/A	N/A	131	wasylenki@bmc.emp.ca

Appendix C

Patients (BMC and Student Spreadsheets)

PATIENTS – BMC SPREADSHEET

Patient No.	Last Name	First Name	Middle Initial	Sex	Date of Birth	Street Address	City	Province	Postal Code	Home Phone	Work/Cell	OHIP	Version Code
1	Thomas	Douglas	T	M	1959-03-31	108 Second Avenue	Ottawa	ON	K2S 1C5	613-592-1234	N/A	1080 331 195	DT
2	Thomas	Kyle	T	M	1988-03-16	108 Second Avenue	Ottawa	ON	K2S 1C5	613-592-1234	N/A	1080 316 198	KT
3	Thomas	Kaylea	A	F	1991-06-01	108 Second Avenue	Ottawa	ON	K2S 1C5	613-592-1234	N/A	1080 601 199	KT
4	Thomas	Cindy	L	F	1958-12-25	108 Second Avenue	Ottawa	ON	K2S 1C5	613-592-1234	613-767-4689	1081 225 195	CT
5	Johnson	Kingsland	G	M	1933-06-13	8 Sewell Way	Kanata	ON	K2G 2X1	613-224-1146	N/A	8061 319 333	KJ
6	Johnson	Erna	E	F	1934-08-01	8 Sewell Way	Kanata	ON	K2G 2X1	613-224-1146	N/A	8080 119 334	EJ
7	Kelly	Lynn	S	F	1956-01-14	56 Westwood Drive	Nepean	ON	K2Z 1X4	613-432-4774	N/A	5601 141 955	LK
8	Kelly	Kenneth	D	M	1954-07-04	56 Westwood Drive	Nepean	ON	K2Z 1X4	613-432-4771	N/A	5607 041 954	KK
9	Kelly	Maddison	S	F	1986-11-21	56 Westwood Drive	Nepean	ON	K2Z 1X4	613-432-7447	613-732-7447	5611 211 986	LK
10	Mudda	Brenda	L	F	1960-01-19	71 Gagnon Lane	Arnprior	ON	K2S 7V3	613-722-2100	613-722-2100	7101 141 960	BM
11	Mudda	James	E	M	1958-06-30	71 Gagnon Lane	Arnprior	ON	K2S 7V3	613-722-2100	613-623-4123	7106 301 958	JM
12	Fry	Chris	D	M	1980-07-30	37 Bunting Lane	Stittsville	ON	K2S 0S1	613-234-4123	613-729-1111	3707 301 980	CF
13	Fry	Nat	N	F	1981-03-07	37 Bunting Lane	Stittsville	ON	K2S 0S1	613-234-4123	N/A	3703 071 981	NF
14	Fry	Peter	C	M	2012-07-10	37 Bunting Lane	Stittsville	ON	K2S 0S1	613-234-4123	N/A	3707 132 015	KE
15	Fry	Alex	C	M	2011-09-11	37 Bunting Lane	Stittsville	ON	K2S 0S1	613-234-4123	N/A	3709 112 011	AF
16	Kerr	Justin	P	M	1996-05-18	55 Riverview Lane	Portsmith	BC	V5Z 1E0	250-224-1146	N/A	55051819.96	N/A
17	Smith	John	S	M	1998-03-17	89 Bear Lake Road	Bear Lake	SK	S4P 1E0	306-831-4123	N/A	8903171.99	N/A
18	Arie	Jules	Q	F	1988-09-01	1200 - 45 Rue La Montagne	Gatineau	QC	J6M 8N9	819-454-3233	819-800-2888	ARIJ77561710	20xx
19	Woods	Cameron	S	M	1986-10-22	1958 Cathcart Blvd.	Stittsville	ON	K2J 2V6	613-596-3197	613-596-3198	WSIB	29505003-Q
20	Yu	Le	F	M	1988-01-01	45 Song Le	Kobe	Japan		011-81-78-458-0101	N/A	N/A	N/A

PATIENTS – STUDENT SPREADSHEET

Patient No.	Last Name	First Name	Middle Initial	Alias	Sex	DOB YYYY-MM-DD	Relationship	Street Address	City	Province	Postal Code	Home Phone	Work/Cell	OHIP	Version Code
1					M	1959-				ON					
2					M	1988-				ON					
3					F	1991-				ON					
4					F	1958-				ON					
5					M	1933-				ON					
6					F	1934-				ON					
7					F	1956-				ON					
8					M	1954-				ON					
9					F	1986-				ON					
10					F	1960-				ON					
11					M	1958-				ON					
12					M	1980-				ON					
13					F	1981-				ON					
14					M	present year				ON					
15					M	2011-				ON					
16					M	1996-				non-ON					
17					M	1998-				non-ON					
18					F	1988-				QC					
19					M	1986-				ON				WSIB	
20					M	1988-				Foreign					

Appendix D

Templates

EXTENDED HEALTH CARE CLAIM FORM (Page 1)

Extended Health Care Claim Form

sain® gezond® 健康® gesund khỏe mạnh® sláintiúil

Healthy Life Insurance Co.

Sano ® 健康 ® Saludable® בריא® здоровый® υγιής

- Form used for all medical expenses and services.
- Please print clearly and complete all sections.
- Attach original receipts for any expenses incurred.
- Sign on page 2 of the form.
- Submit to www.healthylifeinsurance.ca

1 Your Information

Contract No.		Member ID No.		Your Plan Employer		Preferred Language	E ☐ F ☐
Last Name		First Name		M ☐ F ☐	Birthdate (yyyy-mm-dd)	Phone No.	
Address (Street)		Apt.		City		Province		Postal Code	

2 Complete section if you or your spouse are covered under another plan

Send your claims to your own plan first. When you receive your claim statement, send a copy plus copies of your receipts to your spouse's plan to claim any unpaid amount. Send your spouse's expenses to their plan first and then send remaining amount to your plan. Send your children's claims first to the plan of the parent whose birthday falls earlier in the year.

Is your spouse a member of another benefit plan?	N ☐ Y ☐	**If yes, please provide details below**

Spouse's Last Name		First Name		Birthdate (yyyy-mm-dd)	Coverage Type
Are you claiming any expenses that are **NOT** covered under your spouse's plan?	N ☐ Y ☐	If yes, please specify			
If spouse's benefit plan is with Healthy Life, do you want us to process the claim through both benefit plans?	N ☐ Y ☐	Contract No.		Member ID No.	

Spouse's Signature	**X**	**Date (yyyy-mm-dd)**

Is your spouse a member of another benefit plan?	N ☐ Y ☐	**If yes, please provide details below**

Type of Coverage	Single ☐ Family ☐	Are you claiming any expenses that are NOT covered under your other plan?	N ☐ Y ☐	If yes, please specify	
What is your employment status under your other benefit plan	Full-time ☐ Part-time ☐ Retired ☐	If your other benefit plan is with Healthy Life Insurance Co., do you want us to process the claim through both benefit plans?	N ☐ Y ☐	Contract No.	Member ID No.

3 Information about your claim

List the names of all persons for whom you are claiming expenses. Add up all the receipts and insert the total amount claimed. Ensure each receipt clearly indicates the type of expense being claimed.

Persons for whom you are making the claim

Last Name		First Name		Date of birth (yyyy-mm-dd)	Relationship to You	Full-time student N ☐ Y ☐	Disabled N ☐ Y ☐	Amount Claimed $
Last Name		First Name		Date of birth (yyyy-mm-dd)	Relationship to You	Full-time student N ☐ Y ☐	Disabled N ☐ Y ☐	Amount Claimed $
Last Name		First Name		Date of birth (yyyy-mm-dd)	Relationship to You	Full-time student N ☐ Y ☐	Disabled N ☐ Y ☐	Amount Claimed $
Last Name		First Name		Date of birth (yyyy-mm-dd)	Relationship to You	Full-time student N ☐ Y ☐	Disabled N ☐ Y ☐	Amount Claimed $
								Total Claimed **$**

EXTENDED HEALTH CARE CLAIM FORM (Page 2)

<table>
<tr><td colspan="6">Page 2 of 2</td></tr>
<tr><td rowspan="2">Are you attaching receipts for out-of-Canada expenses?
If yes, tell us the date of departure from claimant's home province. We will assess expenses in Canadian dollars.</td><td>N Y</td><td>Date (yyyy-mm-dd)</td><td colspan="3">Out-of-Canada expenses claimed</td></tr>
<tr><td>☐ ☐</td><td></td><td colspan="3"></td></tr>
<tr><td>Are any of the expenses you are claiming the result of work injury?</td><td>N Y
☐ ☐</td><td colspan="3">If yes, did you submit your claim to the workers' compensation plan in your province?</td><td>N Y
☐ ☐</td></tr>
<tr><td>Are any of the expenses you are claiming the result of a motor vehicle accident?</td><td>N Y
☐ ☐</td><td colspan="3">If yes, did you submit your claim to the automobile insurance plan in your province?</td><td>N Y
☐ ☐</td></tr>
<tr><td colspan="6">4 Authorization and Signature</td></tr>
<tr><td colspan="6">I certify that all goods and services claimed by me/and or my spouse or dependents have been received by me and/or my spouse or dependents. I certify that all information on this form is true and complete and does not contain any expenses paid for in previous claims. I am authorized to disclose any information necessary about my spouse or dependents in order to complete this form correctly. I have authorized my spouse to disclose any information about me if necessary in order for Healthy Life to assess and pay any benefits. I authorize Healthy Life to collect, use and disclose information about me, my spouse, and my dependents, if necessary, for the underwriting, administration and adjudicating of any claims from health professionals, institutions, investigative agencies and insurers. I also am aware that this plan can be audited and any information from that may be reviewed. I acknowledge that any suspicion or evidence of fraud will incur further investigation of me by Healthy Life Insurance Co. If there is an overpayment, I acknowledge that I will be responsible for repaying the funds. I agree that any photocopy or electronic version of this claim is as valid as the original and may remain so for the effect and continuation of the administration of this plan.</td></tr>
<tr><td>Member's Signature</td><td colspan="2">X</td><td>Date (yyyy-mm-dd)</td><td colspan="2"></td></tr>
<tr><td colspan="3">Mailing Instructions</td><td>Phone Inquiries</td><td colspan="2">Fax No.</td></tr>
<tr><td colspan="3">Healthy Life Insurance Co.
5555 Main Street
Ottawa, ON K2L 3T7</td><td>613-222-4444</td><td colspan="2">613-222-5555</td></tr>
</table>

INVOICE FOR BROOKLANE MEDICAL CENTRE

INVOICE

33 Brooklane Avenue
Ottawa, ON K2B 6M7
613-224-2308 [telephone]
613-224-2300 [fax]
info@bmc.emp.ca
www.bmc.emp.ca

To:

Date:

From:

DESCRIPTION	AMOUNT
HST (Registration No. 139092416RT0001):	
TOTAL	

Payment is due within 30 days from date of invoice or a 2 percent per month interest charge will be applied.

Thank you for choosing Brooklane Medical Centre.

INVOICE FOR HOPE GENERAL HOSPITAL

HOPE GENERAL HOSPITAL
77 Gladview Avenue
Ottawa, ON K2S 3G8
613-813-1234 [telephone]
613-813-1235 [fax]

info@hgh.emp.ca
www.hgh.emp.ca

INVOICE

To:

Date:

From:

DESCRIPTION	AMOUNT
HST (Registration No. 139092416RT0002)	
TOTAL	

Payment is due within 30 days from date of invoice or a 2 percent per month interest charge will be applied.

Thank you for choosing Hope General Hospital for your medical needs.

PROVINCIAL AND TERRITORIAL HEALTH CARDS

Jurisdiction	Abbreviation	No. of Digits	Expiry Date	Letters or Version Code (if applicable)	Registration Unit (i.e. individual, subscriber, or family)	Website
Alberta	AB	9			Individual	
British Columbia	BC	10 or 11			Individual	
Manitoba	MB	9			Subscriber/family group	
New Brunswick	NB	9			Individual	
Newfoundland and Labrador	NL	12			Individual	
Northwest Territories	NT	7 + 1 letter			Individual	
Nova Scotia	NS	10			Individual	
Nunavut	NU	9			Individual	
Ontario	ON	10			Individual	
Prince Edward Island	PE	9			Individual	
Quebec	PQ	10			Individual	
Saskatchewan	SK	9			Individual	
Yukon	YT	9			Individual	

PUBLIC SERVICE HEALTH CARE PLAN CLAIM FORM (Page 1)

Public Service Health Care Plan (PSHCP)

- Form used for all medical expenses and services.
- Please print clearly and complete all sections.
- Attach original receipts for any expenses incurred.
- Sign on page 2 of the form.
- Submit to www.healthylifeinsurance.ca

sain®gezond®健康®gesund khỏe mạnh®sláintiúil

Healthy Life Insurance Co.

Sano ® 健康 ® Saludable®בריא® здоровый®υγιής

1	Member Information						
Certificate Number				Preferred Language		E ☐	F ☐
Last Name		First Name		M ☐ F ☐	Birthdate (yyyy-mm-dd)		Phone No.
Address (Street)		Apt.		City			
Province	ON	Postal Code					

2	Coordination of Benefits			
Send your claims to your own plan first. When you receive your claim statement, send a copy plus copies of your receipts to your spouse's plan to claim any unpaid amount. Send your spouse's expenses to their plan first and then send remaining amount to your plan. Send your children's claims first to the plan of the parent whose birthday falls earlier in the year				
Is your spouse a member of PSHCP?	N ☐	Y ☐	**If yes, please provide details below**	
Does your spouse authorize us to process the claim under his/her certificate number?	N ☐	Y ☐	**If yes, provide details below**	
Spouse's Last Name		First Name		Spouse's Gender M ☐ F ☐
If spouse's benefit plan is with PSHCP, do you want us to process the claim through both benefit plans?	N ☐	Y ☐	**Certificate Number**	**Spouse's Contract Number**
Spouse's Signature	**X**			**Date (yyyy-mm-dd)**

3	Complete if Claiming Expenses for Your Spouse or Dependent Children							
List the names of all persons for whom you are claiming expenses. Add up all the receipts and insert the total amount claimed. Ensure each receipt clearly indicates the type of expense being claimed.								
Persons for Whom You are Making the Claim								
Last Name		First Name		Date of Birth (yyyy-mm-dd)	Spouse ☐	Dependent Daughter ☐ Son ☐	Other ☐	Amount Claimed
Last Name		First Name		Date of Birth (yyyy-mm-dd)	Spouse ☐	Dependent Daughter ☐ Son ☐	Other ☐	Amount Claimed $
Last Name		First Name		Date of Birth (yyyy-mm-dd)	Spouse ☐	Dependent Daughter ☐ Son ☐	Other ☐	Amount Claimed $
Last Name		First Name		Date of Birth (yyyy-mm-dd)	Spouse ☐	Dependent Daughter ☐ Son ☐	Other ☐	Amount Claimed $
Page 1 of 2								**Total Claimed** **$**

PUBLIC SERVICE HEALTH CARE PLAN CLAIM FORM (Page 2)

Page 2 of 2

Are you attaching receipts for out-of-Canada expenses? If yes, tell us the date of departure from claimant's home province. We will assess expenses in Canadian dollars.	N ☐ Y ☐	Date (yyyy-mm-dd)	Out-of-Canada expenses claimed
Are any of the expenses you're claiming the result of work injury?	N ☐ Y ☐	If yes, did you submit your claim to the workers' compensation plan in your province?	N ☐ Y ☐
Are any of the expenses you're claiming the result of a motor vehicle accident?	N ☐ Y ☐	If yes, did you submit your claim to an automobile insurance plan in your province?	N ☐ Y ☐
Are any of the expenses you are claiming the result of government travel?			N ☐ Y ☐

4 Authorization and Signature

I certify that all goods and services claimed by me/and or my spouse or dependents have been received by me and/or my spouse or dependents. I certify that all information on this form is true and complete and does not contain any expenses paid for in previous claims. I am authorized to disclose any information necessary about my spouse or dependents in order to complete this form correctly. I have authorized my spouse to disclose any information about me if necessary in order for Healthy Life to assess and pay any benefits. I authorize Healthy Life to collect, use and disclose information about me, my spouse, and my dependents, if necessary, for the underwriting, administration, and adjudicating of any claims from health professionals, institutions, investigative agencies, and insurers. I also am aware that this plan can be audited and any information from that may be reviewed. I acknowledge that any suspicion or evidence of fraud will incur further investigation of me by Healthy Life. If there is an overpayment, I acknowledge that I will be responsible for repaying the funds. I agree that any photocopy or electronic version of this claim is as valid as the original and may remain so for the effect and continuation of the administration of this plan.

Member's Signature	X	Date (yyyy-mm-dd)	
Mailing Instructions		**Phone Inquiries**	**Fax No.**
Healthy Life Insurance Co. 5555 Main Street Ottawa, ON K2L 3T7		613-222-4444	613-222-5555

RECEIPT FOR BROOKLANE MEDICAL CENTRE

RECEIPT

33 Brooklane Avenue
Ottawa, ON K2B 6M7
613-224-2308 [telephone]
613-224-2300 [fax]
info@bmc.emp.ca
www.bmc.emp.ca

To:

Date:

From:

DESCRIPTION	AMOUNT
HST (Registration No. 139092416RT0001): Total: Amount Paid: Method of Payment:	
BALANCE OWING:	

Thank you for choosing Brooklane Medical Centre.

RECEIPT FOR HOPE GENERAL HOSPITAL

HOPE GENERAL HOSPITAL
77 Gladview Avenue
Ottawa, ON K2S 3G8
613-813-1234 [telephone]
613-813-1235 [fax]

info@hgh.emp.ca
www.hgh.emp.ca

RECEIPT

To: **Date:**

From:

DESCRIPTION	AMOUNT
HST (Registration No. 139092416RT0002): Total: Amount Paid: Method of Payment:	
TOTAL	

Thank you for choosing Hope General Hospital for your medical needs.

UNIVERSITY HEALTH INSURANCE PLAN CLAIM FORM (Page 1)

UHIP Claim Form

sain® gezond® 健 康® gesund khỏe mạnh® sláintiúil
Healthy Life Insurance Co.
Sano ® 健 康 ® Saludable® בריא® здоровый® υγιής

All claims must be submitted no more than TWELVE MONTHS following the date on which the expenses are incurred.

Claimants must provide a valid Canadian address for reimbursement.

1	**Member Information**						
University Name		Member Identification Number		Email Address			
Last Name		First and Middle Name		Birthdate (yyyy-mm-dd)		Phone No.	
Address (Street)		Apt.		City		Province	Postal Code
Do you or your dependents have additional Health coverage with Healthy Life Insurance?	N ☐	Y ☐	If yes, policy no.				
2	**Claimant Information**						
Last Name		First Name		Birthdate (yyyy-mm-dd)			
Relationship to Member	Member ☐	Spouse ☐	Son ☐	Daughter ☐			

3 Authorization and Signature – Attach Original Receipts

I understand that the information provided by me on this claim form, and otherwise in respect of my claim, is required by Health Life Insurance, their insurers and authorized administers to assess my entitlement to benefits as well as to administer and underwrite claims, including but not limited to determining if coverage is in effect, investigating the applicability of exclusions and coordinating coverage with each other and other insurers. Additional information may be obtained from existing insurance files about me.

CERTIFICATION

The statements I provide in completing this claim form and otherwise in respect of my claims are true and complete to the best of my knowledge and belief. False or misleading statements can result in cancelled coverage and payment denial. In this case, any refund to the Insurers, I agree to refund.

AUTHORIZATION

I authorize for a period of not less than twelve months from the date hereof, any physician, practitioner, health care provider, hospital, health care institution, medical organization, or any other medically related facility, insurance company or association. In this I include any personal health information, benefit payment, employment or financial information about me, my spouse, and/or dependents in its possession that is requested while administering this claim.

I authorize to disclose any information about me, and I am authorized to disclose any information about my spouse or dependents. I acknowledge that auditing may occur of my records or my spouse's or dependent's records. I authorize any investigation that needs to be made.

I acknowledge that any photocopy of this authorization stands legally the same as the original I am signing.

Check one of the following boxes	Payment to be made to the member	Payment is to be made directly to the provider
	☐	☐

Claimant's Signature	**X**	**Date (yyyy-mm-dd)**	

4	**Provider Information**				
Section 4 and 5 is to only be completed by the provider when the reimbursement is to be made directly to the					
Provider's Name		Physician's Name			
Address of Provider (Street number and name)		Apt or Suite			
City		Province		Postal Code	
Provider ID No.		Telephone Number			

Page 1 of 2

UNIVERSITY HEALTH INSURANCE PLAN CLAIM FORM (Page 2)

Page 2 of 2

5 Statement of Services (Physicians and hospitals must provide the diagnosis)

Service Date (yyyy-mm-dd)	Description of Service	Provincial Billing Procedure Code	Charge	Diagnosis

I declare that the above is a correct statement of the services rendered.

Provider's Signature	X	Date (yyyy-mm-dd)	

Direct All Claims To:	Phone Inquiries	Fax No.
Healthy Life Insurance Co. 5555 Main Street Ottawa, ON K2L 3T7	613-222-4444	613-222-5555

WSIB COVER PAGE

Health Professional's Report (Form 8)

Health Professional, please use this form for:

- Patients who are claiming benefits under the WSIB insurance plan for an injury/illness related to work, or
- You think that the cause of your patient's injury/illness is workplace factors.

Section 37 of the *Workplace Safety and Insurance Act, 1997* provides the legal authority for health professionals, hospitals and health facilities to submit, without consent, information relating to a worker claiming benefits to the Workplace Safety and Insurance Board (WSIB).

Completing the form:

- **Give a copy of page two only to your patient to give to employer.**
- **Please send pages one and two to the Workplace Safety and Insurance Board.**
- **On the worker's initial visit, ONLY the Form 8 will be paid. A Functional Abilities Form (FAF) will not be paid if completed on the same date.**

For Electronic Submission

To register for electronic form submission and electronic billing, please go to www.telushealth.com/wsib or call Telus at 1-866-240-7492 for more information.

By Fax to:

416-344-4684 or 1-888-313-7373

Or by Mail to:

Workplace Safety and Insurance Board
200 Front Street West
Toronto, ON M5V 3J1

www.wsib.on.ca

0008A1

WSIB FORM 8 (Page 1)

print reset save

wsib cspaat ONTARIO

Fax To: 416-344-4684 OR 1-888-313-7373

Start > Claim Number (if known)

8 Health Professional's Report (Form 8)

A. Patient and Employer Information - (Patient to complete Section A)

Last Name | First Name | Init. | Sex ☐M ☐F

Address (no., street, apt.) | City/Town | Prov. ON | Postal Code

Telephone | Social Insurance No. | Date of Birth dd mm yyyy | Language ☐Eng. ☐Fr. ☐Other

Employer Name

The Workplace Safety and Insurance Board (WSIB) collects your information to administer and enforce the Workplace Safety and Insurance Act. The Social Insurance Number may be used to identify workers and to issue income tax information statements as authorized by the Income Tax Act. Questions should be directed to the decision maker responsible for your file or toll free at 1-800-387-5540.

B. Incident Dates and Details Section

1. How did the injury/reinjury or illness occur at work?

Occupation

Date of incident/or when did the symptoms start? dd mm yyyy

C. Clinical Information Section - (Please check all that apply)

1. Area of Injury/Illness

☐ Brain ☐ Head ☐ Face ☐ Eyes ☐ Other:

☐ Ears ☐ Teeth ☐ Neck ☐ Chest

☐ **Upper back** ☐ **Lower back** ☐ Abdomen ☐ Pelvis

Left / Right: **Shoulder**, Arm, Elbow, Forearm

Left / Right: Wrist, Hand, Fingers

Left / Right: Hip, Thigh, Knee, Lower Leg

Left / Right: Ankle, Foot, Toes

2. Description of Injury/Illness Physical Examination Findings

☐ Pain at rest/Night Pain

Pain Rating Scale 0 1 2 3 4 5 6 7 8 9 10

☐ Abrasion ☐ Amputation ☐ Bite ☐ Burn ☐ Contusion/Hematoma/Swelling ☐ Crush Injury

☐ Disc Herniation ☐ Dislocation ☐ **Fall from Height** ☐ Foreign Body ☐ **Fracture** ☐ Hernia ☐ Infection

☐ Inflammation ☐ Internal Joint Derangement ☐ Joint Effusion ☐ Laceration ☐ **Neurological Dysfunction** ☐ Psychological ☐ Puncture (non-needlestick)

☐ Repetitive Strain Injury ☐ Spinal Cord Injury ☐ Sprain/Strain ☐ **Surgical Intervention** ☐ Tendonitis/Tenosynovitis ☐ ▼ Range of Motion

☐ Other

Exposure/Illness

☐ Asthma ☐ Cancer ☐ Fumes - Inhalation ☐ Hand-arm Vibration ☐ Hearing Loss ☐ Infectious Disease ☐ Needle Stick ☐ Poisoning/Toxic Effects ☐ Skin Condition

3. Are you aware of any pre-existing or other conditions/factors that may impact recovery? ☐ yes ☐ no

If yes, describe

4. Diagnosis

D. Treatment Plan

1. What is the treatment plan (type of treatment, duration) including prescribed medications?

2. To be completed by physicians only.

Work Injury/Illness Medications	Dose	Frequency	Duration	Work Injury/Illness Medications	Dose	Frequency	Duration
1.				3.			
2.				4.			

3. Investigations & Referrals:

☐ None ☐ Labs ☐ Xrays ☐ CT Scan ☐ MRI ☐ EMG ☐ Ultrasound ☐ Other

☐ FP/GP ☐ Specialist/Specialty ☐ Chiropractor

☐ Occupational Health Centre ☐ Occupational Therapist ☐ Other

☐ Physiotherapist ☐ Psychologist

Would the patient benefit from the following referrals? ☐ Specialty Clinic ☐ Regional Evaluation Centre (REC)

Name of Referral or Facility (if known) | Telephone | Appointment Date dd mm yyyy

E. Billing Section

Health Professional Designation ☐ Chiropractor ☐ Physician ☐ Physiotherapist ☐ Registered Nurse (Extended Class) | Service Code **8M** | WSIB Provider ID

HST Registration No. | HST Amount Billed (if applicable) **$** | Service Code **ONHST** | Your Invoice No. | Service Date dd mm yyyy

Health Professional Name (please print) | Address

Telephone | Fax

WSIB FORM 8 (Page 2)

Claim Number (If known)

8 Health Professional's Report (Form 8)

Return To Work Information

Once completed, please ensure that a copy of this page only is provided to the worker.

Last Name	First Name	Init.	Birth Date dd mm yyyy
Area(s) of Injury(ies)/Illness(es)			

Date of Incident dd mm yyyy

F. Return To Work Information - Must be completed by a Health Professional

When work injury/illness occurs, focus on return to usual activity including return to safe and appropriate work is best practice. Most workers who experience soft tissue injury are able to remain at work.

1. Have you discussed return to work with your patient? ☐ yes ☐ no

2. ☐ **This worker can resume Regular duties. Start date** dd mm yyyy **If graduated hours required please specify** ______

☐ **This worker can begin Modified duties. Start date** dd mm yyyy **If graduated hours required please specify** ______

☐ **This worker is not able to work because of the workplace injury/illness.**

Please provide explanation ______

3. Please indicate the worker's status and functional abilities in relation to the workplace injury and diagnosis.

A. Full Functional Abilities ☐

B. Worker Functional Abilities

	Able to	Not Able to		Able to	Not Able to		Able to	Not Able to
Bend/Twist	☐	☐	Operate Heavy Equipment	☐	☐	Stand	☐	☐
Climb	☐	☐	Operate a Motor Vehicle	☐	☐	Use of Public Transportation	☐	☐
Kneel	☐	☐	Push/Pull	☐	☐	Use of Upper Extremities	☐	☐
Lift	☐	☐	Sit	☐	☐	Walk	☐	☐

C. Other Limitations: eg. Environmental Conditions, Medication, Use of Protective Equipment.

Please describe: ______

4. From the date of this assessment, the above limitations will apply for approximately:

☐ 1 - 2 days ☐ 3 - 7 days ☐ 8 - 14 days ☐ 14 + days

5. Follow-up Appointment

☐ None required ☐ As Needed Date of next appointment dd mm yyyy

Health Professional's Name (Please print)		Address
Health Professional's Signature PLEASE PRINT AND SIGN	Telephone	Service Date dd mm yyyy

G. Worker's Signature

By signing below I am authorizing the above noted health professional, who is treating me, to provide my employer with a copy of this page outlining my functional abilities. I understand a copy will be sent to the Workplace Safety and Insurance Board (WSIB) by my health professional.

Signature	Date dd mm yyyy
PLEASE PRINT AND SIGN	

Once completed, please ensure that a copy of this page only is provided to the worker.

0008A

visit our website at at: **www.wsib.on.ca**

Page 2/2

print reset save

Appendix E

Sample Documents

EXTENDED HEALTH CARE CLAIM FORM (Page 1)

Extended Health Care Claim Form

- Form used for all medical expenses and services.
- Please print clearly and complete all sections.
- Attach original receipts for any expenses incurred.
- Sign on page 2 of the form.
- Submit to www.healthylifeinsurance.ca

sain® gezond® 健康® gesund khỏe mạnh® sláintiúil

Healthy Life Insurance Co.

Sano® 健康® Saludable® בריא® здоровый® υγιής

1 Your Information

Contract No.	198772	Member ID No.	89822	Your Plan Employer	Achieve Gold Inc.	Preferred Language	E [X] F [ ]
Last Name	Smithers	First Name	Justin	M [X] F [ ]	Birthdate (yyyy-mm-dd) 19xx-07-29	Phone No. 613-877-1000	
Address (Street)	78 Elm Street	Apt.		City	Ottawa	Province ON	Postal Code K2G 9M5

2 Complete section if you or your spouse are covered under another plan

Send your claims to your own plan first. When you receive your claim statement, send a copy plus copies of your receipts to your spouse's plan to claim any unpaid amount. Send your spouse's expenses to their plan first and then send remaining amount to your plan. Send your children's claims first to the plan of the parent whose birthday falls earlier in the year.

Is your spouse a member of another benefit plan?	N [X] Y [ ]	**If yes, please provide details below**	
Spouse's Last Name		First Name	Birthdate (yyyy-mm-dd) / Coverage Type
Are you claiming any expenses that are **NOT** covered under your spouse's plan?	N [X] Y [ ]	If yes, please specify	
If spouse's benefit plan is with Healthy Life, do you want us to process the claim through both benefit plans?	N [ ] Y [ ]	Contract No.	Member ID No.

Spouse's Signature	X	**Date (yyyy-mm-dd)**

Is your spouse a member of another benefit plan?	N [X] Y [ ]	**If yes, please provide details below**		
Type of Coverage	Single [ ] Family [ ]	Are you claiming any expenses that are NOT covered under your other plan?	N [ ] Y [ ]	If yes, please specify
What is your employment status under your other benefit plan	Full-time [X] Part-time [ ] Retired [ ]	If your other benefit plan is with Healthy Life Insurance Co., do you want us to process the claim through both benefit plans?	N [X] Y [ ]	Contract No. / Member ID No.

3 Information about your claim

List the names of all persons for whom you are claiming expenses. Add up all the receipts and insert the total amount claimed. Ensure each receipt clearly indicates the type of expense being claimed.

Persons for whom you are making the claim

Last Name	First Name	Date of birth (yyyy-mm-dd)	Relationship to You	Full-time student N Y	Disabled N Y	Amount Claimed
Smithers	Justin	19xx-07-29	Self	[X] [ ]	[X] [ ]	$ 395.00
				[ ] [ ]	[ ] [ ]	$
				[ ] [ ]	[ ] [ ]	$
				[ ] [ ]	[ ] [ ]	$

Total Claimed
$ 395.00

EXTENDED HEALTH CARE CLAIM FORM (Page 2)

Page 2 of 2

Are you attaching receipts for out-of-Canada expenses? If yes, tell us the date of departure from claimant's home province. We will assess expenses in Canadian dollars.	N Y	Date (yyyy-mm-dd)	Out-of-Canada expenses claimed	
	[X] [ ]			
Are any of the expenses you are claiming the result of work injury?	N [X] Y [ ]	If yes, did you submit your claim to the workers' compensation plan in your province?		N [ ] Y [X]
Are any of the expenses you are claiming the result of a motor vehicle accident?	N [X] Y [ ]	If yes, did you submit your claim to the automobile insurance plan in your province?		N [ ] Y [X]

4 Authorization and Signature

I certify that all goods and services claimed by me/and or my spouse or dependents have been received by me and/or my spouse or dependents. I certify that all information on this form is true and complete and does not contain any expenses paid for in previous claims. I am authorized to disclose any information necessary about my spouse or dependents in order to complete this form correctly. I have authorized my spouse to disclose any information about me if necessary in order for Healthy Life to assess and pay any benefits. I authorize Healthy Life to collect, use and disclose information about me, my spouse, and my dependents, if necessary, for the underwriting, administration and adjudicating of any claims from health professionals, institutions, investigative agencies and insurers. I also am aware that this plan can be audited and any information from that may be reviewed. I acknowledge that any suspicion or evidence of fraud will incur further investigation of me by Healthy Life Insurance Co. If there is an overpayment, I acknowledge that I will be responsible for repaying the funds. I agree that any photocopy or electronic version of this claim is as valid as the original and may remain so for the effect and continuation of the administration of this plan.

Member's Signature	X *Justin Smithers*	Date (yyyy-mm-dd)	20xx-06-06

Mailing Instructions	Phone Inquiries	Fax No.
Healthy Life Insurance Co. 5555 Main Street Ottawa, ON K2L 3T7	613-222-4444	613-222-5555

INVOICE FOR BROOKLANE MEDICAL CENTRE

INVOICE

33 Brooklane Avenue
Ottawa, ON K2B 6M7
613-224-2308 [telephone]
613-224-2300 [fax]
info@bmc.emp.ca
www.bmc.emp.ca

To:
Mr. Robert Moore
115 Meadowview Drive
Ottawa, ON K2G 2S2

Date:
September 7, 20xx

From:
Fred Bones, MD

DESCRIPTION	AMOUNT
Adult Bariatric Heavy Duty Walking Crutches	$102.30
HST (Registration No. 139092416RT0001):	15.35
TOTAL	$117.65

Payment is due within 30 days from date of invoice or a 2 percent per month interest charge will be applied.

Thank you for choosing Brooklane Medical Centre.

INVOICE FOR HOPE GENERAL HOSPITAL

HOPE GENERAL HOSPITAL
77 Gladview Avenue
Ottawa, ON K2S 3G8
613-813-1234 [telephone]
613-813-1235 [fax]

info@hgh.emp.ca
www.hgh.emp.ca

INVOICE

To:
Mr. Robert Shaw
193 Apple Street
Ottawa, ON K4B 6M9

Date:
April 14, 20xx

From:
Fred Bones, MD

DESCRIPTION	AMOUNT
Newborn Circumcision	$125.00
HST (Registration No. 139092416RT0002)	$16.25
TOTAL	$141.25

Payment is due within 30 days from date of invoice or a 2 percent per month interest charge will be applied.

Thank you for choosing Hope General Hospital for your medical needs.

PUBLIC SERVICE HEALTH CARE PLAN CLAIM FORM (Page 1)

Public Service Health Care Plan (PSHCP)

- Form used for all medical expenses and services.
- Please print clearly and complete all sections.
- Attach original receipts for any expenses incurred.
- Sign on page 2 of the form.
- Submit to www.healthylifeinsurance.ca

sain®gezond®健康®gesund khỏe mạnh®sláintiúil

Healthy Life Insurance Co.

Sano ® 健康 ® Saludable®בריא® здоровый®υγιής

1 Member Information

Certificate Number		Preferred Language	E [X] F [ ]

Last Name	Thompson	First Name	Emily	M [X] F [ ]	Birthdate (yyyy-mm-dd) 19xx-07-14	Phone No. 613-788-1222
Address (Street)	29 Maple Street	Apt.		City Ottawa	Province ON	Postal Code K9V 5B8

2 Coordination of Benefits

Send your claims to your own plan first. When you receive your claim statement, send a copy plus copies of your receipts to your spouse's plan to claim any unpaid amount. Send your spouse's expenses to their plan first and then send remaining amount to your plan. Send your children's claims first to the plan of the parent whose birthday falls earlier in the year

	N	Y	
Is your spouse a member of PSHCP?	[X]	[ ]	**If yes, please provide details below**
Does your spouse authorize us to process the claim under his/her certificate number?	[ ]	[ ]	**If yes, provide details below**

Spouse's Last Name		First Name		Spouse's Gender M [ ] F [ ]
If spouse's benefit plan is with PSHCP, do you want us to process the claim through both benefit plans? N [ ] Y [ ]		**Certificate Number**		**Spouse's Contract Number**
Spouse's Signature	X			**Date (yyyy-mm-dd)**

3 Complete if Claiming Expenses for Your Spouse or Dependent Children

List the names of all persons for whom you are claiming expenses. Add up all the receipts and insert the total amount claimed. Ensure each receipt clearly indicates the type of expense being claimed.

Persons for Whom You are Making the Claim

Last Name	First Name	Date of Birth (yyyy-mm-dd)	Spouse	Dependent Daughter	Dependent Son	Other	Amount Claimed
Thompson	Brian	19xx-12-02	[X]	[ ]	[ ]	[ ]	675.90
			[ ]	[ ]	[ ]	[ ]	$
			[ ]	[ ]	[ ]	[ ]	$
			[ ]	[ ]	[ ]	[ ]	$

Page 1 of 2	**Total Claimed**
	$675.90

PUBLIC SERVICE HEALTH CARE PLAN CLAIM FORM (Page 2)

Page 2 of 2

Question	N	Y				
Are you attaching receipts for out-of-Canada expenses? If yes, tell us the date of departure from claimant's home province. We will assess expenses in Canadian dollars.	☒	☐	Date (yyyy-mm-dd)	Out-of-Canada expenses claimed		
Are any of the expenses you're claiming the result of work injury?	☒	☐	If yes, did you submit your claim to the workers' compensation plan in your province?		N ☐	Y ☐
Are any of the expenses you're claiming the result of a motor vehicle accident?	☒	☐	If yes, did you submit your claim to an automobile insurance plan in your province?		N ☐	Y ☐
Are any of the expenses you are claiming the result of government travel?					N ☒	Y ☐

4 Authorization and Signature

I certify that all goods and services claimed by me/and or my spouse or dependents have been received by me and/or my spouse or dependents. I certify that all information on this form is true and complete and does not contain any expenses paid for in previous claims. I am authorized to disclose any information necessary about my spouse or dependents in order to complete this form correctly. I have authorized my spouse to disclose any information about me if necessary in order for Healthy Life to assess and pay any benefits. I authorize Healthy Life to collect, use and disclose information about me, my spouse, and my dependents, if necessary, for the underwriting, administration, and adjudicating of any claims from health professionals, institutions, investigative agencies, and insurers. I also am aware that this plan can be audited and any information from that may be reviewed. I acknowledge that any suspicion or evidence of fraud will incur further investigation of me by Healthy Life. If there is an overpayment, I acknowledge that I will be responsible for repaying the funds. I agree that any photocopy or electronic version of this claim is as valid as the original and may remain so for the effect and continuation of the administration of this plan.

Member's Signature	X *Emily Thompson*	Date (yyyy-mm-dd)	20xx-06-06

Mailing Instructions	Phone Inquiries	Fax No.
Healthy Life Insurance Co. 5555 Main Street Ottawa, ON K2L 3T7	613-222-4444	613-222-5555

RECEIPT FOR BROOKLANE MEDICAL CENTRE

RECEIPT

33 Brooklane Avenue
Ottawa, ON K2B 6M7
613-224-2308 [telephone]
613-224-2300 [fax]
info@bmc.emp.ca
www.bmc.emp.ca

To:
Mr. Robert Moore
115 Meadowview Drive
Ottawa, ON K2G 2S2

Date:
September 25, 20xx

From:
Kyle Thomas, MD

DESCRIPTION	AMOUNT
Adult Bariatric Heavy Duty Walking Crutches	$102.30
HST (Registration No. 139092416RT0001):	15.35
Total:	$117.65
Amount Paid:	$117.65
Method of Payment: VISA	
BALANCE OWING:	Nil

Thank you for choosing Brooklane Medical Centre.

RECEIPT FOR HOPE GENERAL HOSPITAL

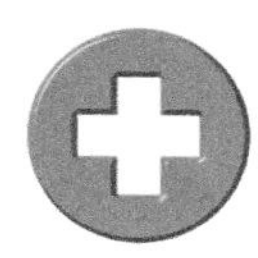

HOPE GENERAL HOSPITAL
77 Gladview Avenue
Ottawa, ON K2S 3G8
613-813-1234 [telephone]
613-813-1235 [fax]

info@hgh.emp.ca
www.hgh.emp.ca

RECEIPT

To:
Mr. Robert Shaw
193 Apple Street
Ottawa, ON K4B 6M9

Date:
April 14, 20xx

From:
Samuel Childs, MD

DESCRIPTION	AMOUNT
Newborn Circumcision	$125.00
HST (Registration No. 139092416RT0002):	16.25
Total: Amount Paid: Method of Payment: Cash	$141.25 $141.25
TOTAL	Nil

Thank you for choosing Hope General Hospital for your medical needs.

UNIVERSITY HEALTH INSURANCE PLAN CLAIM FORM (Page 1)

UHIP Claim Form

sain® gezond® 健康® gesund khỏe mạnh® sláintiúil
Healthy Life Insurance Co.
Sano ® 健康 ® Saludable® בריא® здоровый® սγιής

All claims must be submitted no more than TWELVE MONTHS following the date on which the expenses are incurred.

Claimants must provide a valid Canadian address for reimbursement.

1	Member Information						
University Name	University of Greater Ottawa	Member Identification Number	178993	Email Address	Suj@rogers.com		
Last Name	Su	First and Middle Name	James Graysson	Birthdate (yyyy-mm-dd)	19xx-02-07	Phone No.	613-766-9000
Address (Street)	125 Apple Street	Apt.		City	Ottawa	Province	ON
Postal Code	K1J 6B7						
Do you or your dependents have additional Health coverage with Healthy Life Insurance?	N [X] Y [ ]	If yes, policy no.					

2	Claimant Information				
Last Name	Su	First Name	James	Birthdate (yyyy-mm-dd)	19xx-02-07
Relationship to Member	Member [X]	Spouse [ ]	Son [ ]	Daughter [ ]	

3 Authorization and Signature – Attach Original Receipts

I understand that the information provided by me on this claim form, and otherwise in respect of my claim, is required by Health Life Insurance, their insurers and authorized administers to assess my entitlement to benefits as well as to administer and underwrite claims, including but not limited to determining if coverage is in effect, investigating the applicability of exclusions and coordinating coverage with each other and other insurers. Additional information may be obtained from existing insurance files about me.

CERTIFICATION

The statements I provide in completing this claim form and otherwise in respect of my claims are true and complete to the best of my knowledge and belief. False or misleading statements can result in cancelled coverage and payment denial. In this case, any refund to the Insurers, I agree to refund.

AUTHORIZATION

I authorize for a period of not less than twelve months from the date hereof, any physician, practitioner, health care provider, hospital, health care institution, medical organization, or any other medically related facility, insurance company or association. In this I include any personal health information, benefit payment, employment or financial information about me, my spouse, and/or dependents in its possession that is requested while administering this claim.

I authorize to disclose any information about me, and I am authorized to disclose any information about my spouse or dependents. I acknowledge that auditing may occur of my records or my spouse's or dependent's records. I authorize any investigation that needs to be made.

I acknowledge that any photocopy of this authorization stands legally the same as the original I am signing.

Check one of the following boxes	Payment to be made to the member	Payment is to be made directly to the provider
	[ ]	[X]

Claimant's Signature	X *James Su*	**Date (yyyy-mm-dd)**	20xx-12-12

4 Provider Information

Section 4 and 5 is to only be completed by the provider when the reimbursement is to be made directly to the

Provider's Name	Brooklane Medical Centre	Physician's Name	Kyle Thomas, MD
Address of Provider (Street number and name)	33 Brooklane Avenue	Apt or Suite	
City	Ottawa	Province	ON
Postal Code	K2B 6M7		
Provider ID No.	123456	Telephone Number	613-224-2308

UNIVERSITY HEALTH INSURANCE PLAN CLAIM FORM (Page 2)

Page 2 of 2

5 Statement of Services (Physicians and hospitals must provide the diagnosis)

Service Date (yyyy-mm-dd)	Description of Service	Provincial Billing Procedure Code	Charge	Diagnosis
20xx-12-12	Consultation – A005	A005	$77.20	Acute Bronchitis – 466

I declare that the above is a correct statement of the services rendered.

Provider's Signature	X *Kyle Thomas, MD*	Date (yyyy-mm-dd)	20xx-12-12

Direct All Claims To:	Phone Inquiries	Fax No.
Healthy Life Insurance Co. 5555 Main Street Ottawa, ON K2L 3T7	613-222-4444	613-222-5555

WSIB COVER PAGE

Health Professional's Report (Form 8)

Health Professional, please use this form for:

- Patients who are claiming benefits under the WSIB insurance plan for an injury/illness related to work, or
- You think that the cause of your patient's injury/illness is workplace factors.

Section 37 of the *Workplace Safety and Insurance Act, 1997* provides the legal authority for health professionals, hospitals and health facilities to submit, without consent, information relating to a worker claiming benefits to the Workplace Safety and Insurance Board (WSIB).

Completing the form:

- **Give a copy of page two only to your patient to give to employer.**
- **Please send pages one and two to the Workplace Safety and Insurance Board.**
- **On the worker's initial visit, ONLY the Form 8 will be paid. A Functional Abilities Form (FAF) will not be paid if completed on the same date.**

For Electronic Submission

To register for electronic form submission and electronic billing, please go to www.telushealth.com/wsib or call Telus at 1-866-240-7492 for more information.

By Fax to:

416-344-4684 or 1-888-313-7373

Or by Mail to:

Workplace Safety and Insurance Board
200 Front Street West
Toronto, ON M5V 3J1

www.wsib.on.ca

0008A1

WSIB FORM 8 (Page 1)

print reset save

wsib cspaat ONTARIO

Fax To: 416-344-4684 OR 1-888-313-7373

Claim Number (if known)

Start >

8 Health Professional's Report (Form 8)

A. Patient and Employer Information - (Patient to complete Section A)

Last Name	First Name	Init.	Sex
Fry	Chris	D	■ M ☐ F
Address (no., street, apt.) 37 Bunting Lane	City/Town Stittsville	Prov. ON	Postal Code K2S 0S1

Telephone 613-234-4123 | Social Insurance No. 980301707 | Date of Birth dd 30 mm 07 yyyy 1980 | Language ■ Eng. ☐ Fr. ☐ Other

Employer Name

The Workplace Safety and Insurance Board (WSIB) collects your information to administer and enforce the Workplace Safety and Insurance Act. The Social Insurance Number may be used to identify workers and to issue income tax information statements as authorized by the Income Tax Act. Questions should be directed to the decision maker responsible for your file or toll free at 1-800-387-5540.

B. Incident Dates and Details Section

1. How did the injury/reinjury or illness occur at work?

I was climbing up a 10-rung ladder and my foot slipped on the third rung making me fall off the ladder.

Occupation Window Installer

Date of incident/or when did the symptoms start? dd 10 mm 12 yyyy 20xx

C. Clinical Information Section - (Please check all that apply)

1. Area of Injury/Illness

☐ Brain ■ Head ■ Face ☐ Eyes Other:
☐ Ears ☐ Teeth ☐ Neck ☐ Chest
☐ Upper back ☐ Lower back ☐ Abdomen ☐ Pelvis

Left / Right: ☐ ☐ Shoulder, ☐ ☐ Arm, ☐ ☐ Elbow, ☐ ☐ Forearm

Left / Right: ☐ ☐ Wrist, ■ (Left) ☐ Hand, ☐ ☐ Fingers

Left / Right: ☐ ☐ Hip, ☐ ☐ Thigh, ☐ ☐ Knee, ☐ ☐ Lower Leg

Left / Right: ☐ ■ (Right) Ankle, ☐ ☐ Foot, ☐ ☐ Toes

2. Description of Injury/Illness Physical Examination Findings

☐ Pain at rest/Night Pain

Pain Rating Scale 0 1 2 3 4 5 6 7 8 9 10 (7 marked)

■ Abrasion ☐ Amputation ☐ Bite ☐ Burn ■ Contusion/Hematoma/Swelling ☐ Crush Injury

☐ Disc Herniation ☐ Dislocation ■ Fall from Height ☐ Foreign Body ☐ Fracture ☐ Hernia ☐ Infection

■ Inflammation ☐ Internal Joint Derangement ☐ Joint Effusion ☐ Laceration ☐ Neurological Dysfunction ☐ Psychological ☐ Puncture (non-needlestick)

☐ Repetitive Strain Injury ☐ Spinal Cord Injury ☐ Sprain/Strain ☐ Surgical intervention ☐ Tendonitis/Tenosynovitis ☐ ↓ Range of Motion

Exposure/Illness: ☐ Asthma ☐ Cancer ☐ Fumes - Inhalation ☐ Hand-arm Vibration ☐ Hearing Loss ☐ Infectious Disease ☐ Needle Stick ☐ Poisoning/Toxic Effects ☐ Skin Condition

☐ Other

3. Are you aware of any pre-existing or other conditions/factors that may impact recovery? ☐ yes ■ no

If yes, describe

4. Diagnosis

RT ankle sprain, contusions to face and left hand

D. Treatment Plan

1. What is the treatment plan (type of treatment, duration) including prescribed medications?

Tylenol #3 q4-6n prn, physio for ankle for 1 month, ice to RT ankle prn, dressings

2. To be completed by physicians only.

Work Injury/Illness Medications	Dose	Frequency	Duration	Work Injury/Illness Medications	Dose	Frequency	Duration
1. Tylenol #3	1-2	q4-6h	1 month	3.			
2. Physio				4.			

3. Investigations & Referrals:

☐ None ☐ Labs ■ Xrays ☐ CT Scan ☐ MRI ☐ EMG ☐ Ultrasound ☐ Other

☐ FP/GP ☐ Specialist/Specialty ☐ Chiropractor

☐ Occupational Health Centre ☐ Occupational Therapist ☐ Other

■ Physiotherapist ☐ Psychologist

Would the patient benefit from the following referrals? ☐ Specialty Clinic ☐ Regional Evaluation Centre (REC)

Name of Referral or Facility (if known) | Telephone | Appointment Date dd mm yyyy

E. Billing Section

Health Professional Designation ☐ Chiropractor ■ Physician ☐ Physiotherapist ☐ Registered Nurse (Extended Class)

Service Code 8M | WSIB Provider ID 123790135

HST Registration No. | HST Amount Billed (if applicable) $ | Service Code ONHST | Your Invoice No. | Service Date dd 10 mm 12 yyyy 20xx

Health Professional Name (please print) Kyle Thomas, MD

Address 33 Brooklane Avenue, Ottawa, ON K2B 6M7

Telephone 613-224-2308

Fax 613-224-2300

WSIB FORM 8 (Page 2)

Claim Number (If known)

8 Health Professional's Report (Form 8)
Return To Work Information

Once completed, please ensure that a copy of this page only is provided to the worker.

Last Name	First Name	Init.	Birth Date dd	mm	yyyy
Fry	Chris	D	30	07	1980

Area(s) of Injury(ies)/Illness(es)
Head, face, left hand, and right foot

Date of Incident	dd	mm	yyyy
	10	12	20xx

F. Return To Work Information - Must be completed by a Health Professional

When work injury/illness occurs, focus on return to usual activity including return to safe and appropriate work is best practice. Most workers who experience soft tissue injury are able to remain at work.

1. Have you discussed return to work with your patient? ■ yes ☐ no

2. ■ **This worker can resume Regular duties. Start date** dd 10 mm 01 yyyy 20xx **If graduated hours required please specify** ______

☐ **This worker can begin Modified duties. Start date** dd ___ mm ___ yyyy ___ **If graduated hours required please specify** ______

☐ **This worker is not able to work because of the workplace injury/illness.**
Please provide explanation ______

3. Please indicate the worker's status and functional abilities in relation to the workplace injury and diagnosis.

A. Full Functional Abilities ☐

B. Worker Functional Abilities

	Able to	Not Able to
Bend/Twist	■	☐
Climb	☐	■
Kneel	■	☐
Lift	☐	■
Operate Heavy Equipment	☐	■
Operate a Motor Vehicle	☐	■
Push/Pull	☐	■
Sit	■	☐
Stand	☐	■
Use of Public Transportation	☐	■
Use of Upper Extremities	■	☐
Walk	☐	■

C. Other Limitations: eg. Environmental Conditions, Medication, Use of Protective Equipment.

Please describe: ______

4. From the date of this assessment, the above limitations will apply for approximately:
☐ 1 - 2 days ☐ 3 - 7 days ☐ 8 - 14 days ■ 14 + days

5. Follow-up Appointment
☐ None required ■ As Needed
Date of next appointment dd ___ mm ___ yyyy ___

Health Professional's Name (Please print)
Kyle Thomas, MD

Address
33 Brooklane Avenue, Ottawa, ON, K2B 6M7

Health Professional's Signature
PLEASE PRINT AND SIGN

Telephone
613-224-2308

Service Date dd 10 mm 12 yyyy 20xx

G. Worker's Signature

By signing below I am authorizing the above noted health professional, who is treating me, to provide my employer with a copy of this page outlining my functional abilities. I understand a copy will be sent to the Workplace Safety and Insurance Board (WSIB) by my health professional.

Signature
PLEASE PRINT AND SIGN

Date dd 10 mm 12 yyyy 20xx

Once completed, please ensure that a copy of this page only is provided to the worker.

0008A

visit our website at at: **www.wsib.on.ca**

Page 2/2

print reset save

Appendix F

QHR Technologies Inc.
Accuro®EMR Instructions

DAY SHEET (Page 1)

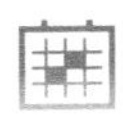

Scheduler

To print a day sheet for a provider, click on the provider's name on the top of the scheduler sheet and then click this icon: . It will bring up the sheet. Print the Day Sheet using the print icon: .

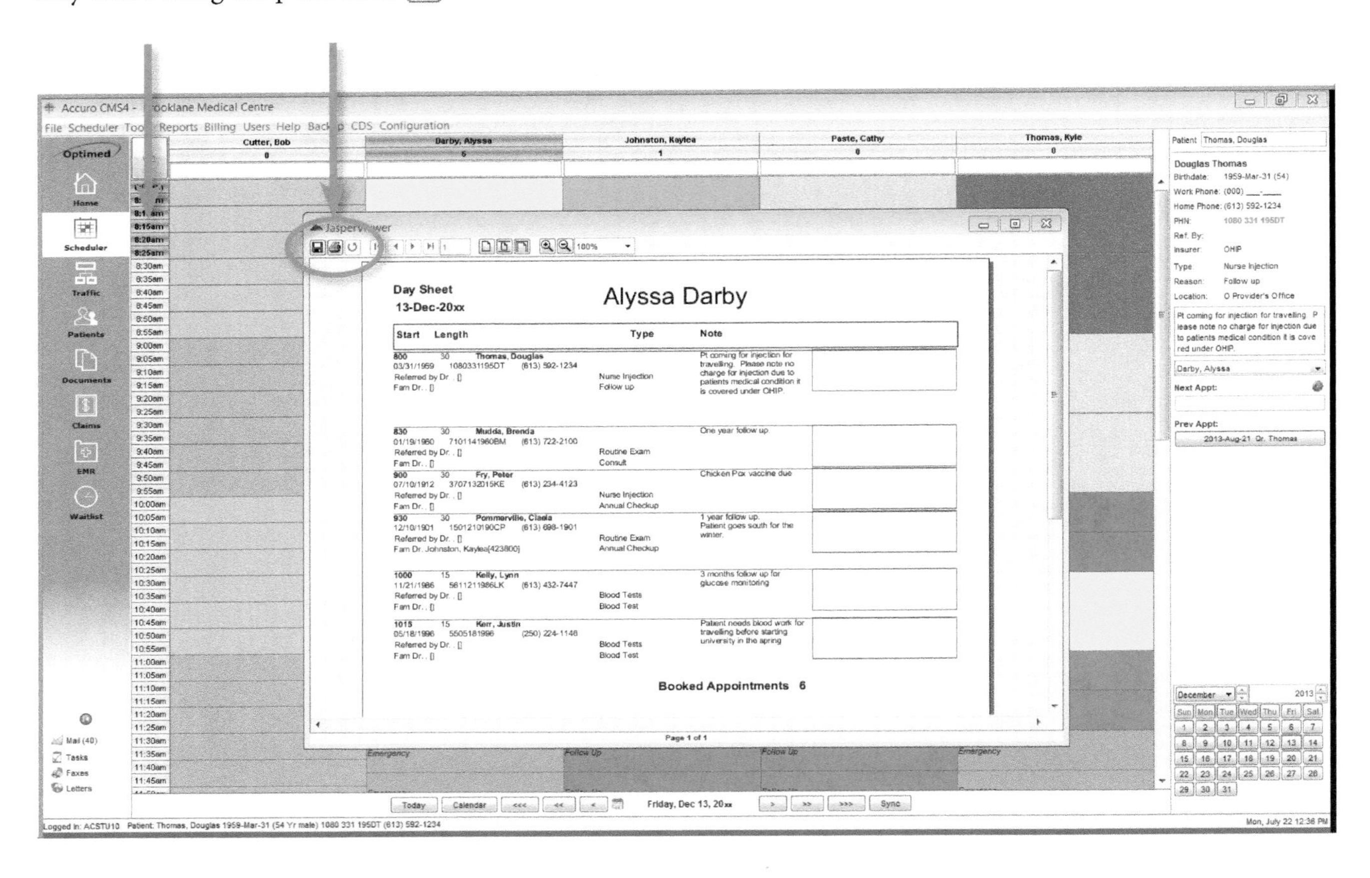

You are also able to print a Day Sheet from the EMR section of the software.

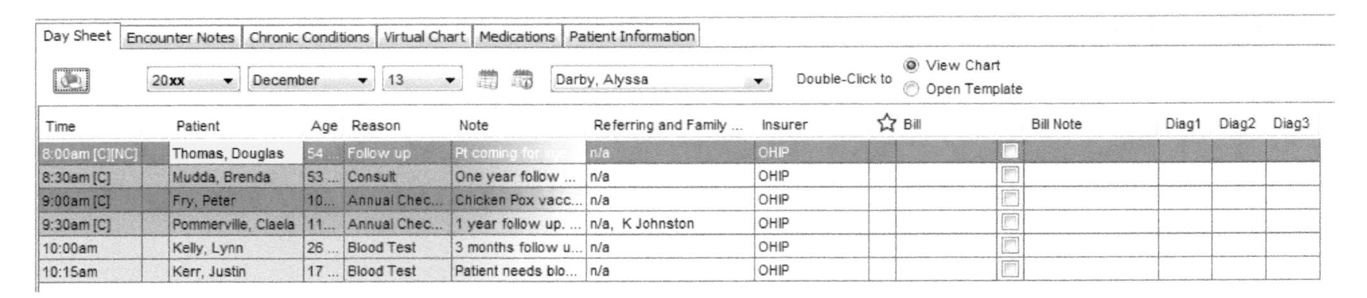

Time	Patient	Age	Reason	Note	Referring and Family ...	Insurer	Bill	Bill Note	Diag1	Diag2	Diag3
8:00am [C][NC]	Thomas, Douglas	54	Follow up	Pt coming for inj...	n/a	OHIP					
8:30am [C]	Mudda, Brenda	53 ...	Consult	One year follow ...	n/a	OHIP					
9:00am [C]	Fry, Peter	10...	Annual Chec...	Chicken Pox vacc...	n/a	OHIP					
9:30am [C]	Pommerville, Claela	11...	Annual Chec...	1 year follow up. ...	n/a, K Johnston	OHIP					
10:00am	Kelly, Lynn	26 ...	Blood Test	3 months follow u...	n/a	OHIP					
10:15am	Kerr, Justin	17 ...	Blood Test	Patient needs blo...	n/a	OHIP					

DAY SHEET (Page 2)

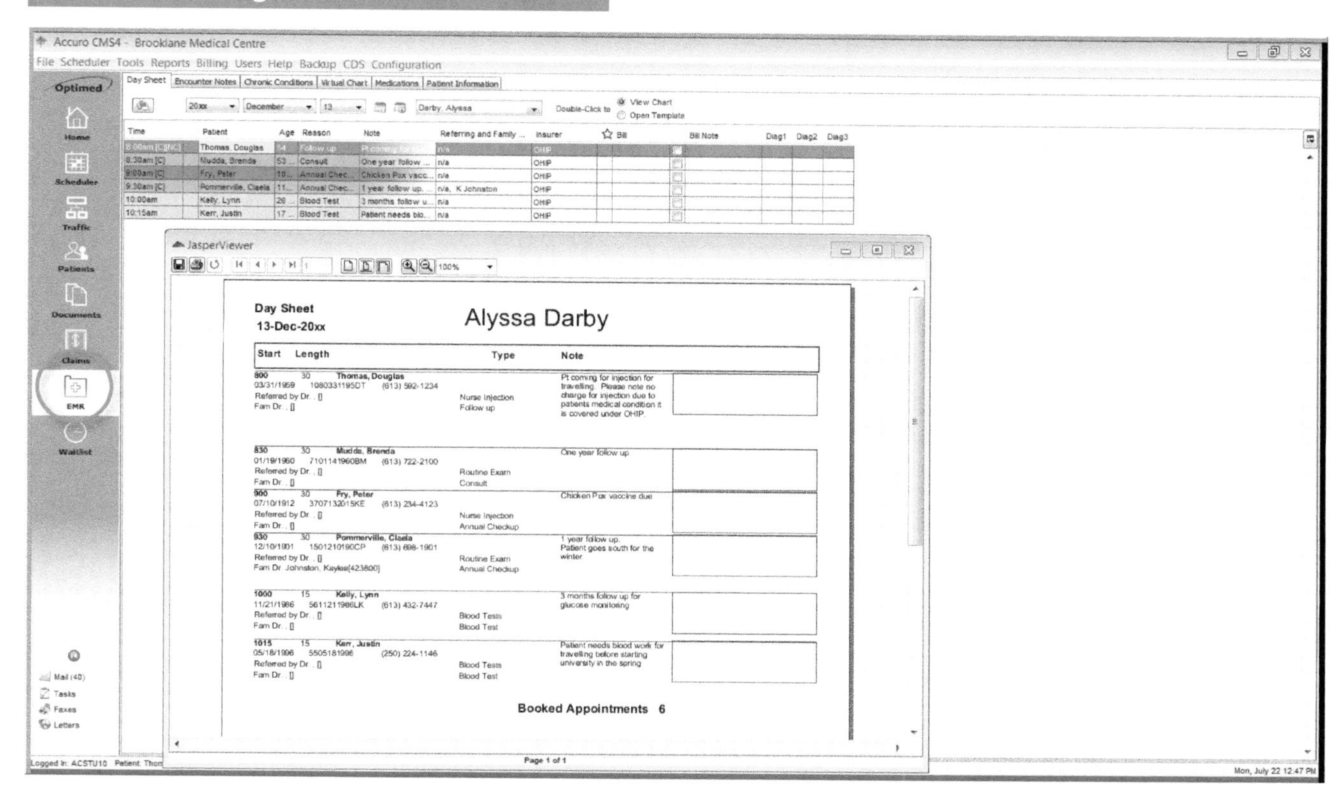

NEW APPOINTMENT (Page 1)

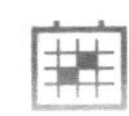

Scheduler

This is the navigation button that you will use to make, change, check in, confirm, register a no show, or not charge for an appointment. When you are in the Navigation Pane, you will notice that it turns white to show you where you are in Accuro®EMR.

Once you have chosen the patient you want to book an appointment for, or check an appointment, you are able to select the patient.

As you will see below, the name we have chosen to search with is James Mudda. Due to the difficultly in the spelling, we chose to use the first few letters and the % symbol so the software will search for a greater number of patients. This will then allow us to narrow down the list.

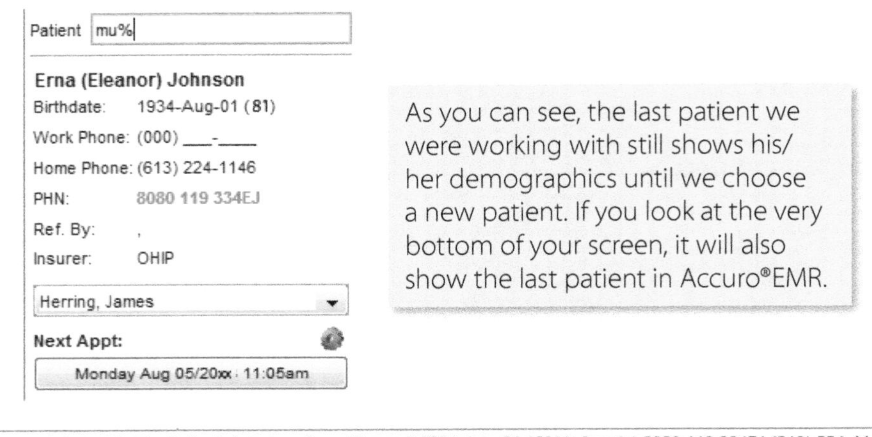

Patients whose names appear in italics have an alias, and patients whose information shows up in red are inactive patients. You are also able to format patients using different colours according to their condition – e.g., pregnant – so the condition is easily identifiable.

NEW APPOINTMENT (Page 2)

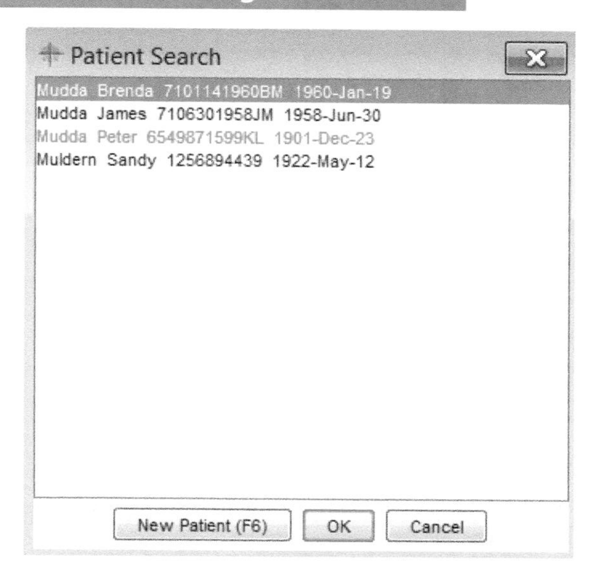

You will see that the patient search chose all the patients in the BMC database whose names started with "mu." It chose one inactive patient and two different last names.

Let's make an appointment for our patient, James Mudda. Once you have selected James, you will notice that his name appears in the box on the right side as well as along the bottom of the screen.

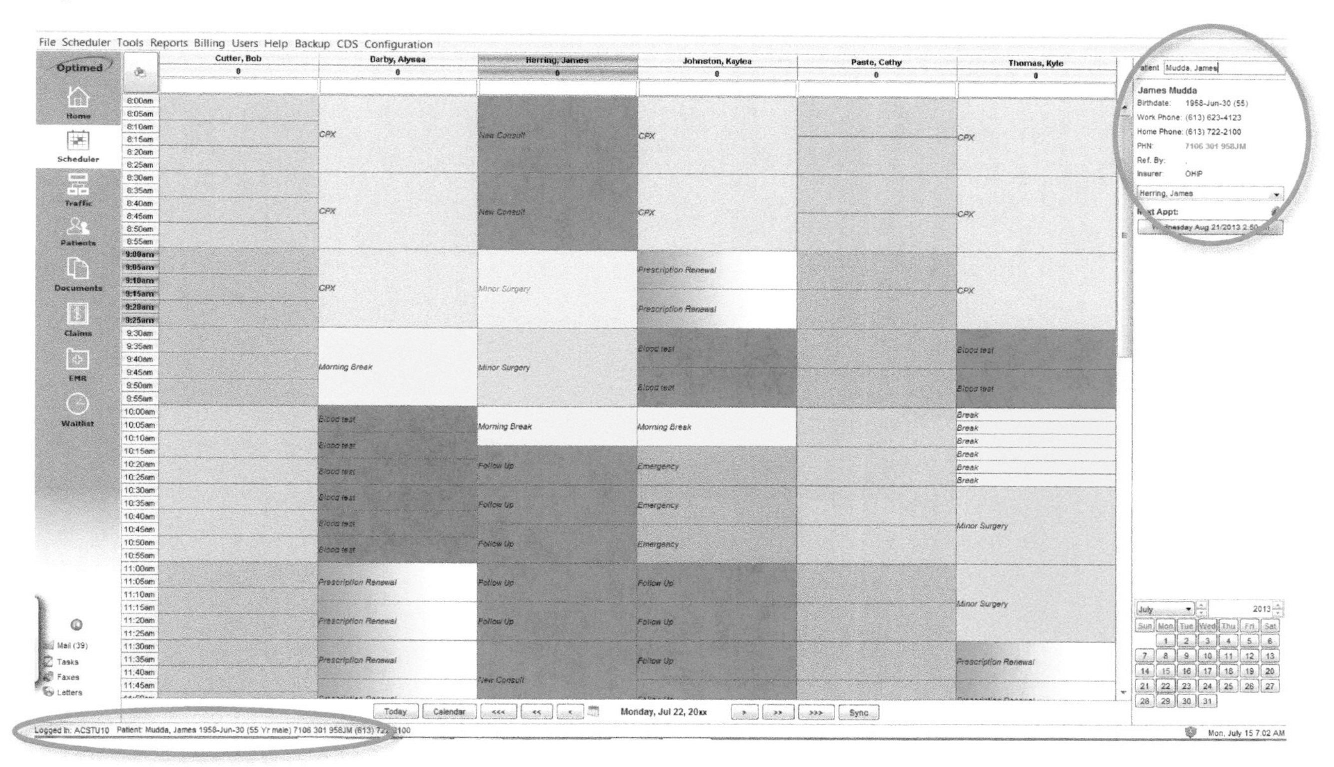

NEW APPOINTMENT (Page 3)

We now go up to the upper left corner and click on the word "Scheduler." A dropbox will appear for us to create an appointment. Click on "Create Appointment."

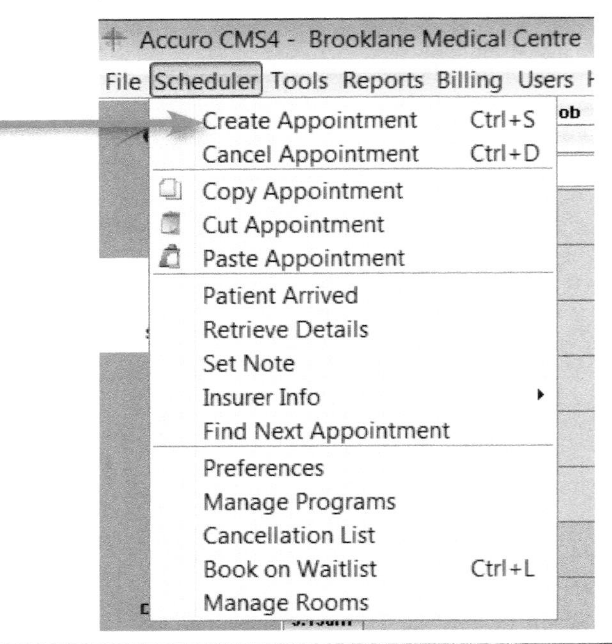

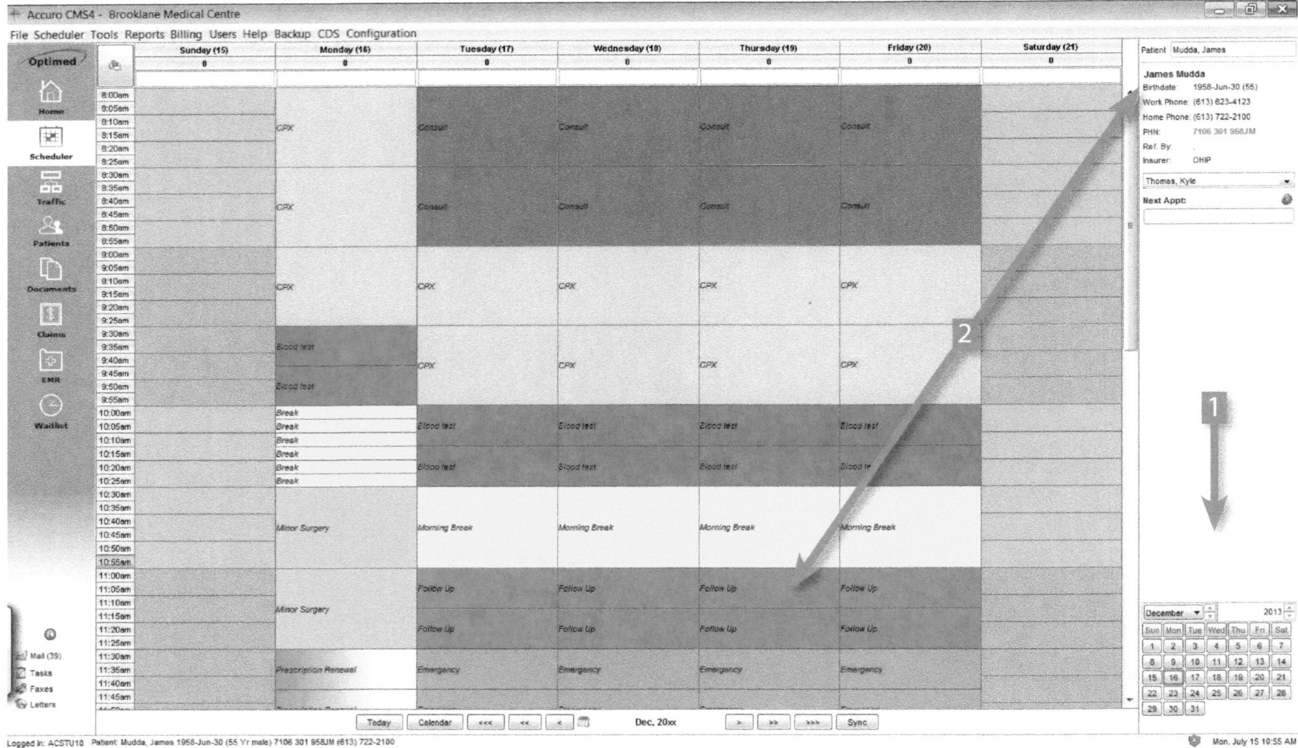

1. Click the dropdown arrow and select the month of the appointment.
2. Click and drag the name of the patient to the appropriate type of appointment. For this patient, we are planning a six-week follow-up appointment. Once we do this, a new box will appear.

NEW APPOINTMENT (Page 4)

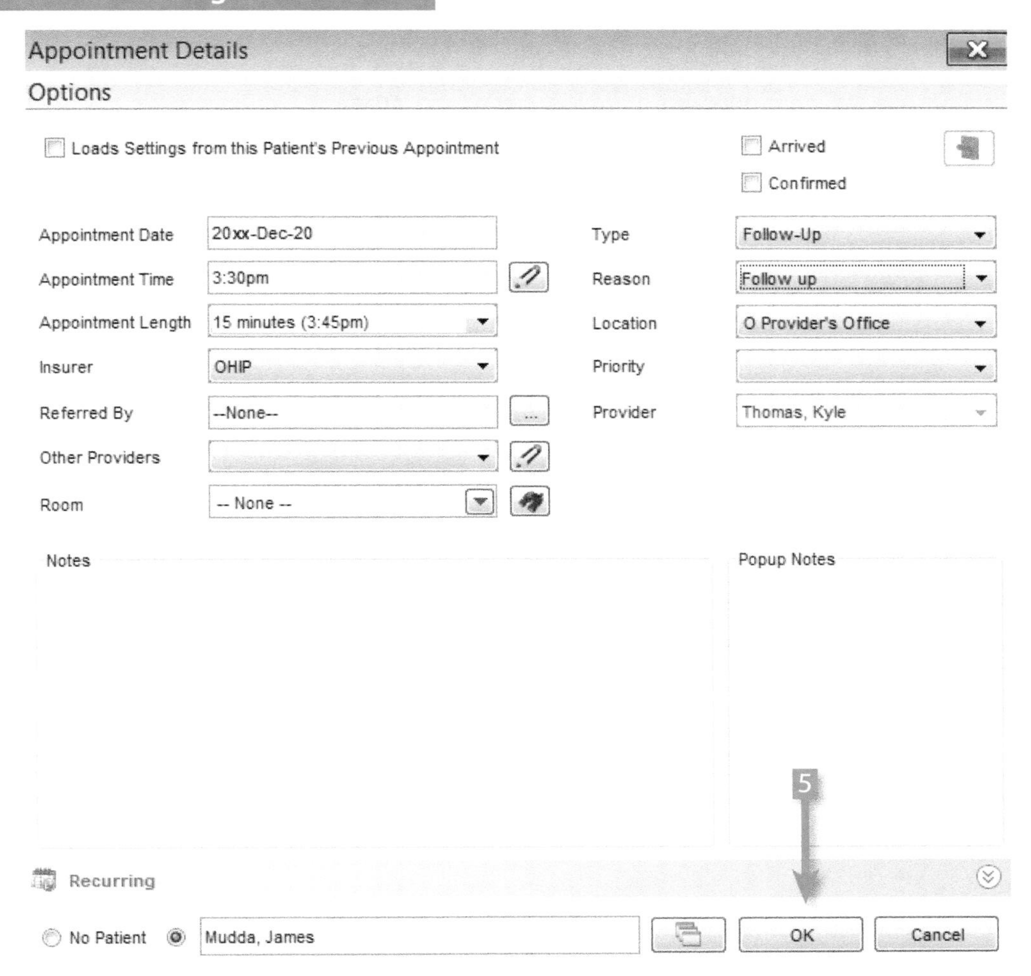

3. In this box are various dropdown arrows. You are able to override the information for the field and time you have chosen, if necessary. If you see the word "manage," you can add reasons or types for your office.
4. You are also able to show a patient as "Confirmed" and "Arrived" in this box. Accuro®EMR has more than one way to perform a function.
5. Click on OK and you have now made an appointment.

NEW APPOINTMENT (Page 5)

6. It is always better to enter as much information as possible when creating an appointment. We know this was a follow-up spot in the calendar, but we also need to know it is a six-month follow-up. Add this to the appointment by right clicking the mouse and searching the dropdown box. In this case, we want to retrieve details and add to the information. As you can see, we are able to do many functions when we click on the patient's appointment in the Scheduler.

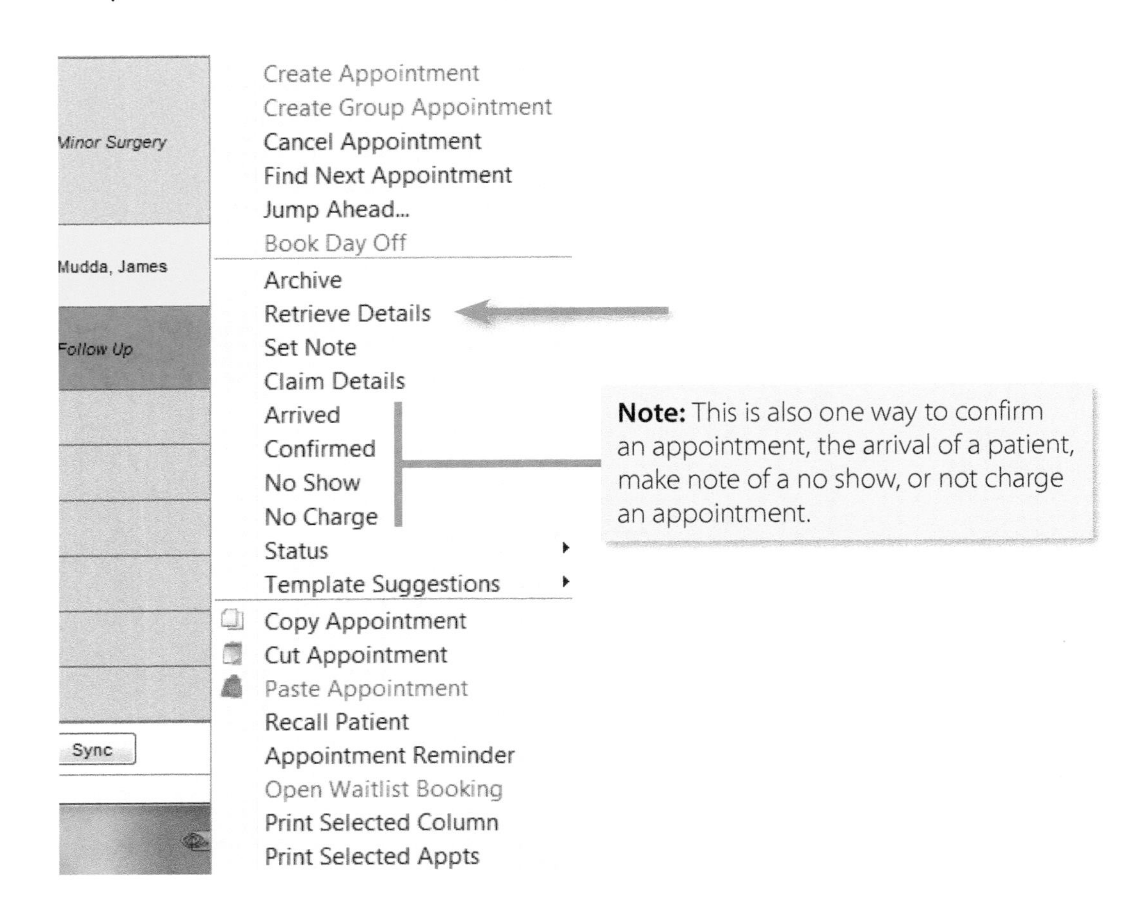

NEW APPOINTMENT (Page 6)

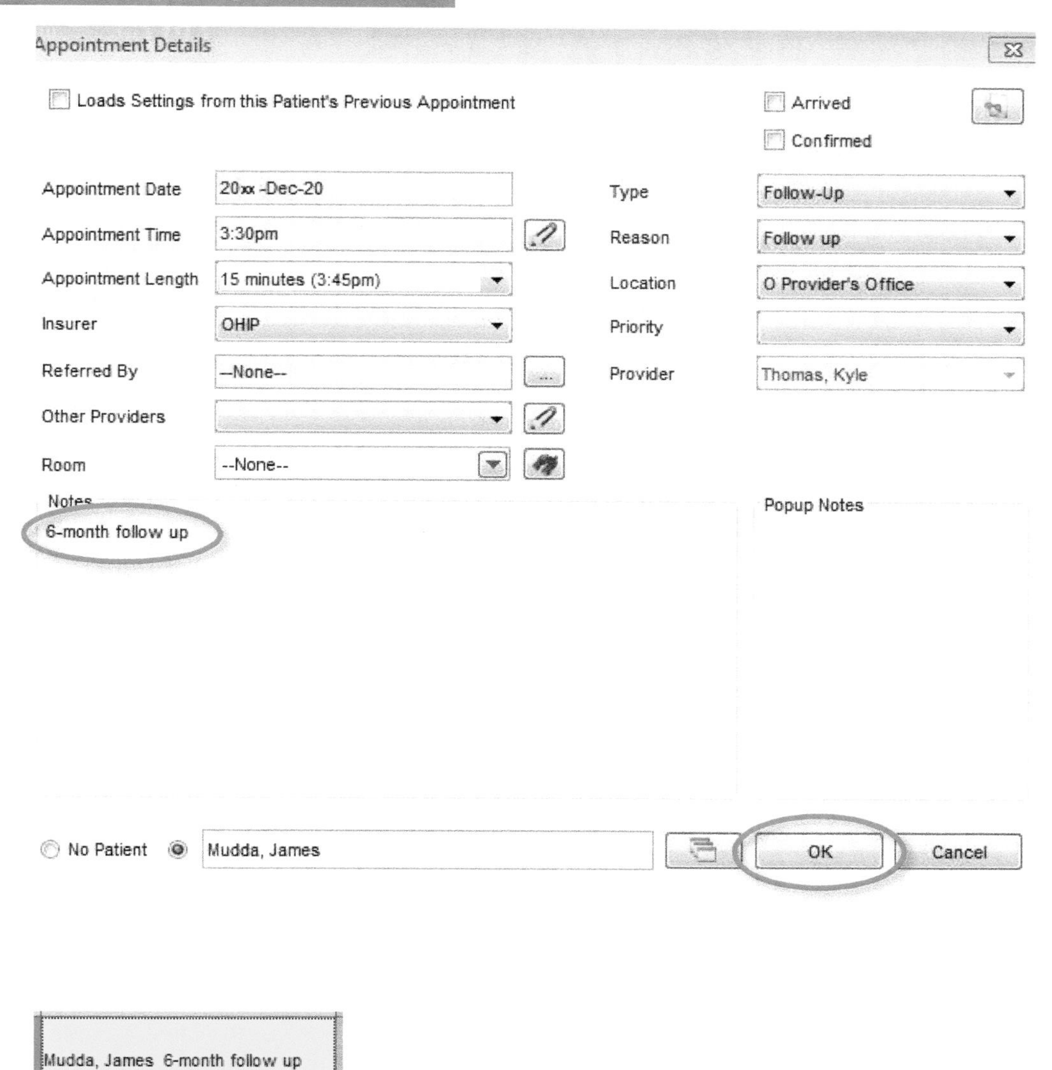

LOGGING ON AND OFF

Log On

Once you have logged on, your username will appear in the top left corner. If you are in a clinic and are using multiple computers, this will assure you that you are using your username and not that of another co-worker.

Due to confidentiality, it is very important to make sure you are signed in under your username and do not use another co-worker's username.

You can also customize your view by changing the select view option.

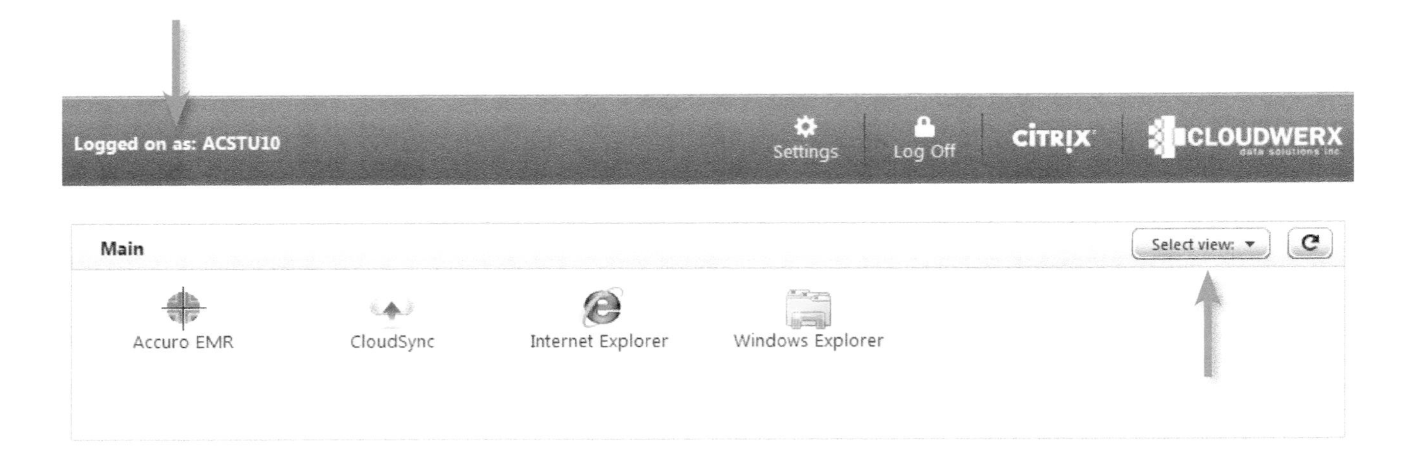

Log Off

Always remember to log off after you are finished your work.

NAVIGATION – HOME PAGE

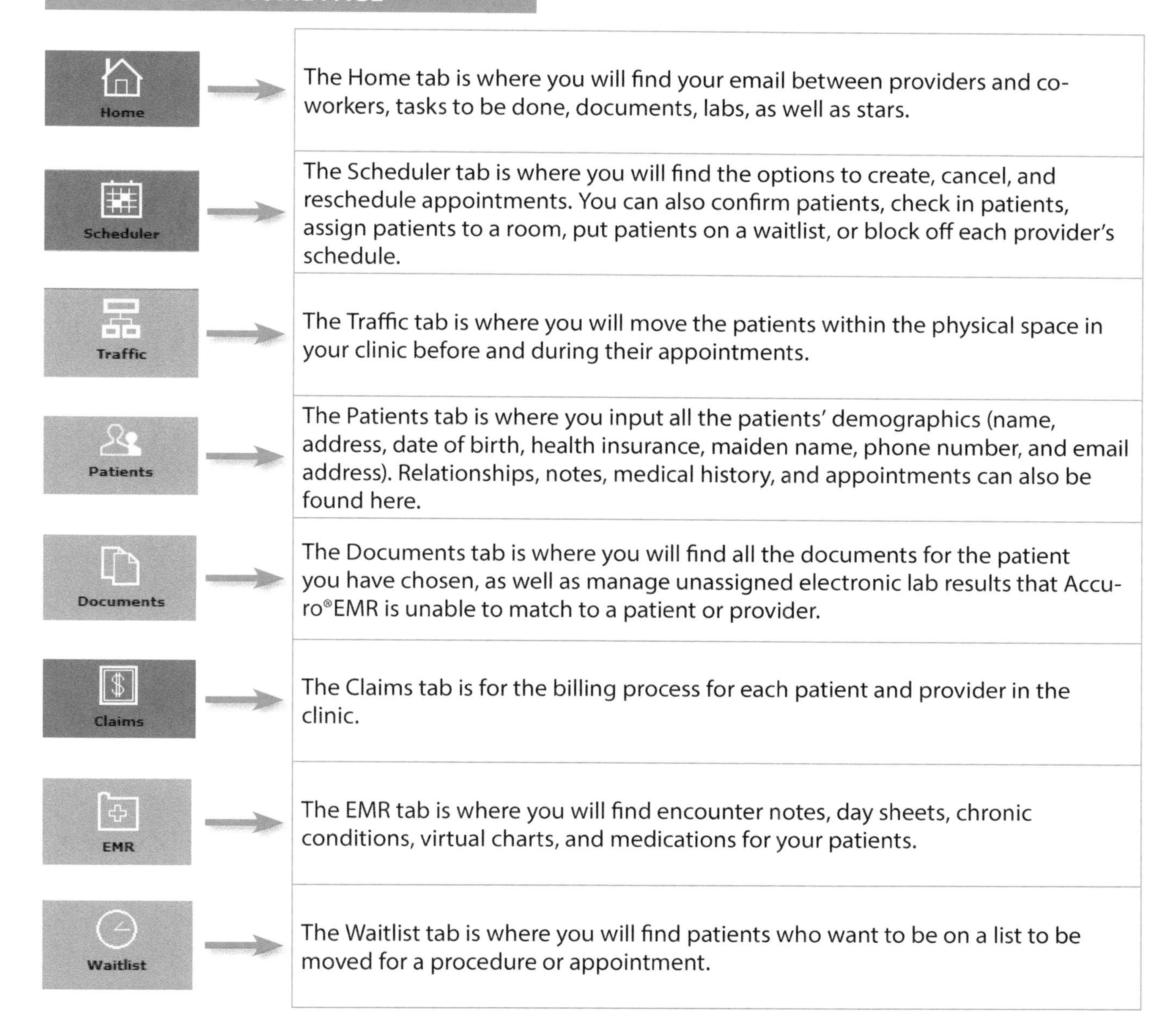

Home	The Home tab is where you will find your email between providers and co-workers, tasks to be done, documents, labs, as well as stars.
Scheduler	The Scheduler tab is where you will find the options to create, cancel, and reschedule appointments. You can also confirm patients, check in patients, assign patients to a room, put patients on a waitlist, or block off each provider's schedule.
Traffic	The Traffic tab is where you will move the patients within the physical space in your clinic before and during their appointments.
Patients	The Patients tab is where you input all the patients' demographics (name, address, date of birth, health insurance, maiden name, phone number, and email address). Relationships, notes, medical history, and appointments can also be found here.
Documents	The Documents tab is where you will find all the documents for the patient you have chosen, as well as manage unassigned electronic lab results that Accuro®EMR is unable to match to a patient or provider.
Claims	The Claims tab is for the billing process for each patient and provider in the clinic.
EMR	The EMR tab is where you will find encounter notes, day sheets, chronic conditions, virtual charts, and medications for your patients.
Waitlist	The Waitlist tab is where you will find patients who want to be on a list to be moved for a procedure or appointment.

SHORTCUT KEYS (PAGE 1)

Keyboard Key	Function
F1	Patient Search
F2	Providers
F3	Quick Summary
F4	Quick Appointment View
F5	Quick Documents View
F6	Quick New Patient
F7	Add/View Patient Tasks
F8	Patient Status History
F9	Generate Registration
F11	Referral Letter
F12	Generate date/time stamp in EMR template
ALT+Home icon	Open Home area in separate window
ALT+Scheduler icon	Open Scheduler area in a separate window
ALT+Traffic icon	Open Traffic area in separate window
ALT+Documents icon	Open Document area in a separate window
ALT+Claims icon	Open Claims area in a separate window
ALT+EMR icon	Open EMR area in a separate window
CTRL+F1	Open User Guide
CTRL+F3	New Patient Summary
CTRL+F10	Open User Guide (Online Help)
CTRL+F11	Adv. Letter
CTRL+ A	Select All
CTRL+B	New Bill
CTRL+D	Cancel Appointment

SHORTCUT KEYS (PAGE 2)

Keyboard Key	Function
CTRL+I	Find Invoice
CTRL+K	Find Claim ID
CTRL+L	Book on Waitlist
CTRL+P	New Procedure
CTRL+Q	Quit
CTRL+R	Reporting
CTRL+S	Create Appointment
CTRL+1	Home
CTRL+2	Scheduler
CTRL+3	Patient
CTRL+4	Documents
CTRL+5	Claims
CTRL+6	EMR
CTRL+8	Waitlist
CTRL+ALT+C	Calculator
CTRL+ (In Scheduler)	CSV Day Sheet

NEW PATIENT RECORD (Page 1)

Accuro CMS4 - Brooklane Medical Centre
File Scheduler Tools Reports Billing Users Help Backup CDS Configuration
Optimed
Home
Scheduler
Traffic
Patients
Documents
Claims
EMR
Waitlist
Last Name
First Name
Middle Name
Health #
Search Only
Identifier
Search Only
Birthdate
MM/DD/YYYY
Mr.
Patient Status: Active
Office Provider: --None--
Demographics | Other | Relationships | Notes | Status History | Private Billing | Insurer Rules | Providers | Provider Enrollment History
Health # ON, Canada Expiry MM/DD/YYYY File Number
Birthdate MM/DD/YYYY Age Gender M Deceased MM/DD/YYYY
Family Phys --None-- Referring Phys --None--
Address Note
City ON, Canada Postal/Zip Type
Phone #s: Home (000) ___-___ Work (000) ___-___ Cell (000) ___-___ Fax (000) ___-___ Preferred Contact Method
Default Insurer OHIP
Current Enrollment Status: Unenrolled
Last Updated:

"Patient Search" is found under the navigation bar under "Patients." You are also able to use F1 to bring you into the patient search field as a shortcut. You are able to search by several criteria as shown below.

In the above screenshot, you will notice the red dots. These fields are the minimum fields required to save a new patient record.

The search criteria are:

- Last name
- First name (as long as you put a comma in front of it)
- Date of birth – mm/dd/yyyy (April 15, 20xx, would be 04/15/20xx)
- File number
- Health card number (search only in box in upper area of the screen)

NEW PATIENT RECORD (Page 2)

Patients who are inactive are in red. If they are in italics (red or black), they have an alias. You can colour-code your patients using different colours for different conditions – e.g., pregnancies.

When a new patient arrives and has filled out the new patient registration, you have to undertake a patient search. The patient has a last name of Pommerville. You will notice that no patients were found. We now have to add the patient's information in the screens provided below.

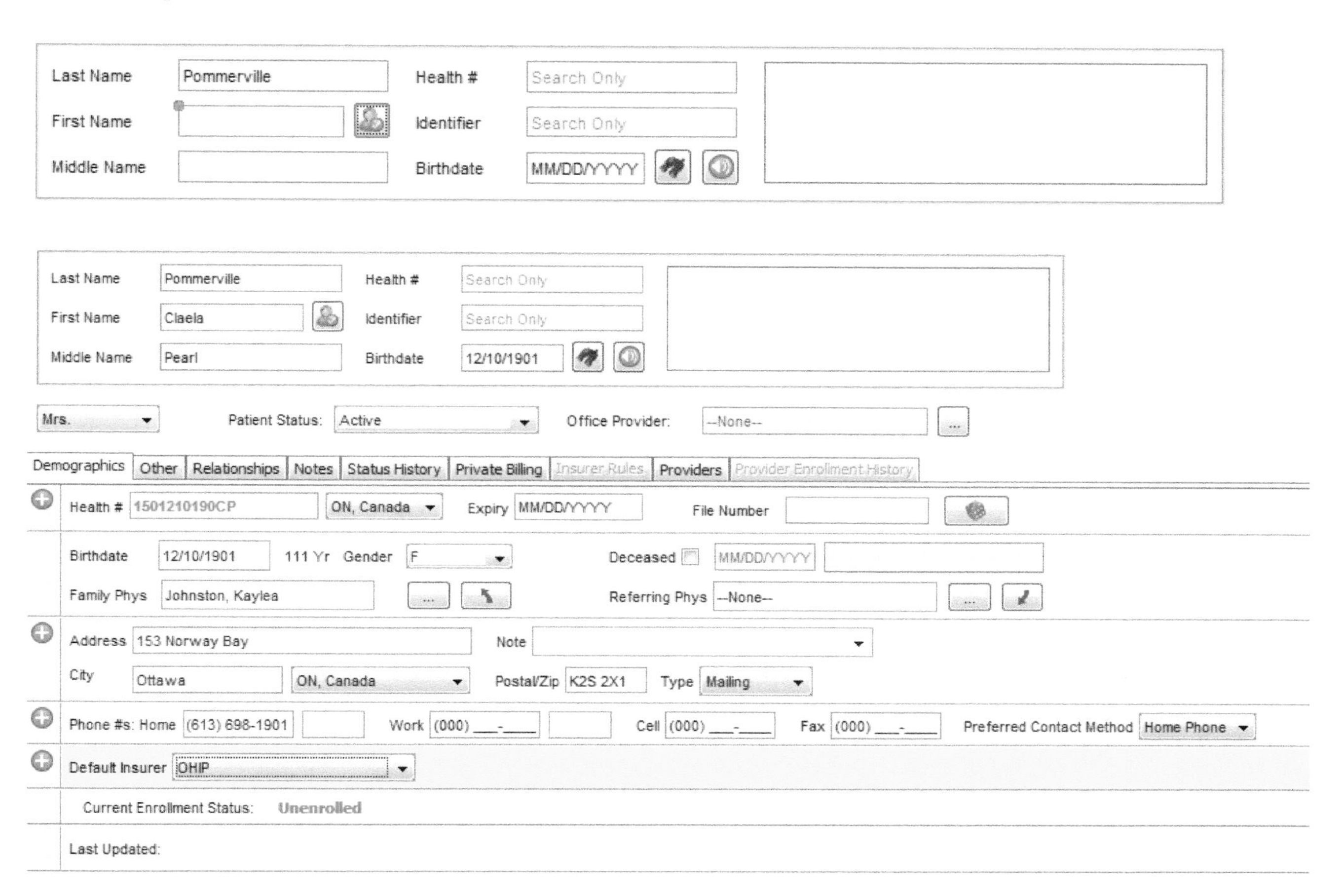

This green button indicates that you can add more information to that specific section. Try each one so you are aware of what information it asks for. For example, we clicked on the address as this patient is away for most of the winter.

You will also note that when you see this symbol ▾, you will have choices to make to fill in the box. If the choices are not appropriate for the patient, you are able to manage the box by adding information.

NEW PATIENT RECORD (Page 3)

To add information, go to Type --Manage-- ▾ Click on the ▼ arrow and the box below will appear. The ⊕ button will now allow you to add in a type. Click OK . This will be available to you in Accuro®EMR for your patient database.

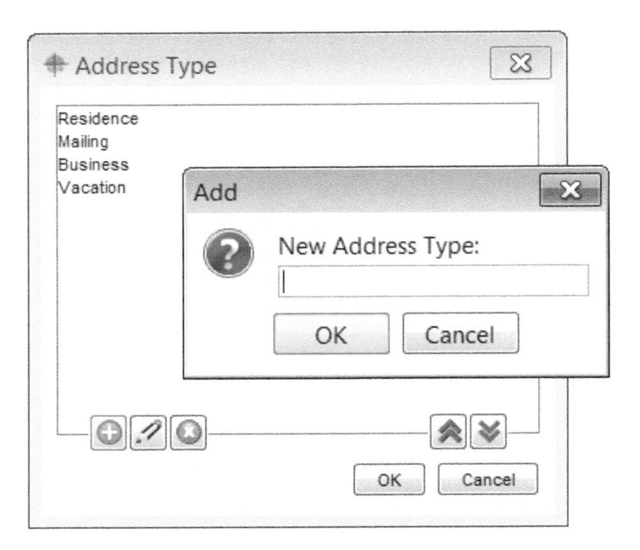

Arrows up and down will also let you navigate in the box or section that you are in and allow you to delete information or scroll through the area. Go to a patient in the BMC database and try this exercise.

Once you have added all this information, you will add the patient to the database. This icon is found at the bottom of the screen. See the arrow below.

You will then search for the patient and add other information – e.g., other clinical specialists seen in the clinic.

ALIAS (Page 1)

An alias is used when a patient has more than one name that is commonly used. It could be a nickname, a different last name such as a maiden name, or a middle name they use.

Entering the alias in an EMR system avoids confusion in identifying the patient.

An alias is entered into the system through the "Patient" screen and the patient must be selected.

We will search for Brenda Mudda and select her. Click on the "Other" tab.

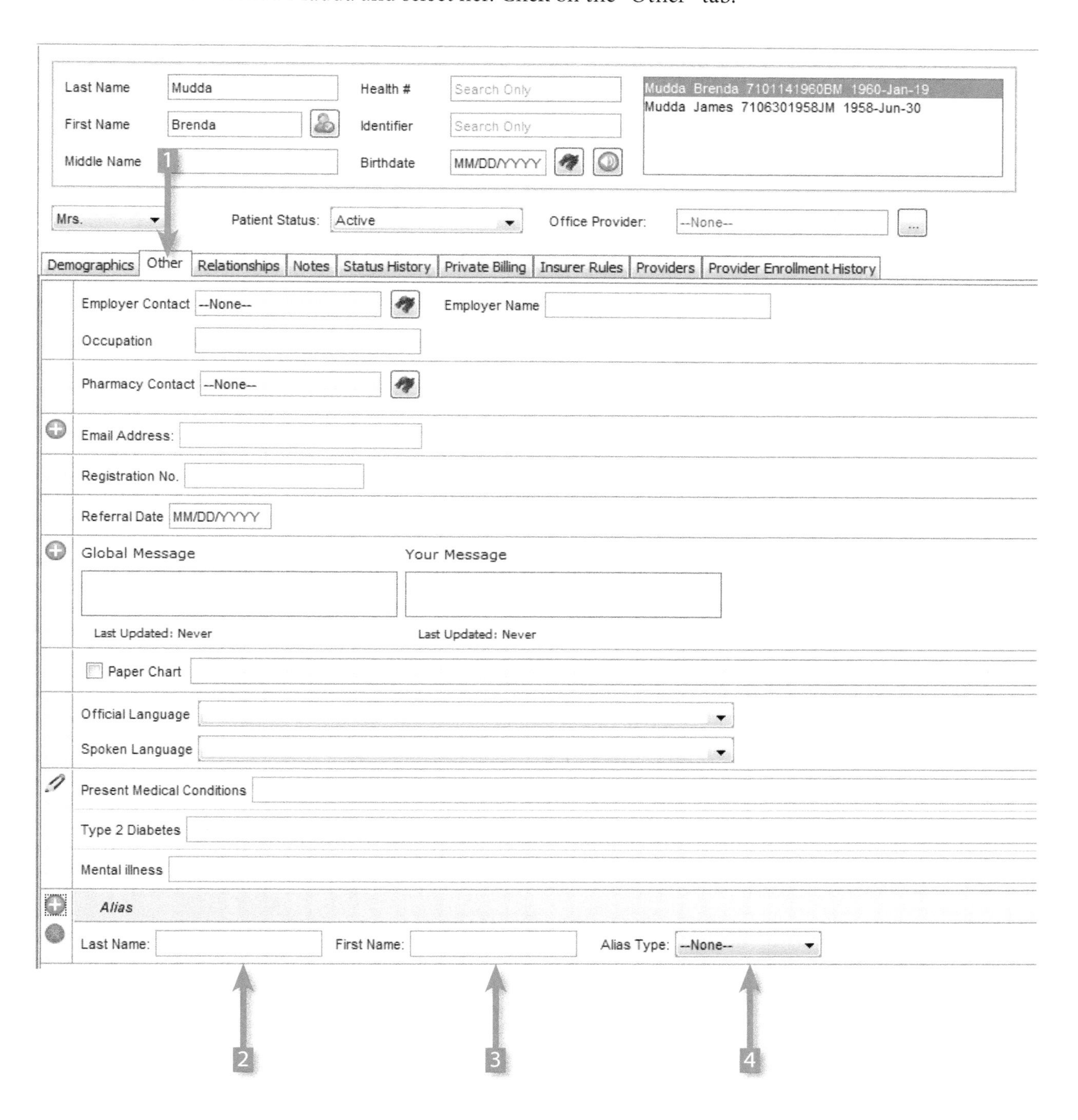

ALIAS (Page 2)

Fill in the information as seen below:

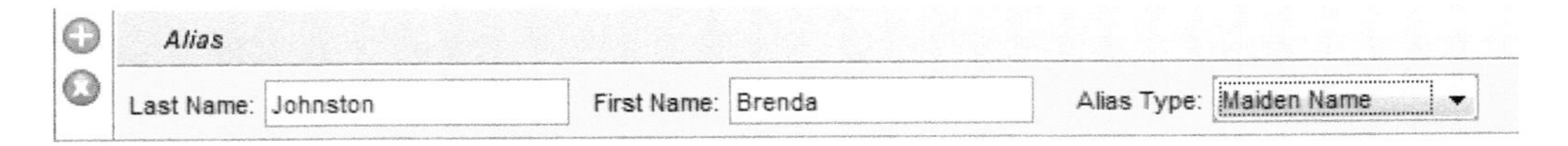

Fill in the information provided from the patient and/or patient registration form as seen below. Choose the appropriate alias type from the dropdown button. If the correct type is not in the system, click on "Manage" and enter a new type.

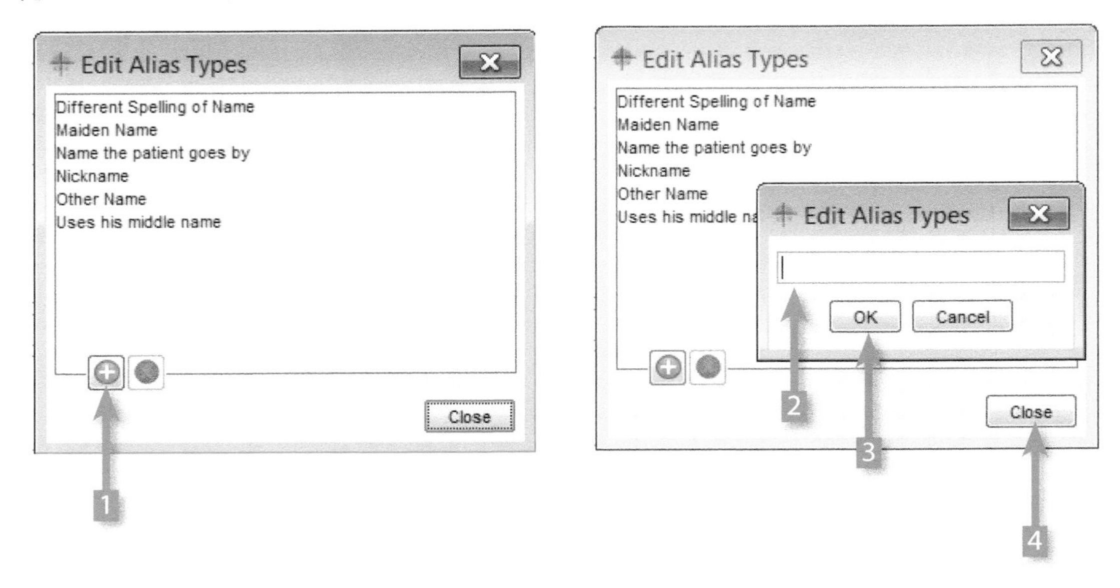

As you can now see, when you type in the alias name it will appear in italics.

When you search for the new name you will see that the alias will appear in the search results box.

Remember to always update your patient record when you have made any changes. The "Update Patient" button is located on the bottom right.

NICKNAME AND PREFERRED NAME

In Ontario, the photo ID health card applications are filled in with various combinations of names used. An example would be someone using the middle name as the first name.

To prevent confusion, Accuro®EMR has a field to enter a nickname or a preferred name.

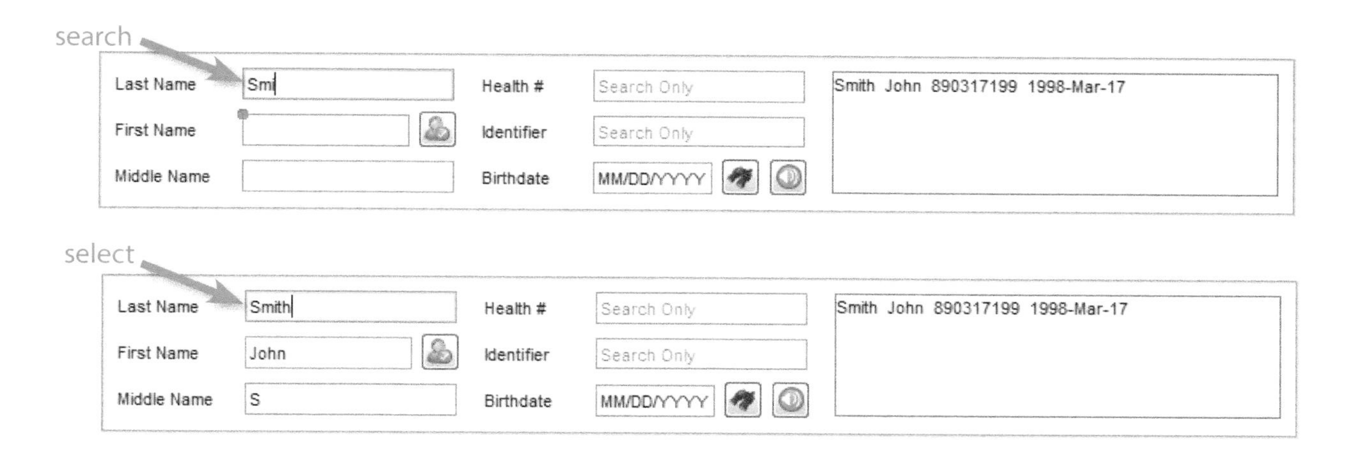

Click on this icon to enter the patient's preferred name. The box below will appear. Once the name is entered, click OK .

If you have made a mistake, click Cancel.

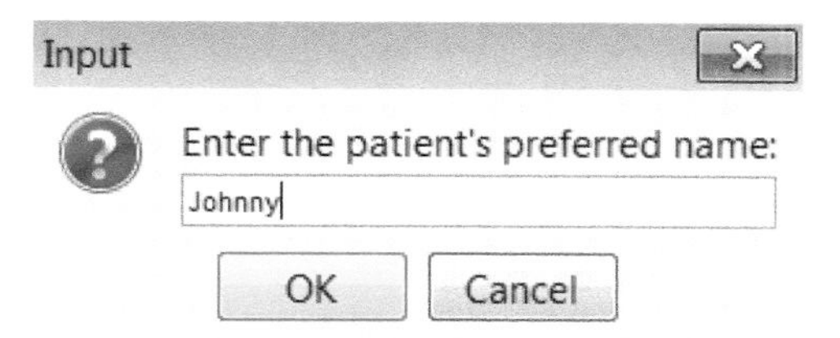

Once you have updated the patient information, press F1 to clear, and do the search again. As you will notice, the preferred name is in brackets beside the first name. This is the name that you would address the patient by in person or on the phone for etiquette purposes.

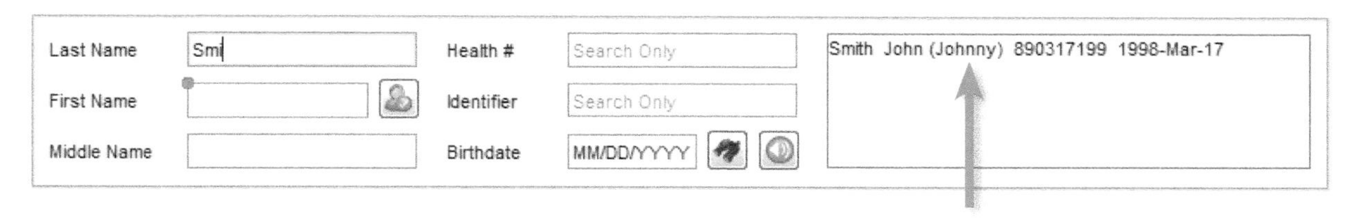

PATIENT INFORMATION – OTHER TAB

As you add each patient and fill in all the patient's information fields, your database, your contact list, and your address book all update with the information you have added.

To search the information in your database, use the icon. As you can see, a pop up with an address book will appear, and then you click on the icon again and the search will be complete. If the correct information is in the search results, you will then select it using the "Select" button. If the contact information is not in your search options, you then have to add the new contact information and select the "Add" button.

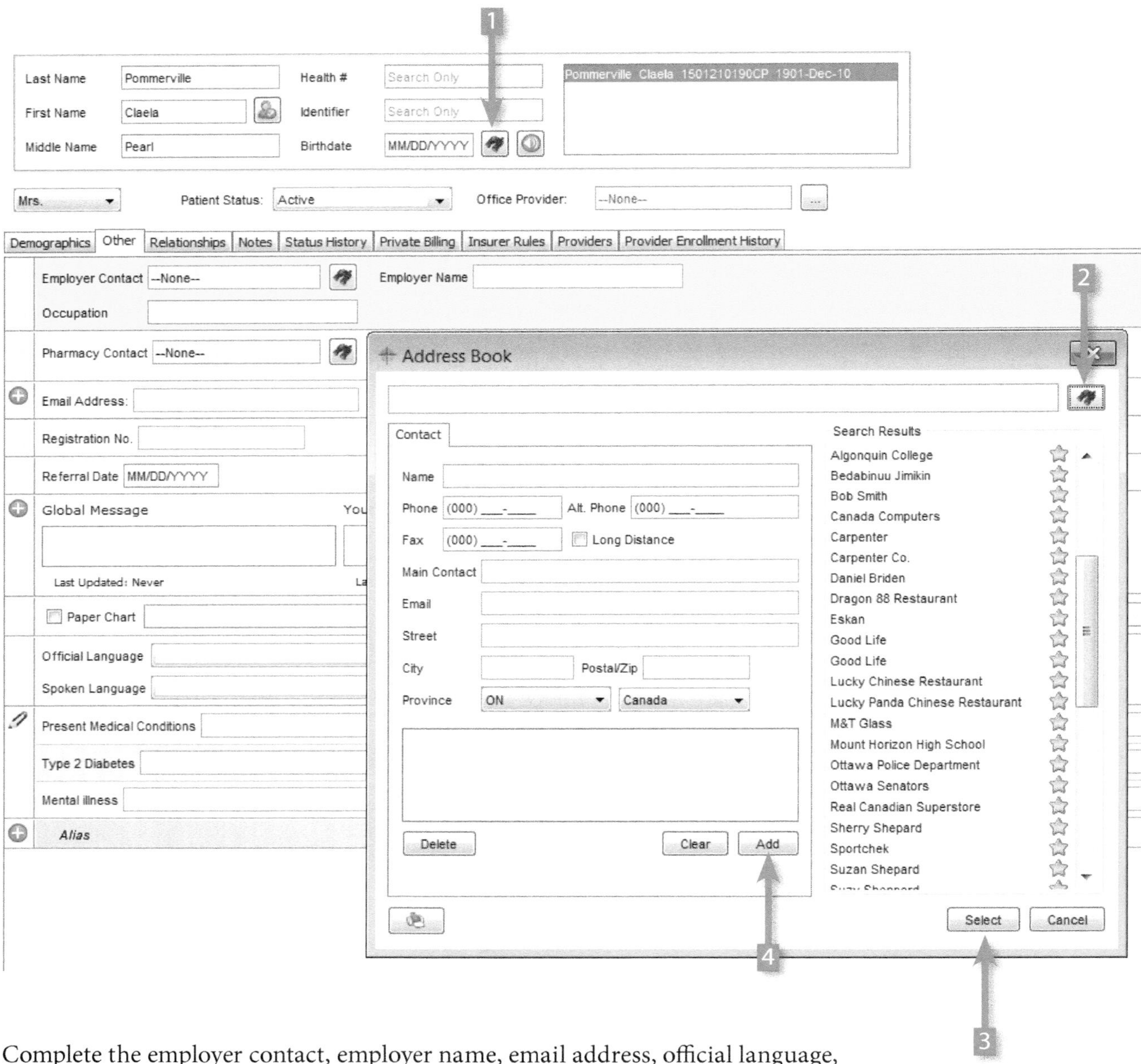

Complete the employer contact, employer name, email address, official language, and spoken language sections using the dropdown buttons to select the correct information. As BMC is Ontario based, the choices for official languages are English and French only.

RELATIONSHIPS AND NEXT OF KIN (Page 1)

Patients

In the health care environment, we need to note the next of kin, as well as family history. It is important for the provider to be aware of any other family members who are registered with the same clinic. This is important in cases of emergency or hereditary diseases. The provider will not be able to tell the patient if a family member is registered with the clinic, but this knowledge could be helpful in the treatment of the patient.

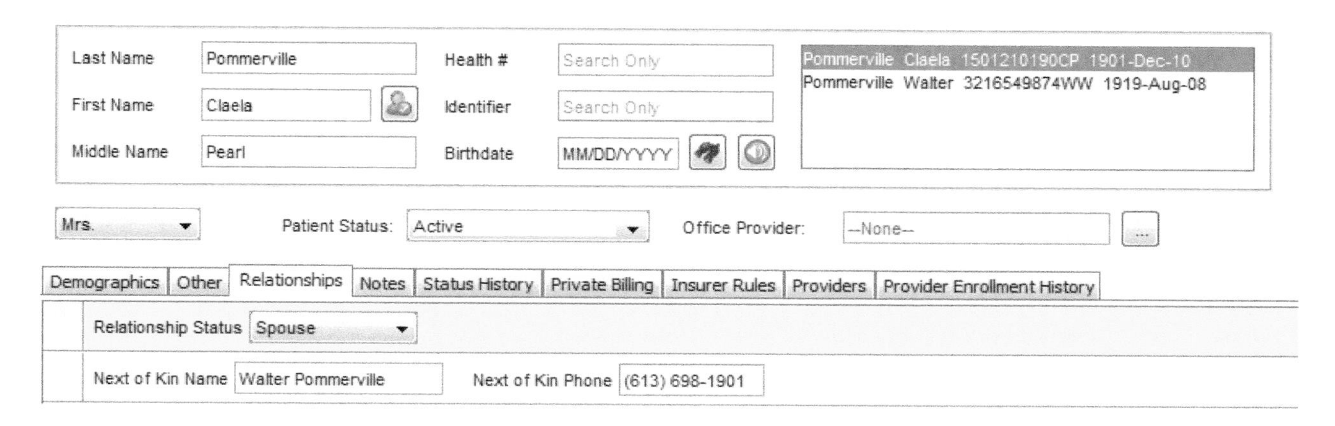

Make sure to use the dropdown arrow to choose a relationship status, and fill in the name of the next of kin and phone number.

When we see this icon ⊕, we can add more information. You are able to add as many relationships as the patient is able to give you. The patient may not know all the answers to the questions, but you can fill in what is available to you. This information can be deleted by using the ⊗.

When you see this icon [...], click on it and choose what is appropriate or use "Manage" to add or edit the selection.

RELATIONSHIPS AND NEXT OF KIN (Page 2)

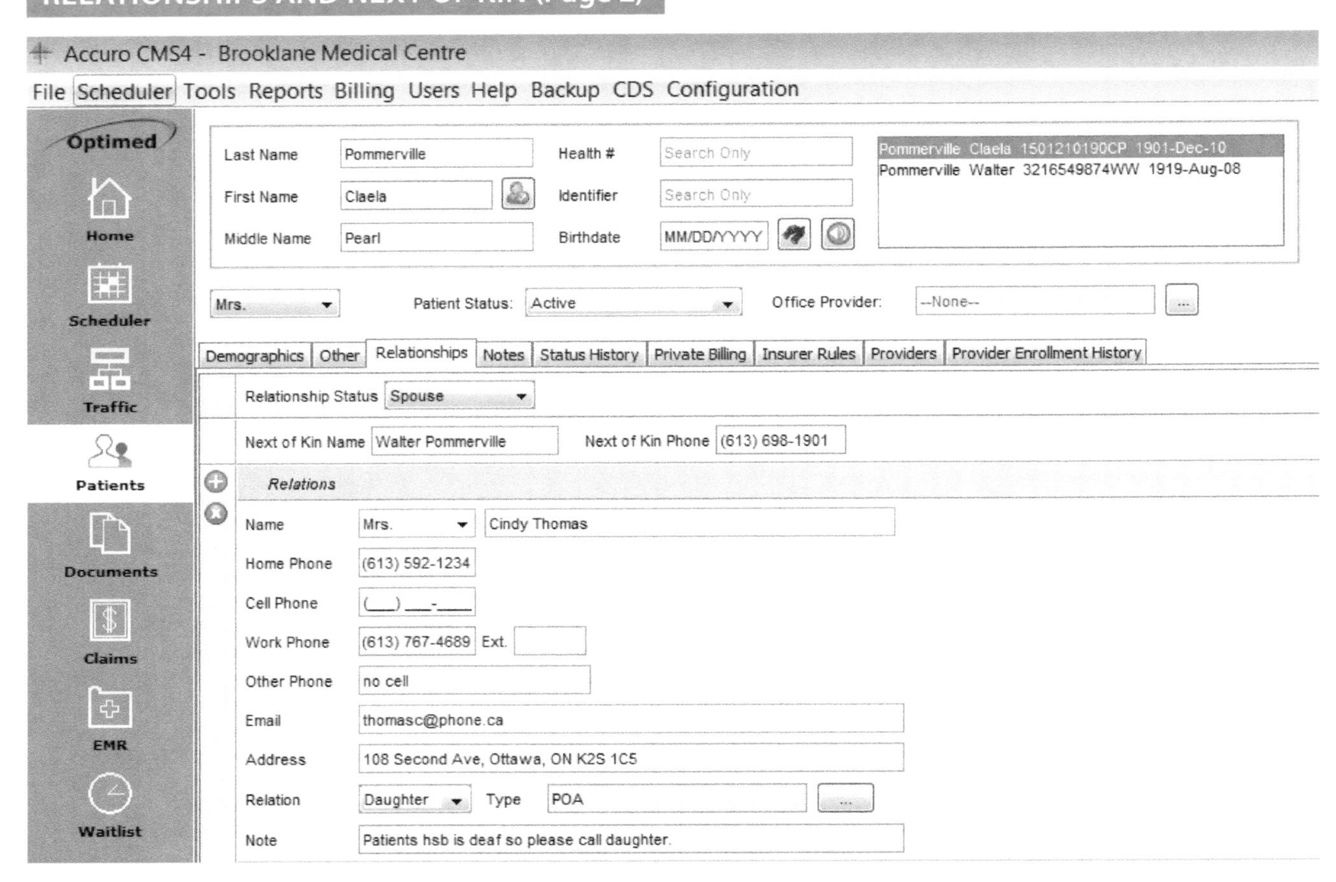

NO CHARGE (Page 1)

Scheduler

The "No Charge" function is used for various reasons. Some appointments are not covered by the OHIP Schedule of Benefits. The physician has decided not to charge the patient whether it is for monetary, personal, or other reasons.

At present, this patient shows as "Arrived" and "Confirmed." To make this a "No Charge," right click on the appointment, scroll down to the appropriate line, and select "No Charge."

Once this is done, you will notice (NC) beside the patient's name. This information also transfers over to the Schedule, the provider's Day Sheet, the Day Sheet, and the EMR.

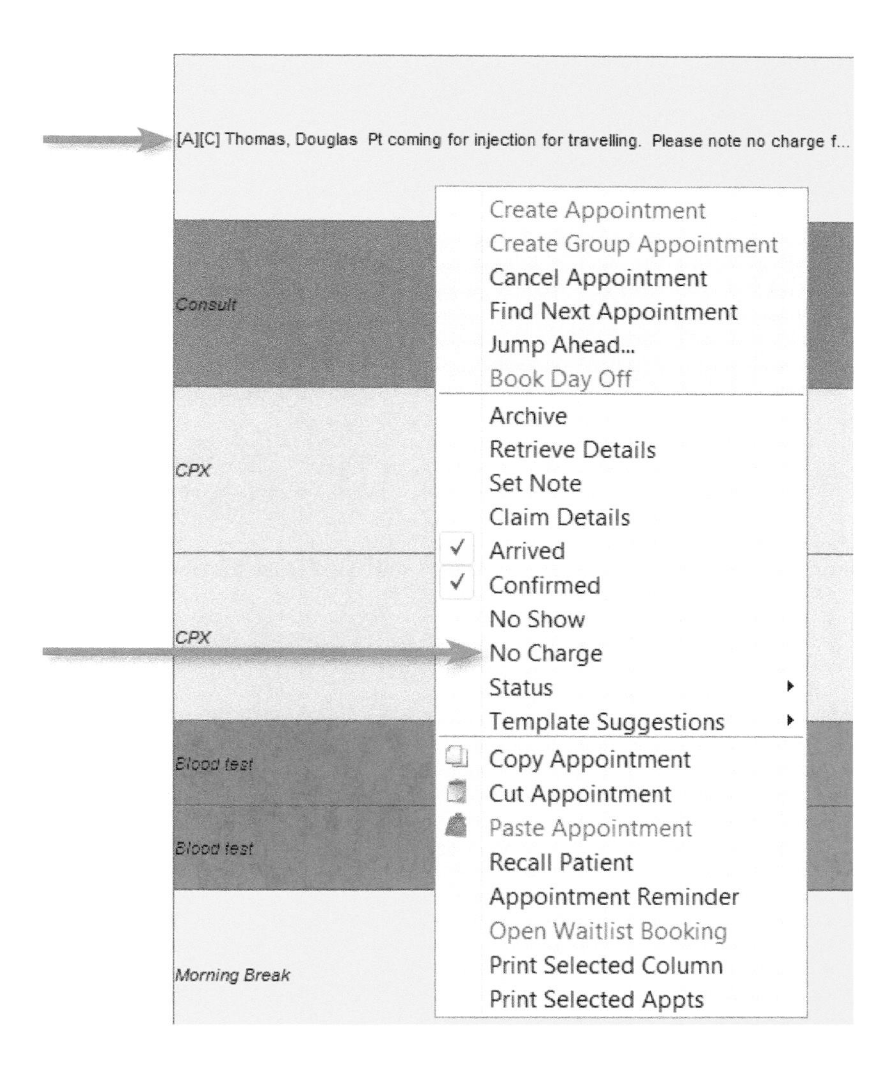

NO CHARGE (Page 2)

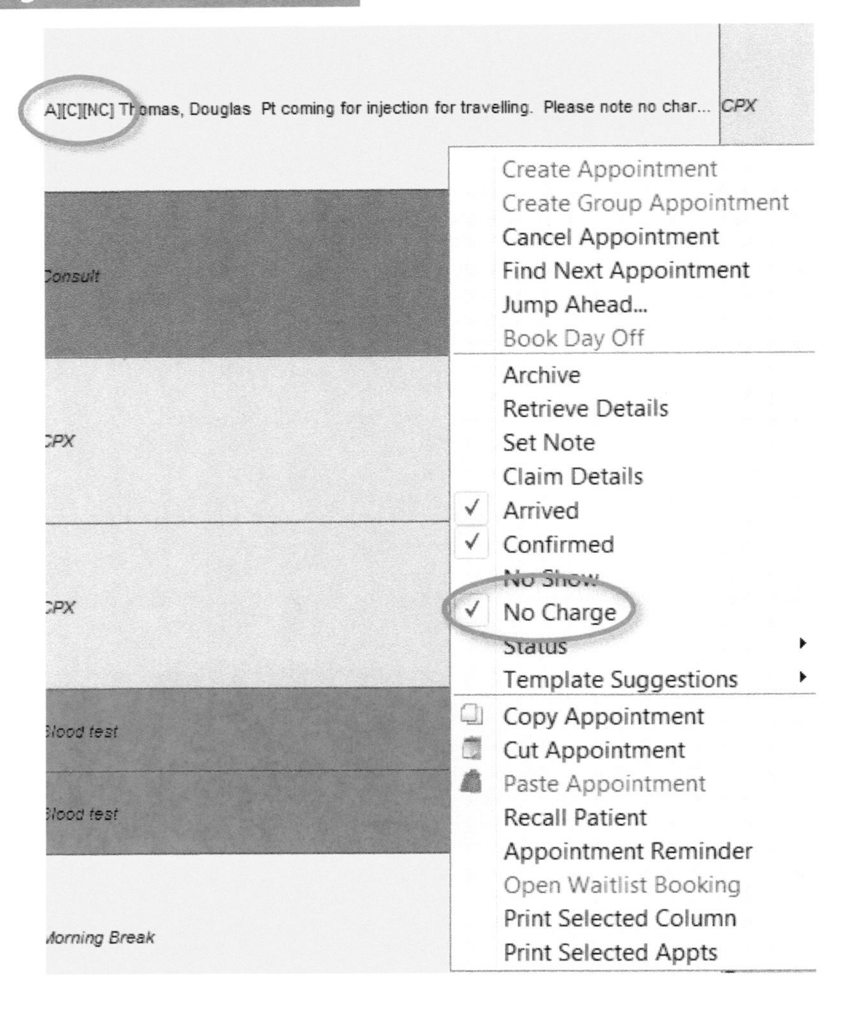

Note: Checking a patient as a "No Show" or a "No Charge" will also transfer over to the Claims section.

NO SHOW (Page 1)

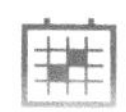

Scheduler

This function is used when a patient does not keep an appointment. This is usually used after one hour has passed to give the patient extra travel time. Some offices will send a bill to the patient, so this function is very important and it needs to be accurate.

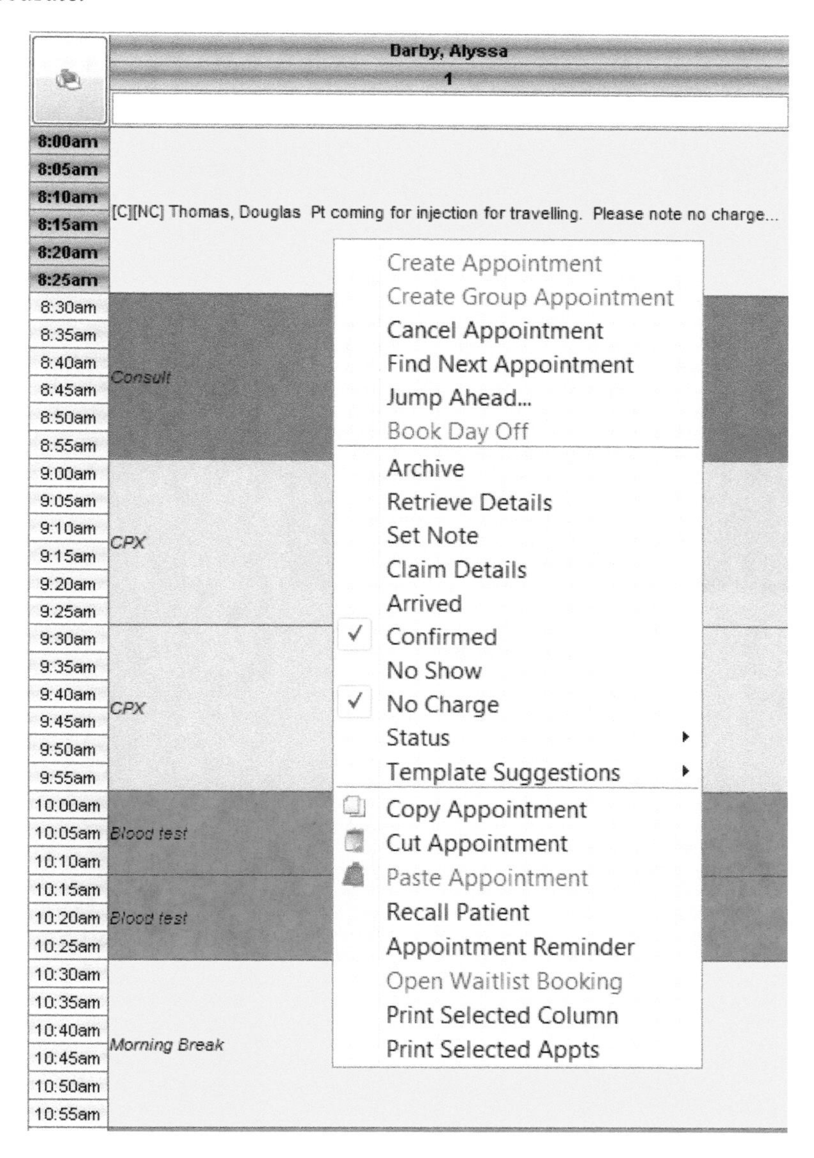

It is now 9:00 a.m. and patient Thomas, Douglas has not arrived. He has been confirmed, and we have noted a "No Charge" for this visit. He has now not shown up, so we must mark him as a "No Show." To do this, we right click on the patient's appointment. Scroll down in the dropdown box and select "No Show."

NO SHOW (Page 2)

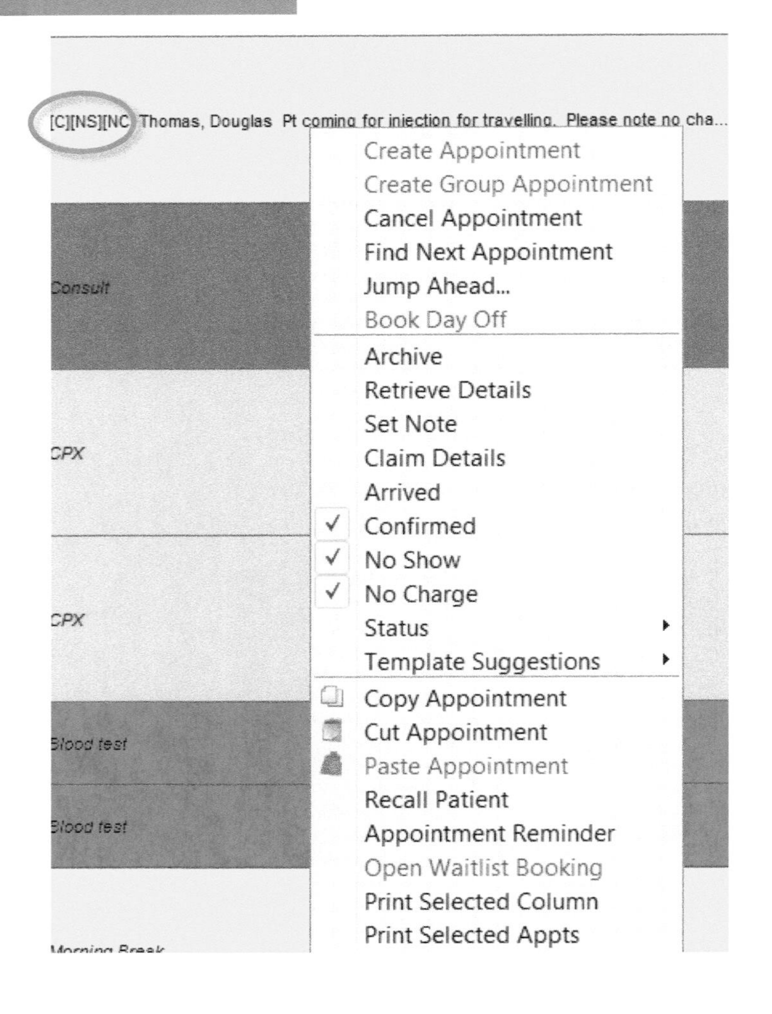

Appendix G

QHR Technologies Inc.

Accuro®EMR Instructions for Medical Billing

CLINIC OR OFFICE BILLING (Page 1)

In Accuro®EMR, there are many methods of navigating within the software to generate a claim.

The **Provider** is the physician who is rendering the care. We are assuming the physician already has the patient's record on the EMR system and available for use on a computer; if not, the physician must first choose the patient and then go to the **EMR** section.

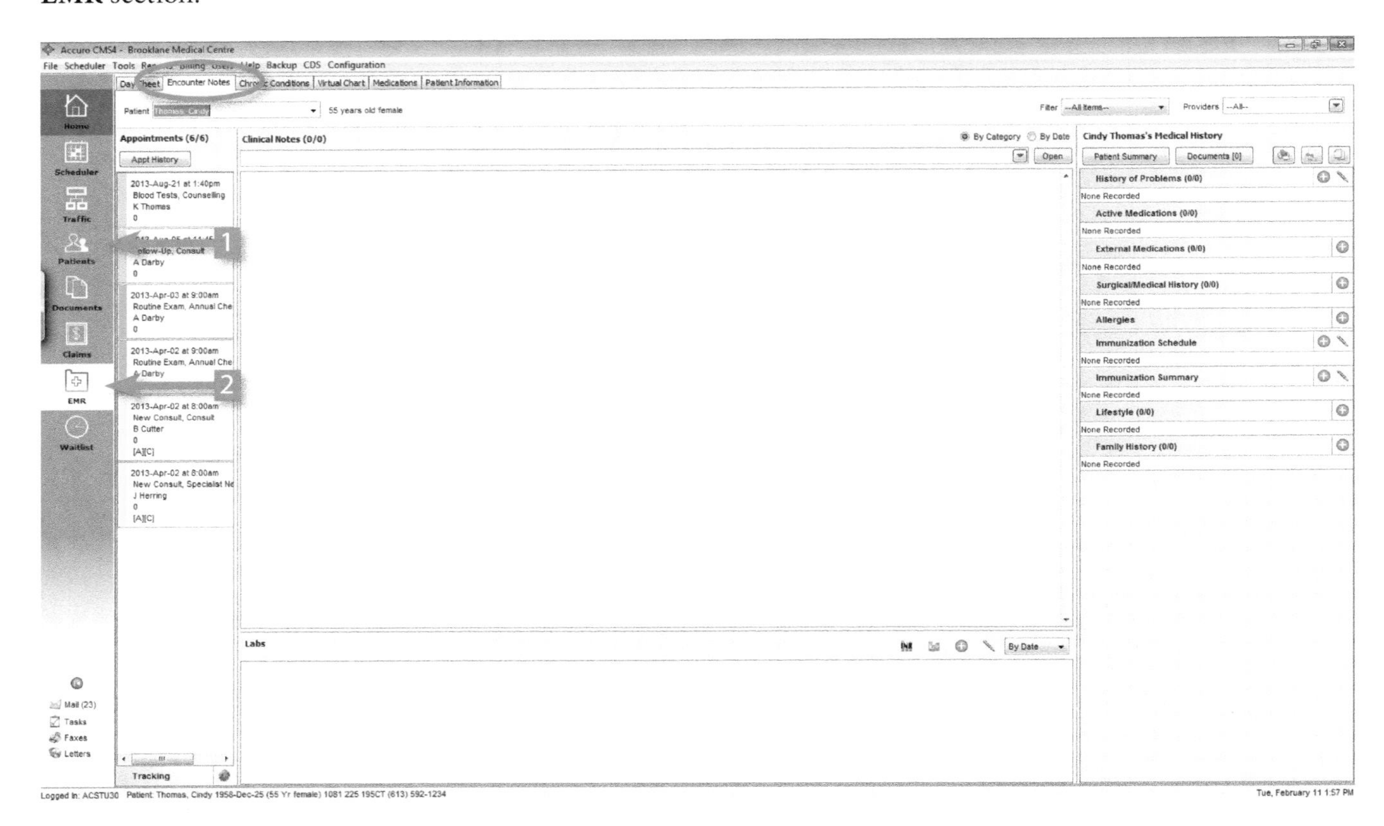

This will bring up all the appointments of the patient. To bill this visit or encounter within the **Encounter Notes** section, right click on the appointment you are processing. This brings you to where you can make a choice: Claim Details, New Bill, or Completed.

CLINIC OR OFFICE BILLING (Page 2)

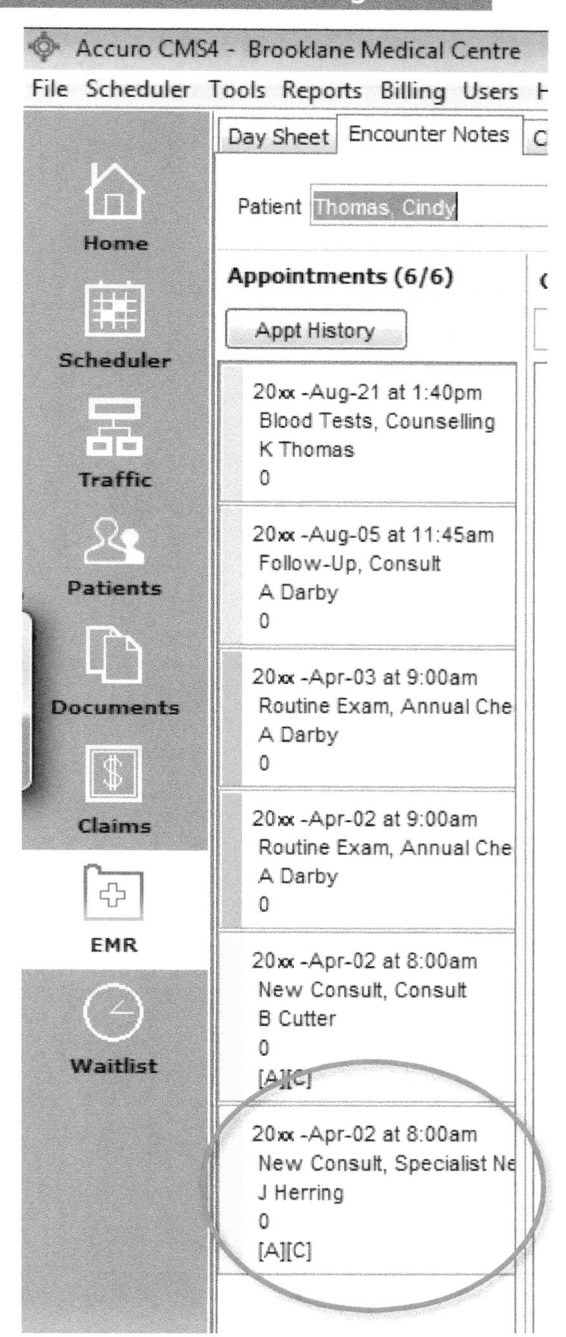

CLINIC OR OFFICE BILLING (Page 3)

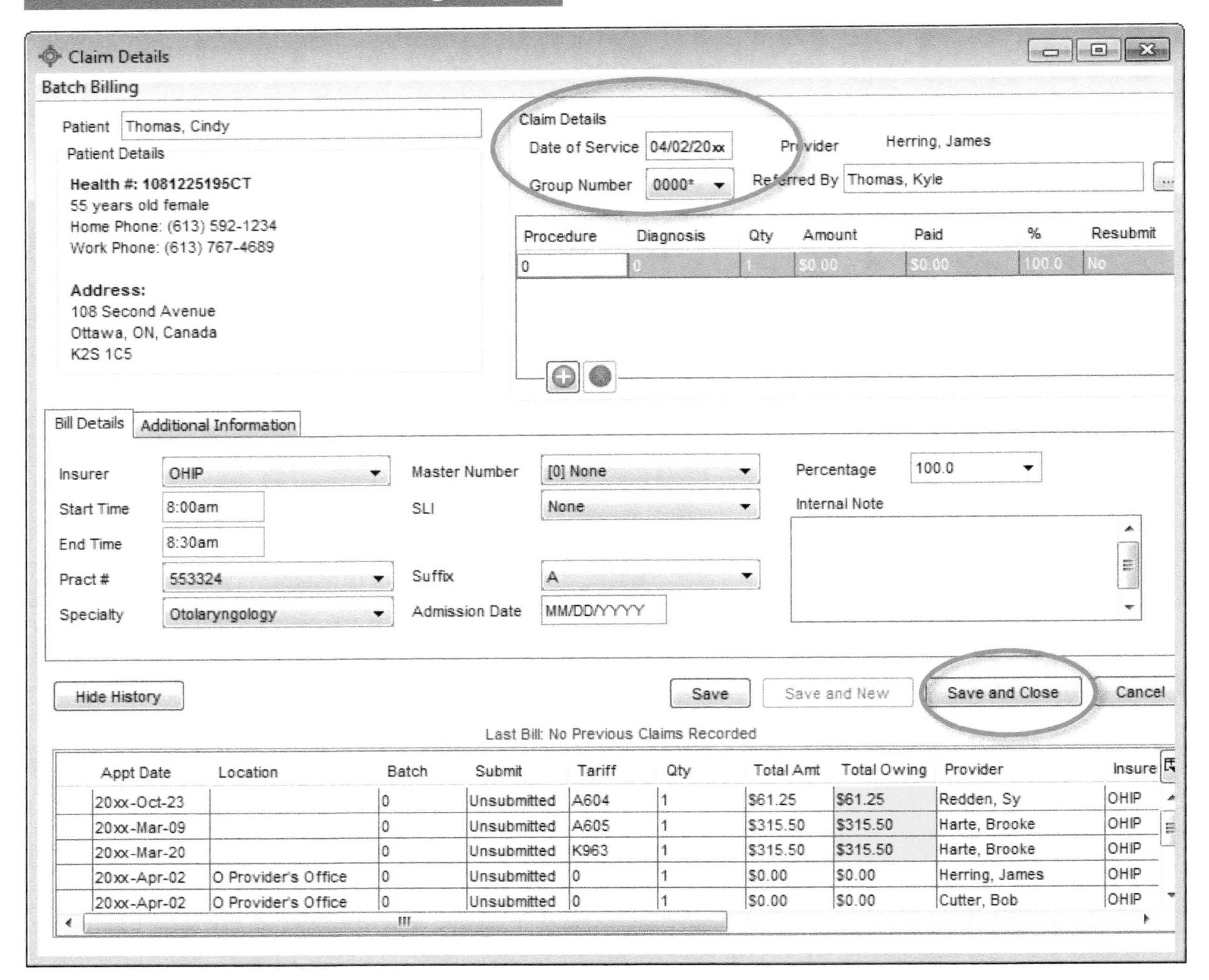

Once you have chosen **Claim Details**, your Claim Details box will appear within your screen. You will notice that some information is already populated with patient information as well as previous visits.

You will also notice on the bottom of the screen that you can scroll over to see the whole claims section where the pop up screen can be enlarged to full screen.

In this section, it is important for you to check that all this information is accurate, and whether any additions or deletions are required. Once this is done, Save and Close.

This claim will then be moved to the Unsubmitted Claims column in the Claims section, awaiting your next Ministry billing submission.

In the Claims Detail pop up, you will notice the Date of Service is the same as the encounter date.

DAY SHEET BILLING (Page 1)

In some offices or clinics, you will have the benefit of the provider using the scheduling software as well as the billing software. If this is how your office works, then you will be able to do your billing from the day sheet. This should be done daily, to help with time management and efficiency in your office.

You will most likely bill from your **Day Sheet**, by each **Provider**. If you have more than one this will keep you organized.

To locate the **Day Sheet**, navigate to the **EMR** section on the side bar. Once you have clicked on the section, click on the Day Sheet tab. You will see that all the patients that were scheduled for the **Provider** and the date that you are billing for will populate the screen. For this exercise, we will use the date May 10, 20xx.

As mentioned before, it is best to get into the routine of processing your billing each day and submitting to the province. This is the most efficient and effective way of managing your time.

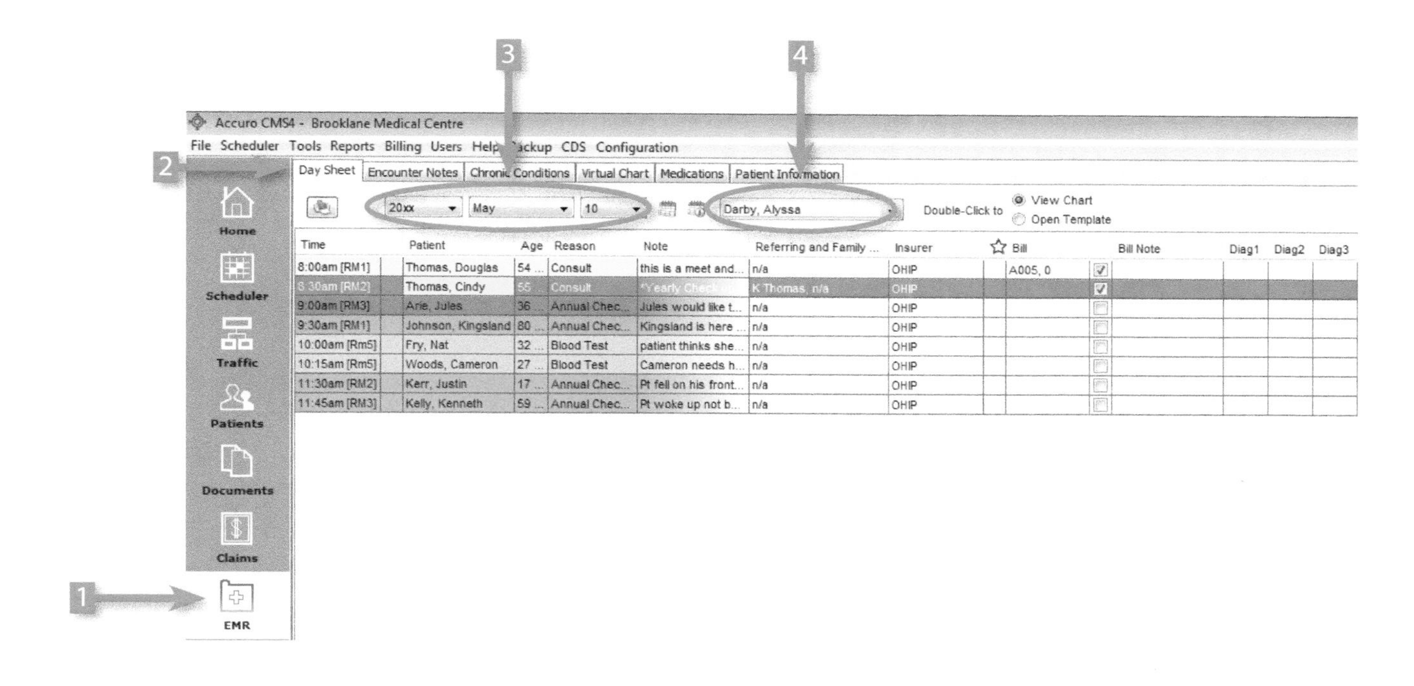

To process the **Day Sheet**, ensure you are in the **EMR system** (Arrow 1), on the Day **Sheet** tab (Arrow 2) and on the correct date (Arrow 3). Start at the top with the first patient and work your way down. This ensures no one will be missed. You need to confirm you are billing for the correct physician. **See Arrow 4.**

Choose the first patient by right clicking on the patient's name. This will give you several options. For the purpose of this workbook, click on **View Bill**.

DAY SHEET BILLING (Page 2)

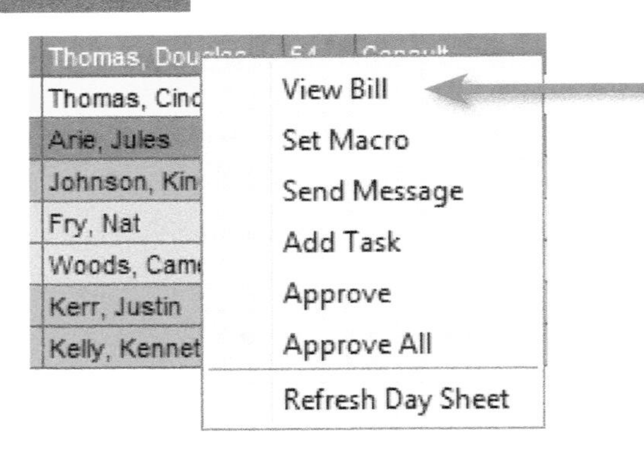

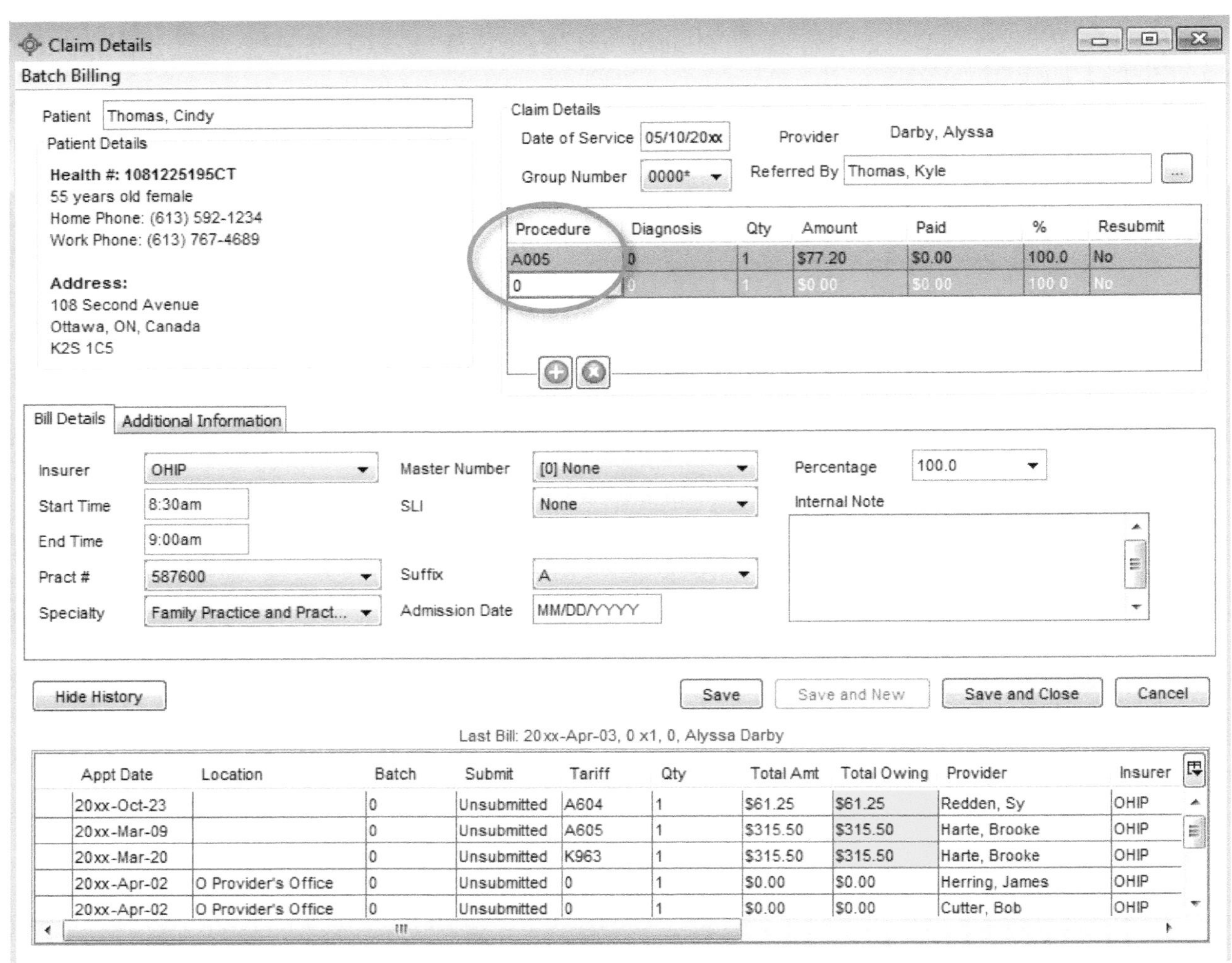

We have added the procedure code A005 as it is for a consultation and the provider is a General Practitioner. This is found in the Schedule of Benefits for Ontario. Each province has its own code.

DAY SHEET BILLING (Page 3)

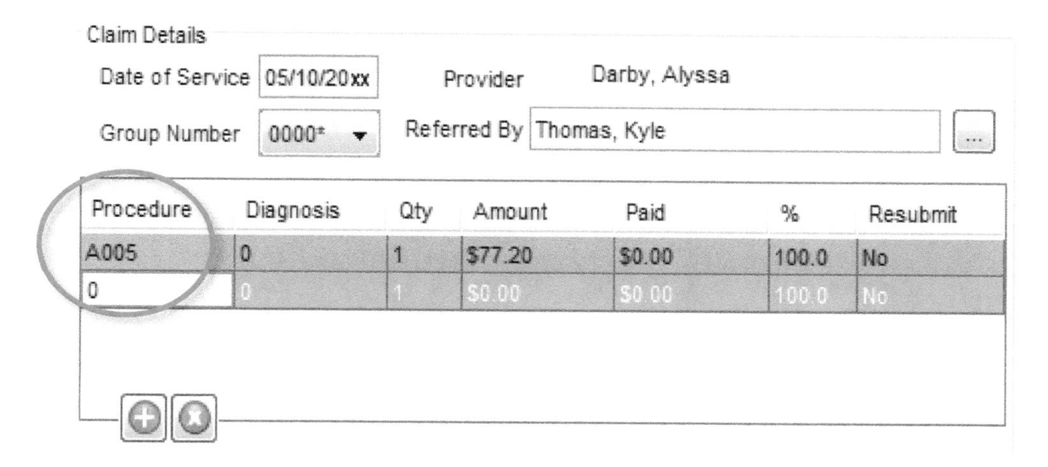

If we had to enter more than one procedure code, we would do so here using the green button for each necessary code(s). If you have to delete a line, use this red botton .

Once you have added all procedures for the service date and reviewed the claim, you then **Save and Close**. This will then be moved to the **Unsubmitted Section** to be processed when you do your next submission to OHIP.

DAY SHEET BILLING (Page 4)

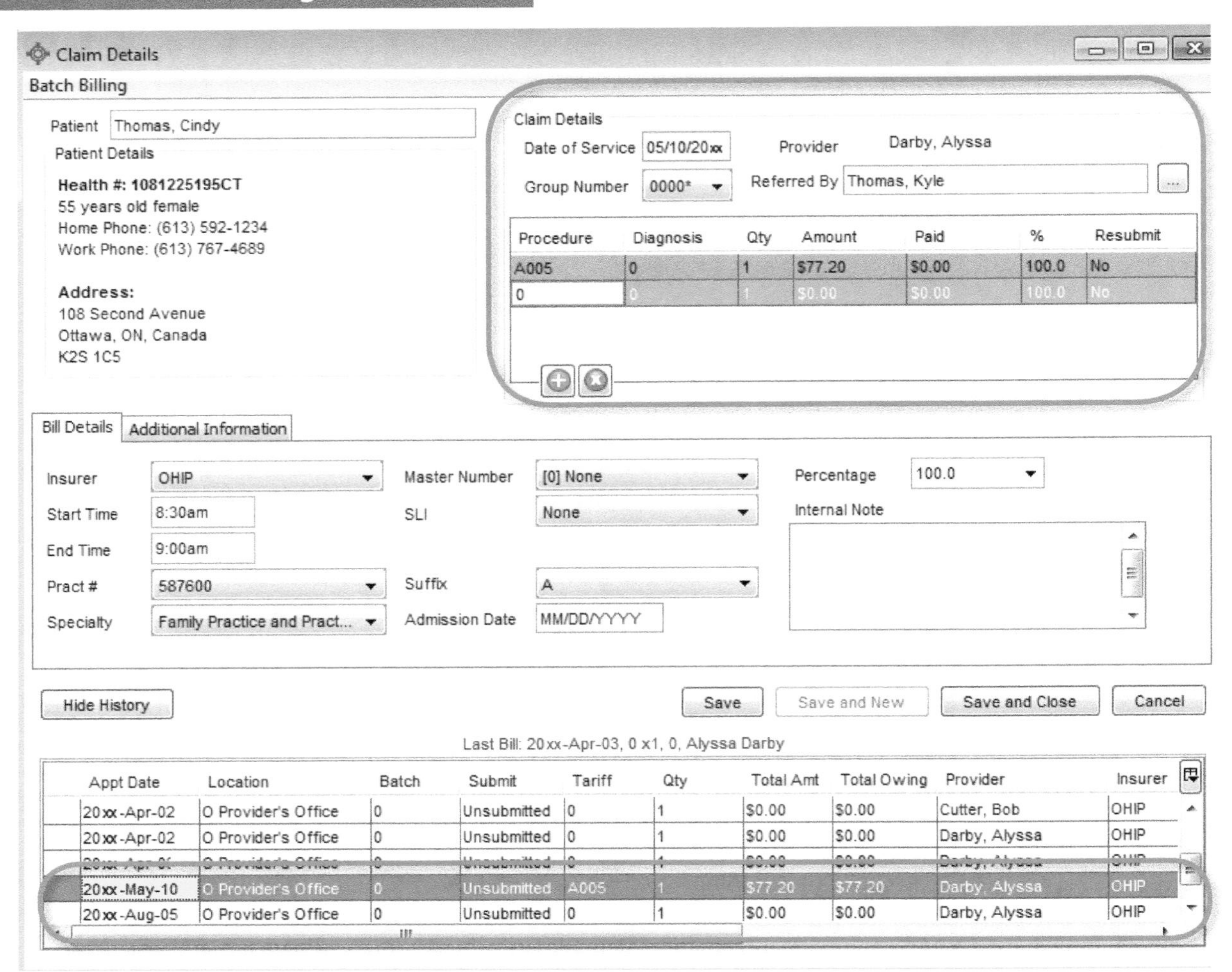

Once you have saved and closed the submission, you will notice that the amount owing from the province has been populated. On the Day Sheet, as seen below, you will notice a ☑ beside the bill you have just processed. Notice that the claims, at this point, are unsubmitted; this will change once you have done your submission to the province.

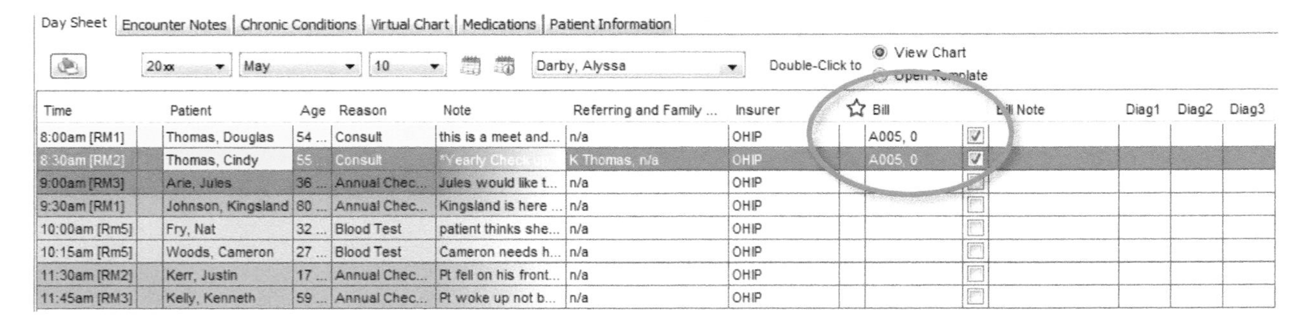

PRIVATE PAY OR THIRD-PARTY BILLING (Page 1)

Depending on the office and specialty you are working with, for the majority of your claims you will be choosing OHIP as the Insurer. This you can see in the Bill Details window shown below. Take note that all services rendered that are medically necessary will be listed in the OHIP Schedule of Benefits and you can process them accordingly. If you are billing for Out-of-Province patients **(except Quebec)**, you bill through OHIP as per the **Reciprocal Medical Billing (RMB)** agreement in Canada.

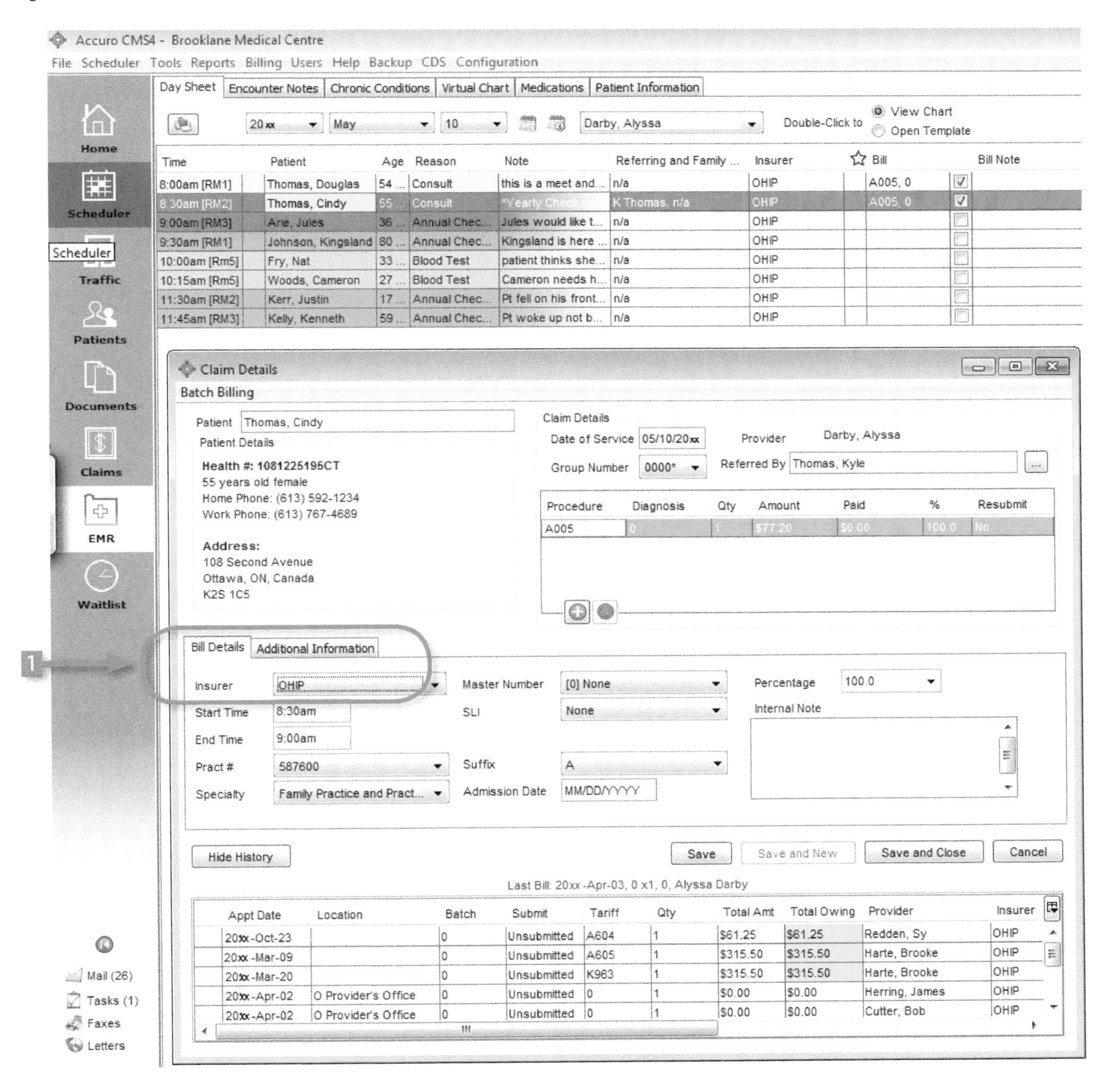

PRIVATE PAY OR THIRD-PARTY BILLING (Page 2)

For your clients who live in Quebec, we will need to treat this claim as a **Private Pay** or **Third-Party Billing**.

You can create a Private Pay or Third-Party claim using any of the claims submission methods (Hospital, EMR Encounter Notes, or Day Sheet). When you are in the **Claims Detail** window, you can identify who the payee will be by using the dropdown arrow in the box beside **Insurer**.

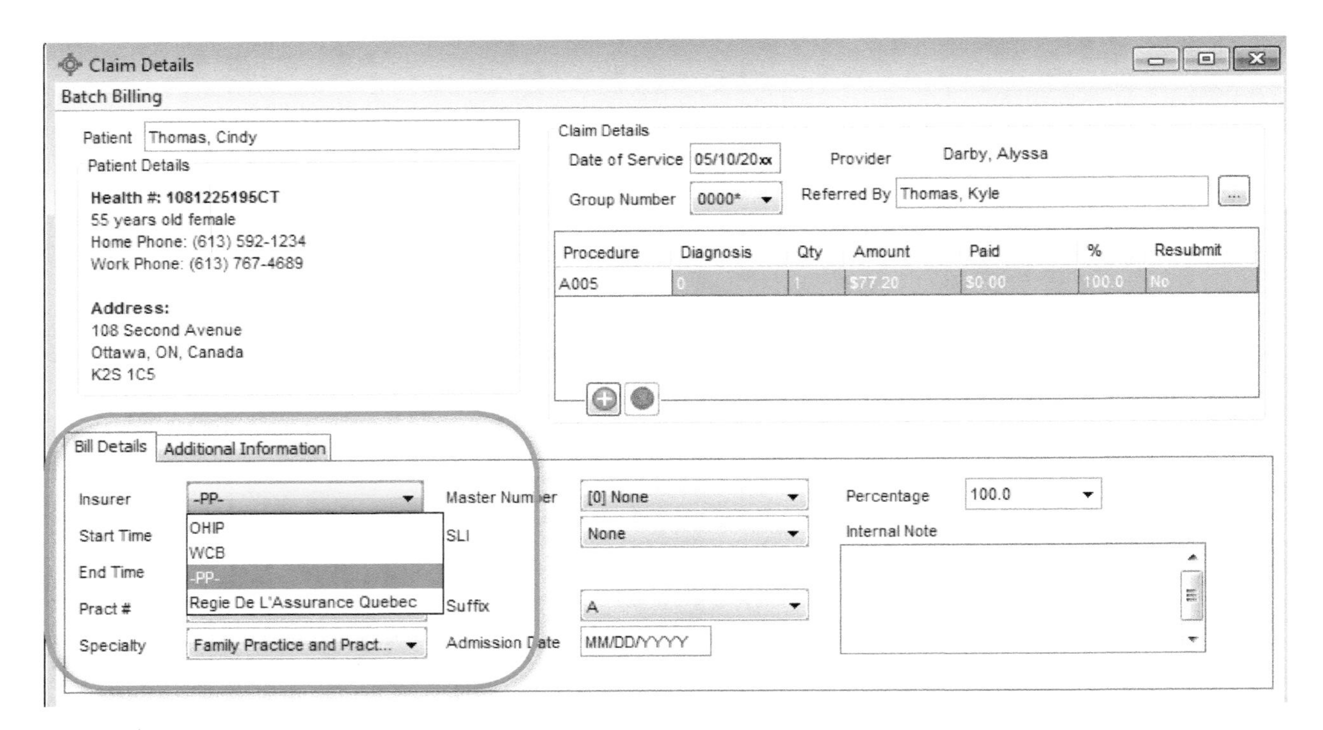

In the figure above, you will see that we have four choices for the insurer; choose accordingly. If the choice you need is not in the dropdown box, you are able to **Add** your **Insurer**. Once this is done, the information will be pre-populated when you select **Generate Invoice**.

TO ADD AN INSURER (Page 1)

To add the information, click on **Billing**. This will give you many choices; choose **Manage Insurers**.

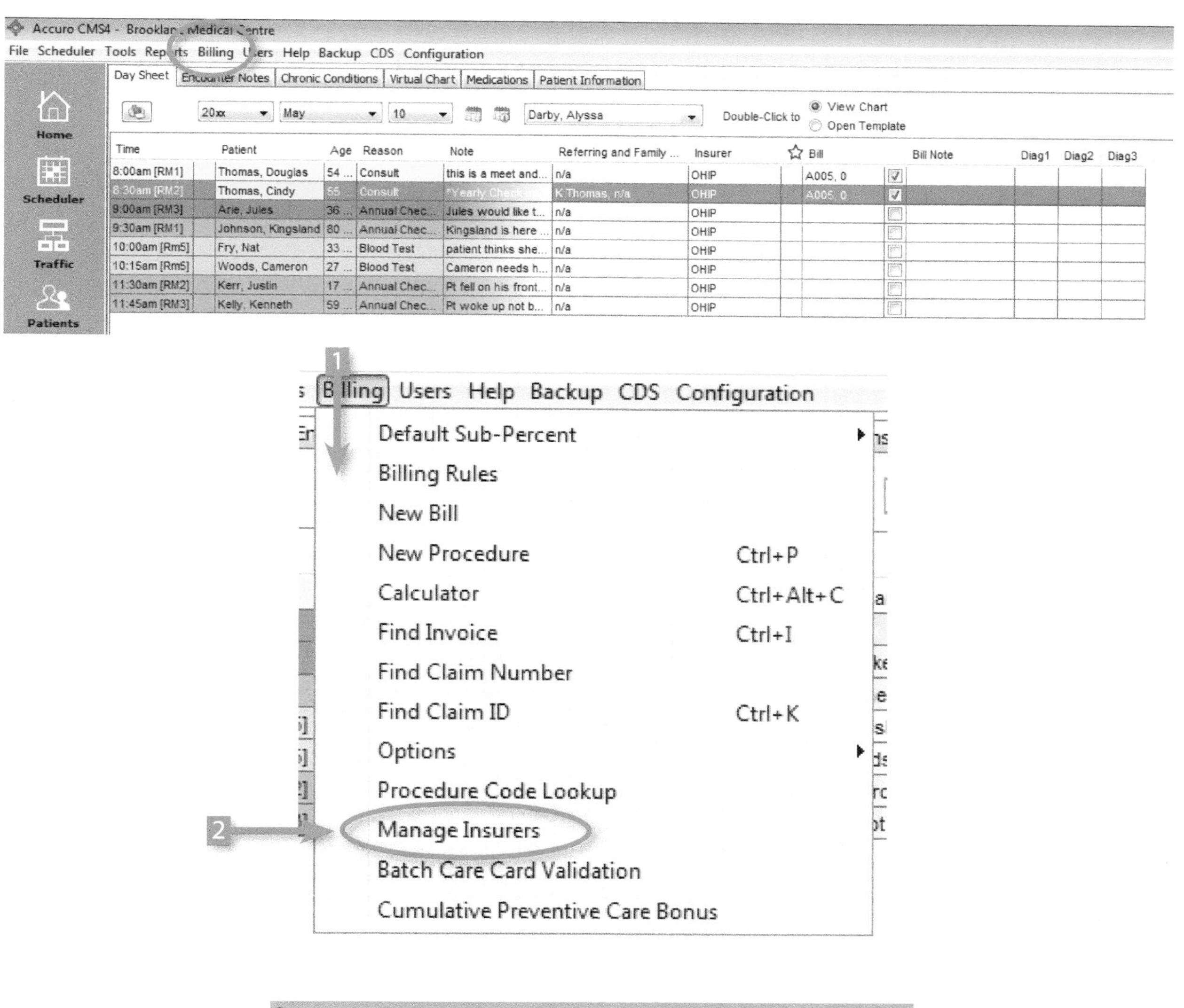

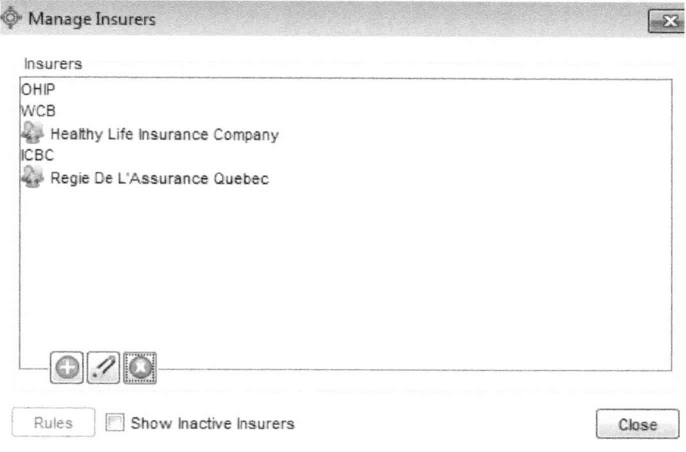

TO ADD AN INSURER (Page 2)

If the insurer has not been added, you will click the green button ⊕.

Fill in all the new information under **Insurer**, and then select **Add**.

The green ⊕ and red ⊗ buttons are to add or delete.

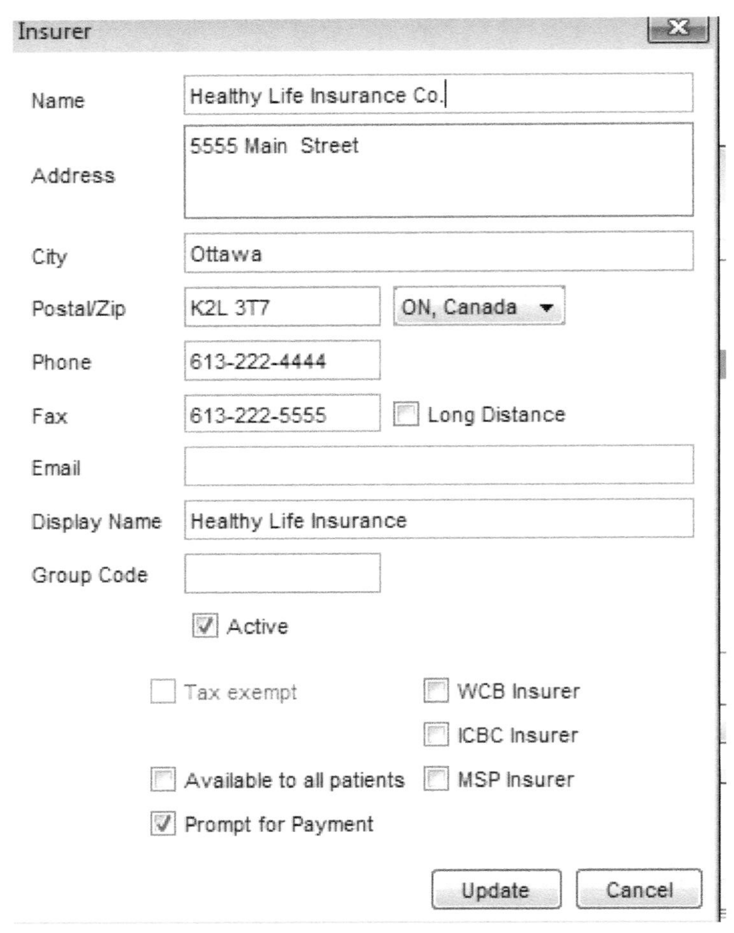

Once you have filled in all the information and selected **Add**, your new **Insurer** will be available in your dropdown list for you to select when required.

The **Insurer** information will now be pre-populated on your invoice when you select **Generate Invoice**, as you will need to do for **Private Pay** or **Third-Party Billing**.

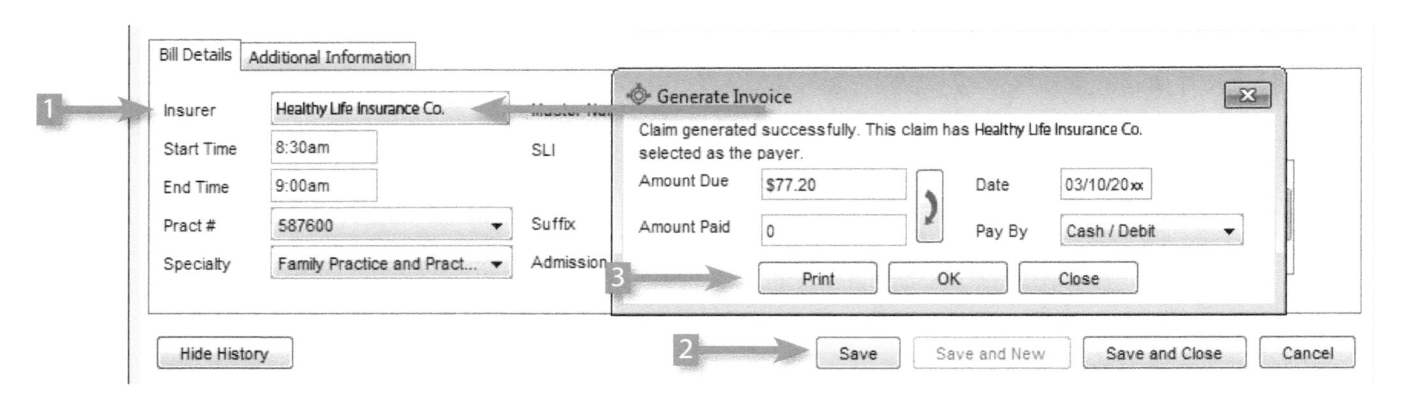

TO ADD AN INSURER (Page 3)

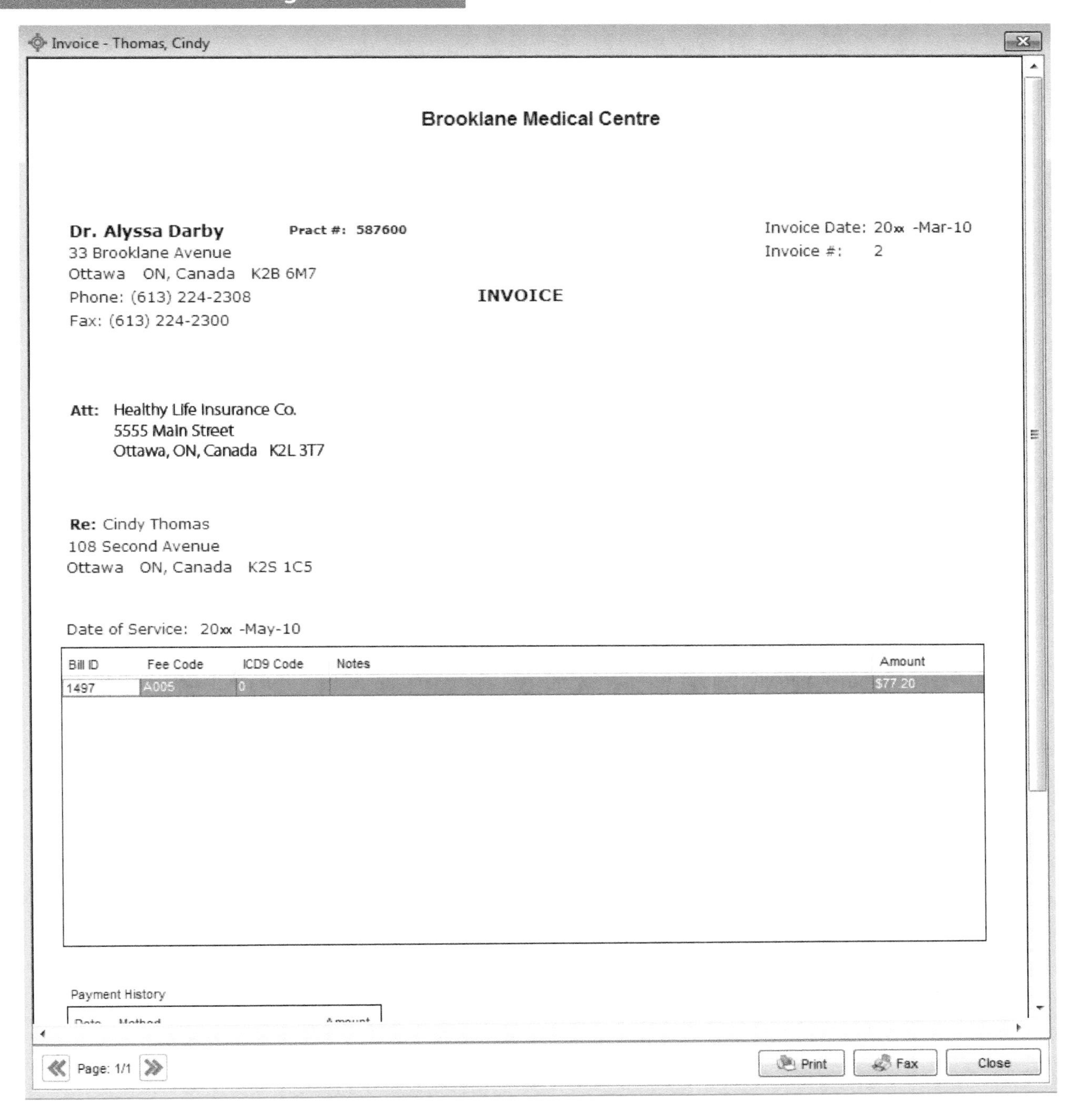

Scroll down the invoice to ensure all information is correct and then print, fax, or close, whichever is the correct function.

Depending on your office policy, you might need to complete an out-of-province claim form for your provider's reimbursement for services rendered or your patient may be required to complete a form for the reimbursement.

HOSPITAL OR OUT-OF-OFFICE BILLING (Page 1)

Claims

Select **Claims** on the Navigation Pane.

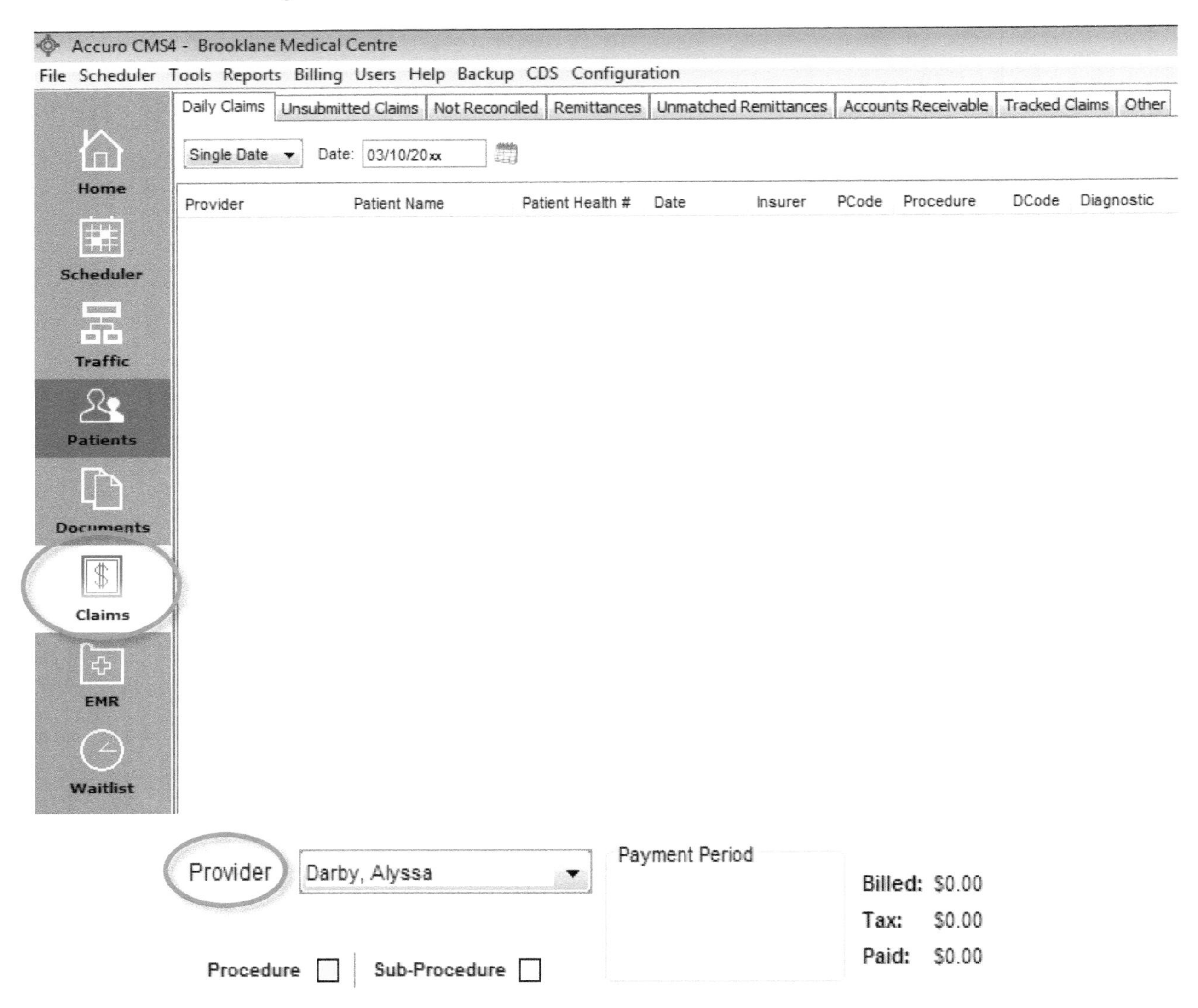

To add a new claim while in the Claims Navigator Pane, you must make sure your provider (for the sake of this workbook, the provider is from BMC) is listed at the bottom left corner of your screen. This will ensure you are entering a claim for the correct physician (many offices have several physicians at the same site).

You are now ready to begin billing for your chosen provider.

HOSPITAL OR OUT-OF-OFFICE BILLING (Page 2)

CTRL+B is the shortcut to use or you can go to the **Billing** tab and select **New Bill**.

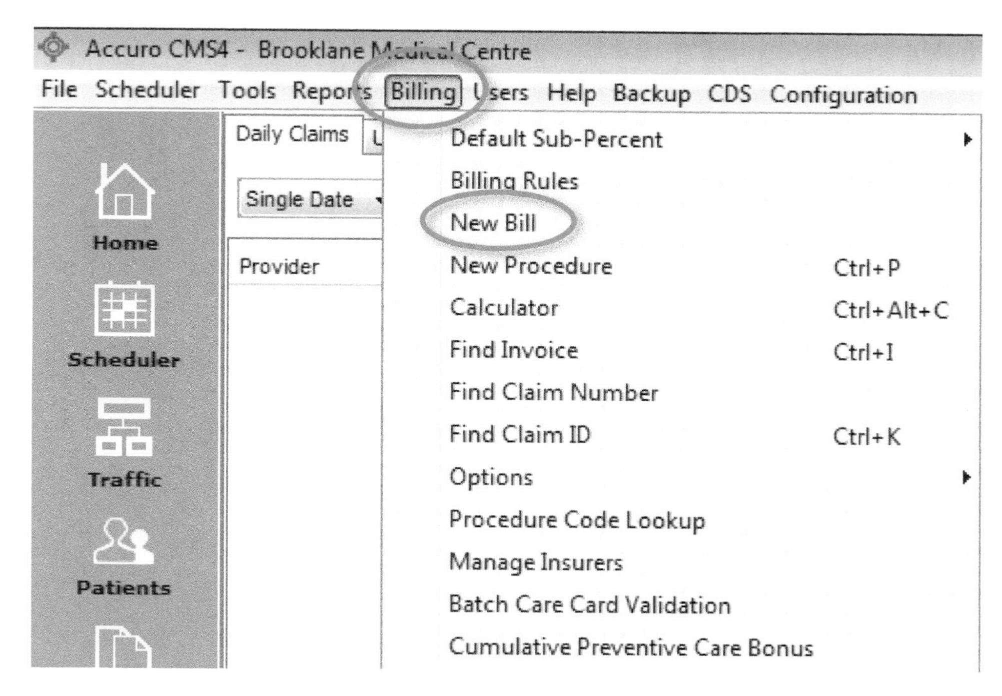

This will open the **Claim Details** window. You can search for your patient by name or health number from your database. The patient's health card number is unique to that patient, so this will ensure that you always pull up the correct patient information.

The **Health Card Number** and **Version Code** are together – e.g., 1081225195CT. The Version Code is not case sensitive, but is more pronounced when in uppercase.

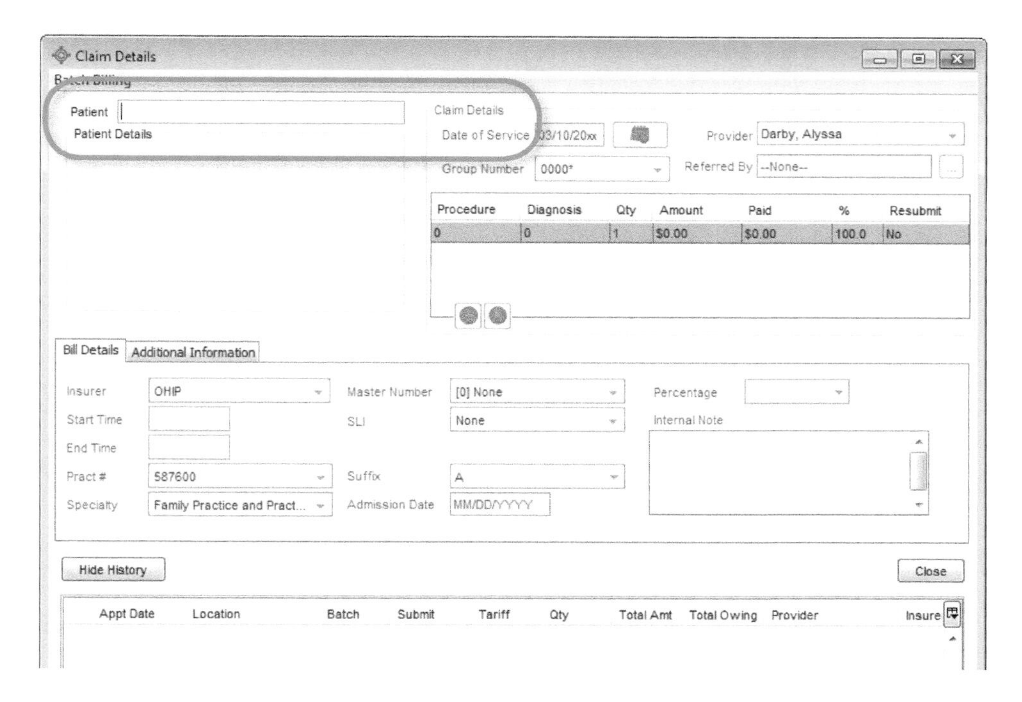

HOSPITAL OR OUT-OF-OFFICE BILLING (Page 3)

Try entering the health card number one digit at a time, and you will see that the database's search begins to narrow and possible patients decrease in number until the software finally locates the correct patient.

If the patient is in the database, ensure all information is correct and up to date in terms of health card number, version code, and personal demographics.

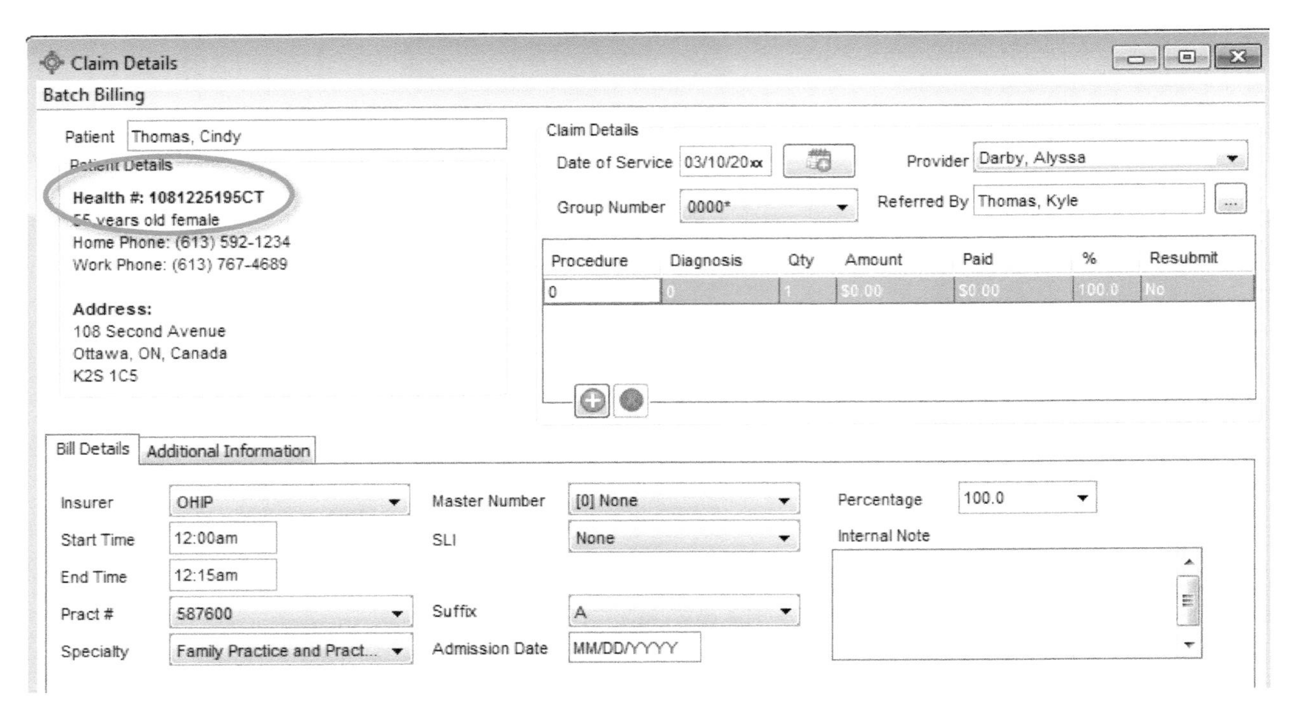

If the database is not current or correct, close the **Claims Details** window, and proceed to the **Patients** icon on the **Navigation Pane** to update all information.

Once you have entered all information, ensure its accuracy and select **Update Patient** at the bottom of the screen to save your information.

HOSPITAL OR OUT-OF-OFFICE BILLING (Page 4)

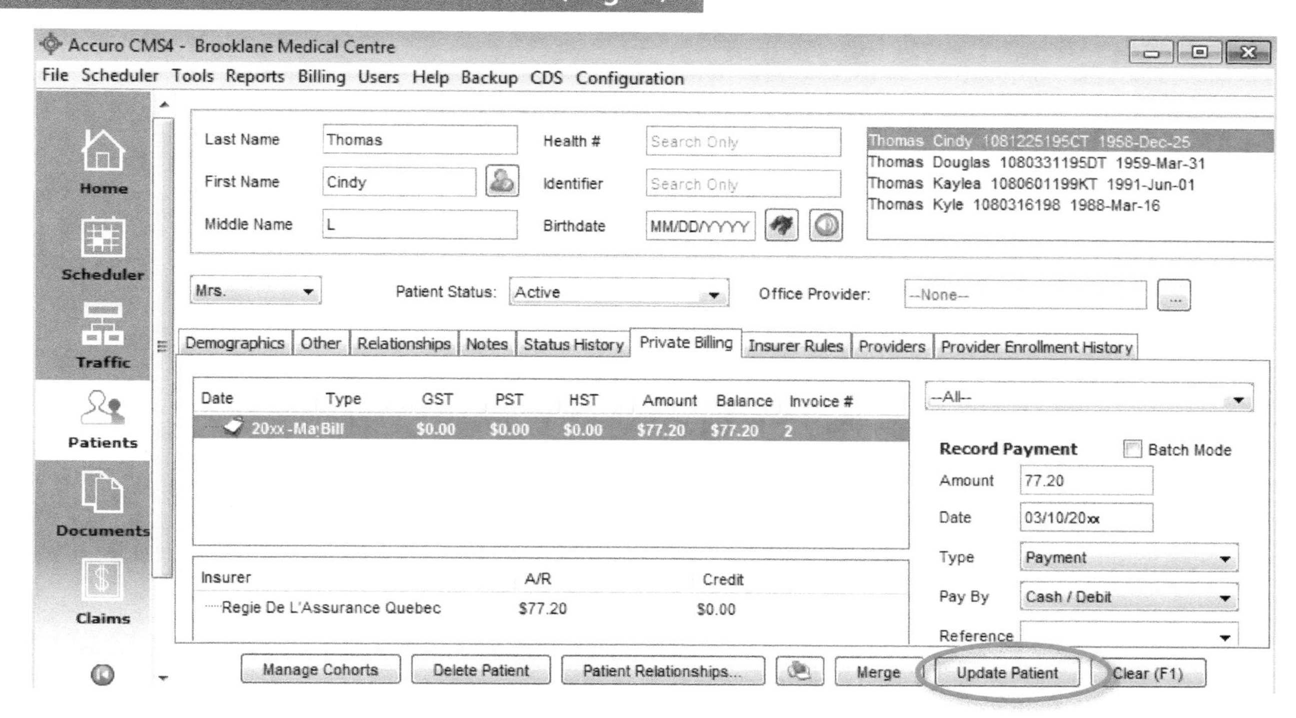

If you have thoroughly searched for your patient or client unsuccessfully, you add the patient to your database. Use the **Patients** icon on the **Navigation Pane**, or the shortcut **ALT+Enter**.

NEW PATIENT RECORD (Page 1)

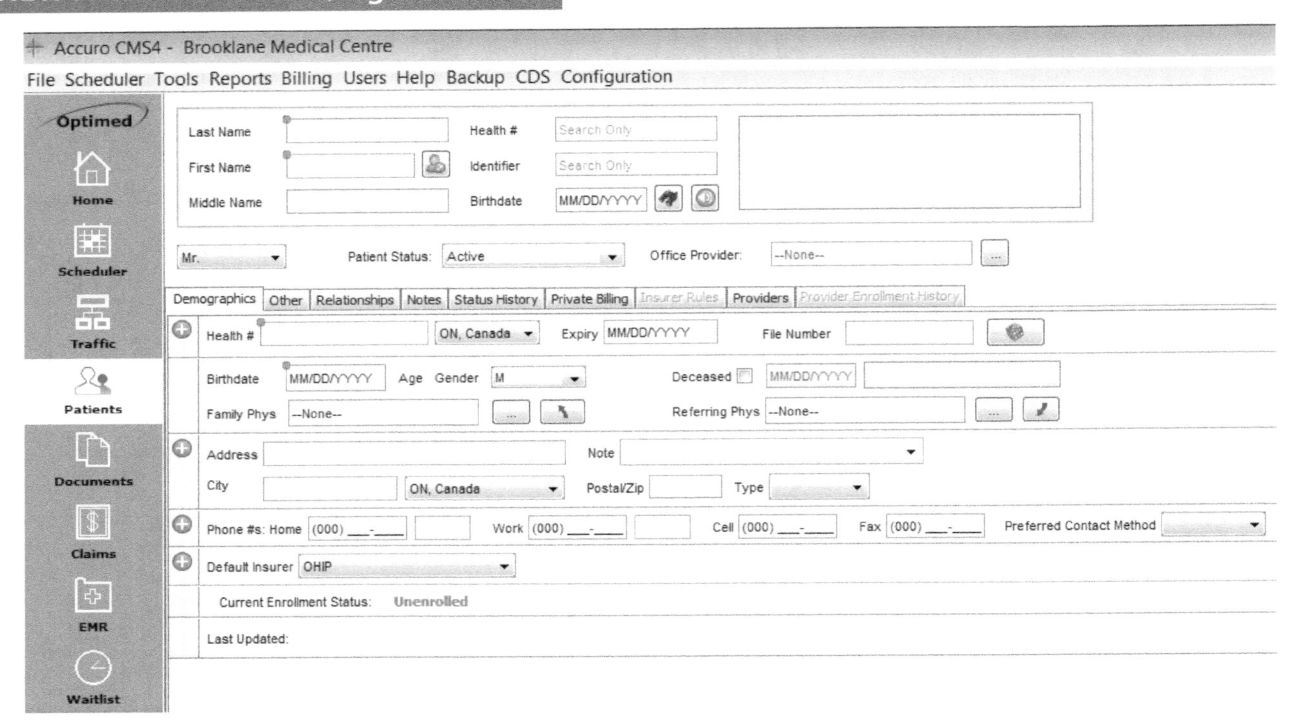

"Patient Search" is found under the navigation bar under "Patients." You can also use F1 as a shortcut to bring you into the patient search field. You are able to search by several criteria, as shown below.

In the screenshot above, you will notice the red dots. These are the minimum fields required to save a new patient record.

The search criteria are:

- Last name
- First name (as long as you put a comma in front of it)
- Date of birth – mm/dd/yyyy (April 15, 20xx, would be 04/15/20xx)
- File number
- Health card number (search only in the box in upper area of the screen)

NEW PATIENT RECORD (Page 2)

Last Name: Cannell | Health #: Search Only
First Name: | Identifier: Search Only
Middle Name: | Birthdate: MM/DD/YYYY

Cannell Avery 6549871235AW 1986-Dec-15
Cannell Ben 987654321 2012-Dec-24
Cannell Benjamin 987654321 2012-Dec-24
Cannell Daniel 6549873215LM 1986-Feb-16
Cannell Daniel 5649874562PP 1988-Dec-30

Mr. | Patient Status: Active | Office Provider: --None--

Patients who are inactive are in red. If they are in italics (red or black), they have an alias. You can colour-code your patients using different colours for different conditions – e.g., pregnancies.

When a new patient arrives and has filled out the new patient registration, you have to undertake a patient search. The patient has a last name of Pommerville. You will notice that no patients were found. We now have to add the patient's information in the screens provided below.

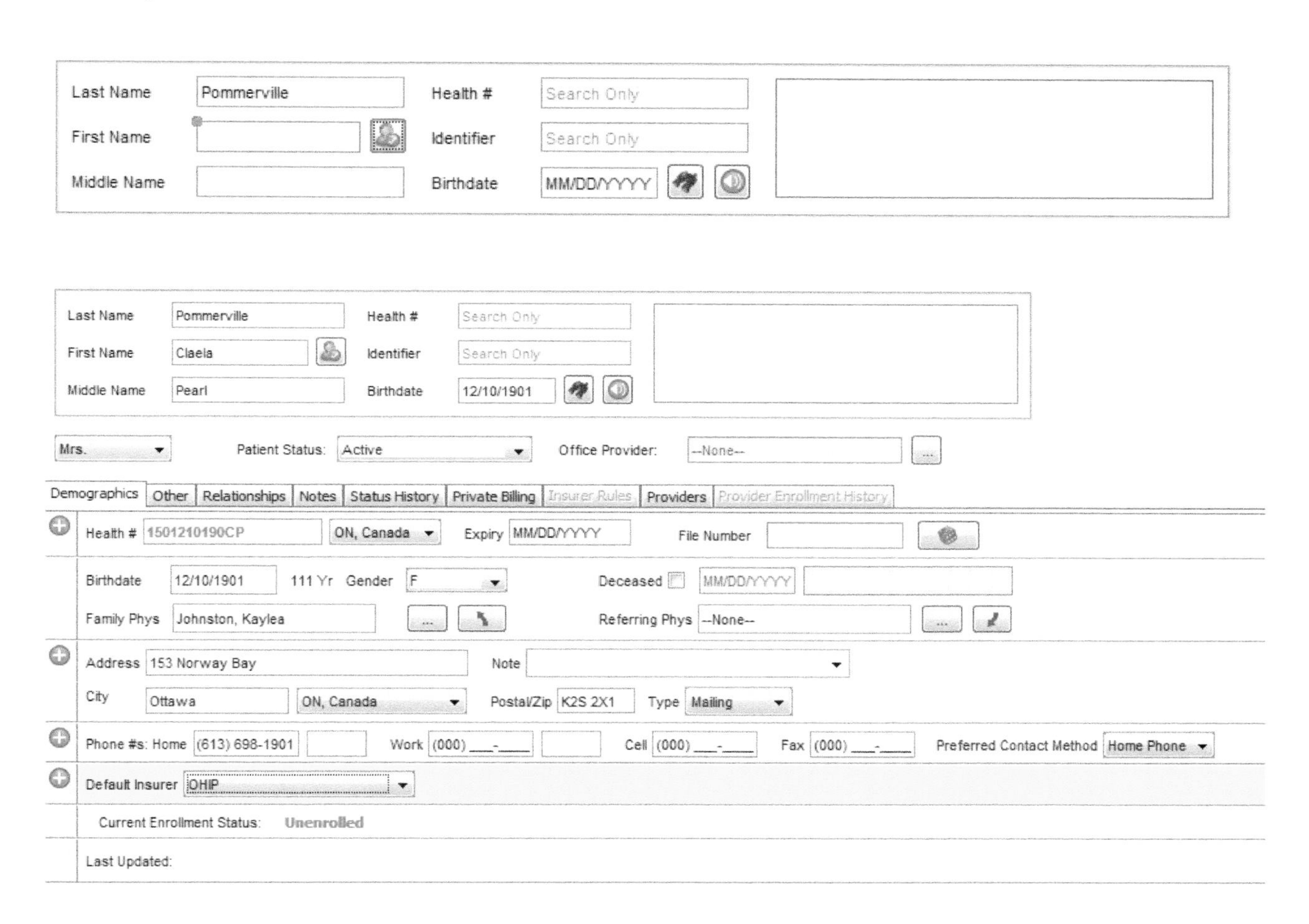

NEW PATIENT RECORD (Page 3)

Where you see this green button, it indicates that you can add more information to that specific section. Try each green button to familiarize yourself with the information required. For example, we clicked on the address as this patient is away for most of the winter.

You will also note that when you see this symbol ▼, you will have choices to fill in the box. If the choices are not appropriate for the patient, you are able to manage the box by adding information.

To add information:

Type --Manage-- ▼ Click on this symbol ▼ and the box below will appear. Using the button will now allow you to add in a new address type, then click OK. This will be available to you in Accuro®EMR for your patient database.

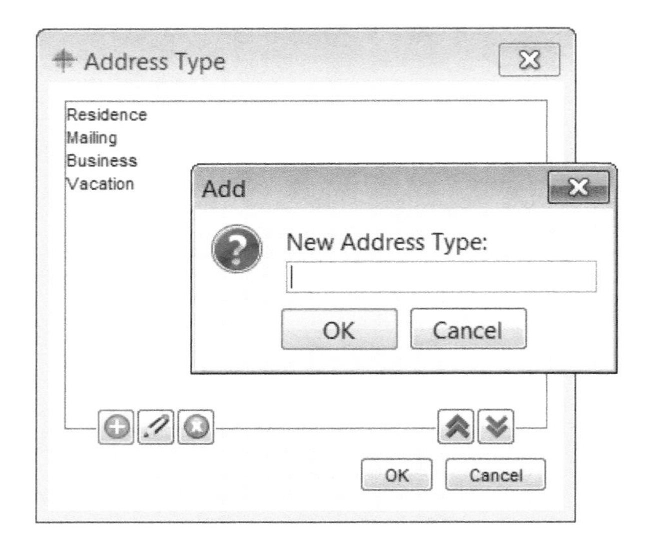

Arrows up and down will also let you navigate in the box or section you are presently in and allow you to delete information or scroll throughout the area. Go to a patient in the BMC database, and try this exercise.

Once you have added all this information, you will add the patient to the database. This icon is found at the bottom of the screen. See below.

You will then search for the patient and add other information – e.g., other clinical specialists seen in the clinic.

NEW PATIENT RECORD (Page 4)

Now that we have our patient in the database, and all the information is correct and current, we can create the claim for this patient.

To create a claim return to the **Claims** icon on the **Navigation Pane** and follow the instructions from above on creating a new bill.

Another way to do this is **CTRL+B** or go to the **Billing** tab and select **New Bill**.

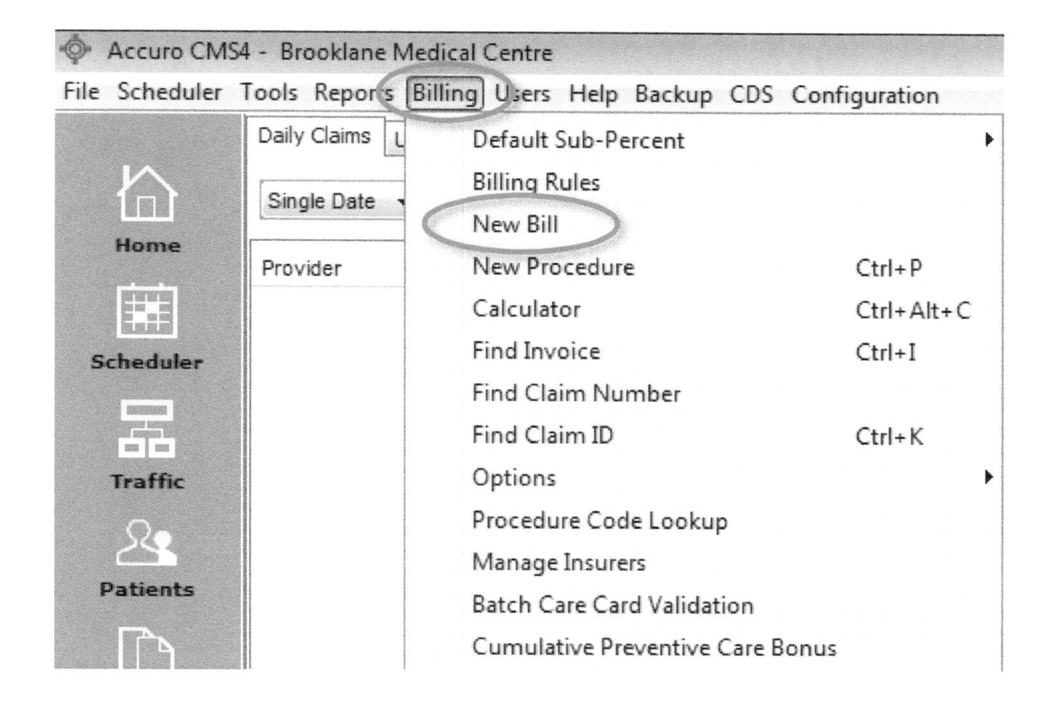

Select the patient that you are creating a new bill for and select **Bill Details**.

NEW PATIENT RECORD (Page 5)

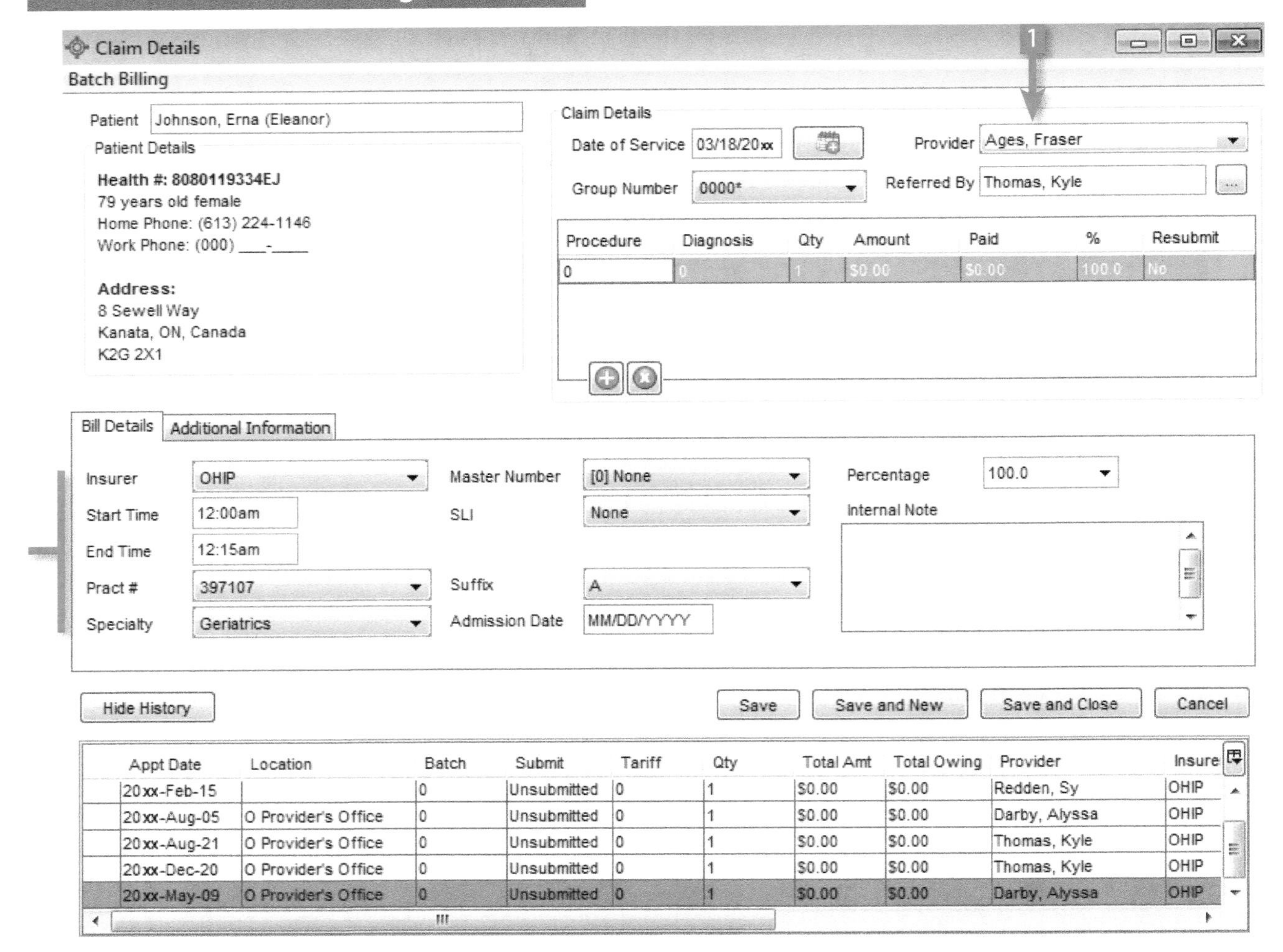

Under **Bill Details**, you will notice some dropdown boxes. Make note of the following for each item.

Insurer: Choose the appropriate insurer from the drop down list. For example, OHIP, Private Pay (PP), or WCB (Workers Compensation Board) or WSIB (Workers Safety Insurance Board)

In addition, you will have several more options. If your patients have additional or individual insurance companies, you should be adding the companies into the database as they arise.

This will be available to personalize the invoices for **Third-Party Billing**. To remind yourself how to do this, go back to **ADD AN INSURER**.

Start Time: Keep this as a default unless identified by your office as a requirement for your billing code.

NEW PATIENT RECORD (Page 6)

End Time: Keep this as a default unless identified by your office as a requirement for your billing code.

Practitioner Number: This will be pre-populated from the Provider Set Up done by Accuro®EMR or the EMR software you are using. Always double-check this number for accuracy.

Specialty: This will be pre-populated from the Provider Set Up done by Accuro®EMR or the EMR software you are using. Always double-check this number for accuracy.

Provider: Choose another Provider from the drop down arrow. The practitioner number and specialty will automatically re-populate the correct information. If you notice an incorrect Provider has been entered for this patient, you are able to correct it.

Master Number: Choose the location where the service was rendered from the dropdown list. This is a four-digit number reflecting the location within a facility.

SLI (Service Location Indicator): SLI codes are used to identify the location where services are performed.

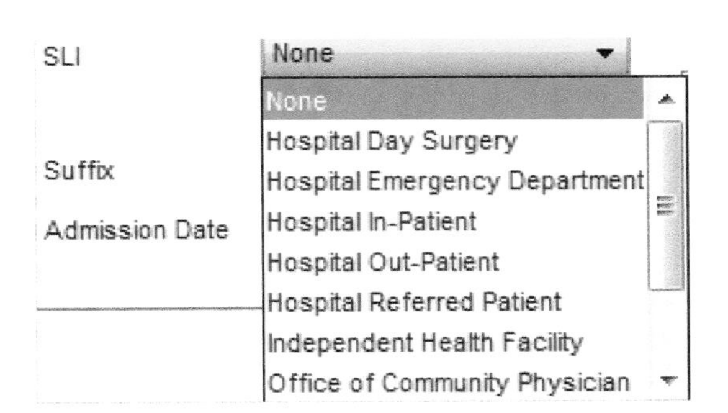

Note: Adding an SLI code to a claim that does not require one, can cause the claim to be rejected. If ever in doubt, it is best to leave it blank.

Suffix: Choose the suffix that identifies the individual who rendered the service. You have three choices: A, B, or C.

Code	Identifier
A	Is the default and identifies the physician
B	Identifies the physician assisting with a procedure
C	Identifies the physician administering an anesthetic

NEW PATIENT RECORD (Page 7)

Or, in the case of **Diagnostic and Therapeutic Procedural Code:**

Code	Identifier
A	Is the technical and professional component
B	Is the technical component only
C	Is the professional component only

Admission Date: A date must be entered if the claim is for an in-patient procedure; otherwise, you can leave this box blank.

Percentage: Keep this as the default (100%) unless your office has instructed otherwise.

Internal Note: This is an area where you can add a note for the internal office. As an example, if you are entering a claim from the EMR and you are not certain of the applicable code, you can add it here, and it will make a note in the EMR Day Sheet tab.

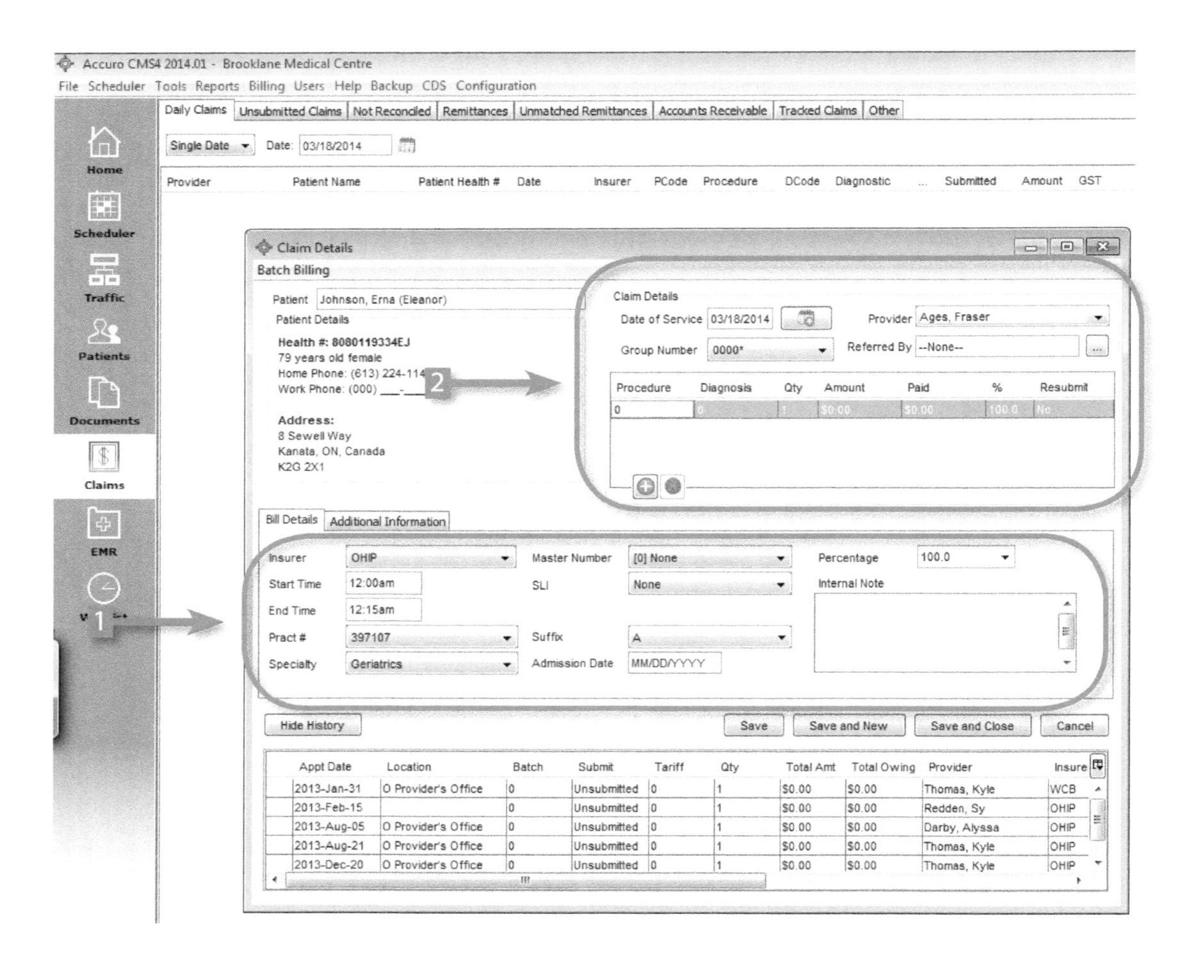

NEW PATIENT RECORD (Page 8)

Now that you have completed the **Bill Details** section, we will go to the **Claim Details** section.

Date of Service: This is the date the physician rendered the service.

Provider: This will have been populated when you chose the Provider at the beginning of the billing process. (See first page of Hospital or Out-of-Office Billing.)

Group Number: You will only need to choose a group number if the physician belongs to a group for the services rendered. This will be a dropdown list to choose from or this number will be pre-populated when you choose your Provider at the beginning of the billing process.

Referred by: Search for the physician who referred this patient. If you are billing for a specialist, the family physician is usually the one who refers to a specialist. If the service rendered does not require a referring physician (as outlined in the OHIP Schedule of Benefits, General Payment Rules), select None for this claim from the dropdown list.

Claims Detail: You are now ready to proceed to input the data required (billing codes) for the services rendered for this claim. You will need to have a good understanding of the OHIP Schedule of Benefits, as well as the Dignostic codes, to proceed.

Procedure: This is the billing code identified in the OHIP Schedule of Benefits for the services rendered. For example, if the patient was sent for a cardiology consultation, you would input A605. If they were seen for a respirology consultation, you would input A475.

Another way to find the codes necessary for the billing is to right click on the box you are populating. The drop down box will give you three choices.

Choose each box and explore.

Search Procedure Codes
Search Diagnostic Codes
Bill Log History

This will also show you a tab that is titled My Codes.

Diagnosis: This is a three-digit code. If you know the three numeric diagnosis code, type it in. If you only know the diagnosis, type it in this section and choose the diagnosis from the drop down list. For example, if the diagnosis is congestive heart failure, type this in and view the list. You will see the dropdown list will show 428 – Ischemic and other forms of heart disease – congestive heart failure.

NEW PATIENT RECORD (Page 9)

Quantity: If the service is time-based (20- or 30-minute units), the quantity may have to be changed. For example, when you refer to the OHIP Schedule of Benefits, A222 (interview) K002, K003, K008. The unit is 30 minutes. If the physician took 1 hour with the patient, then the quantity would have to be changed to 2 units to reflect the actual time. When making the change, you will notice the amount paid reflects the quantity change.

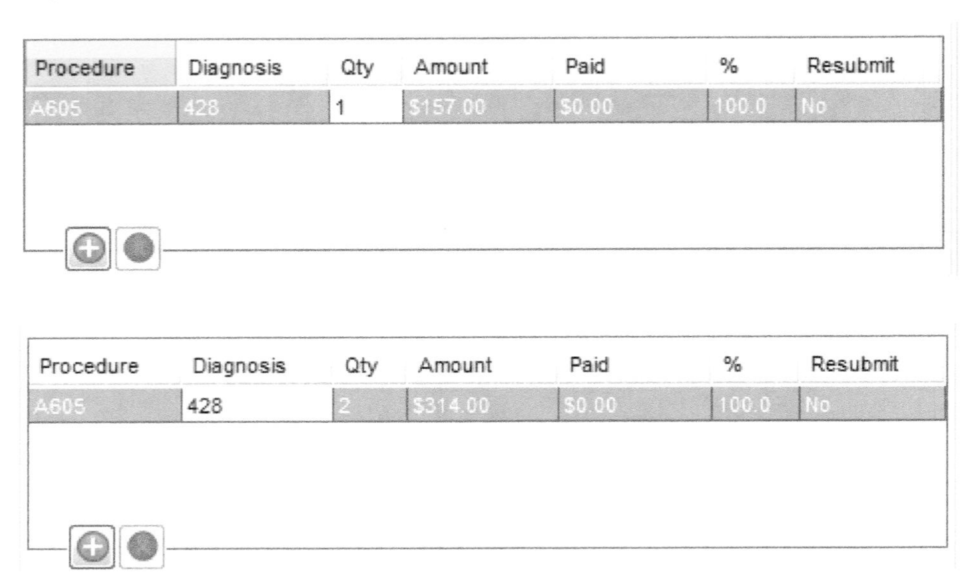

Amount, Paid, Percentage: Once you have entered the Procedure and Diagnosis codes as well as the quantity, the information to complete these fields in the procedure row will be generated.

If your claim has more than one billing code, **CTRL+P** will bring you to a second line to add in a sub-procedure. You can also use the (green button). If you have added in error, you can delete that row by using the (red button). A box will appear to make sure that you are not deleting in error.

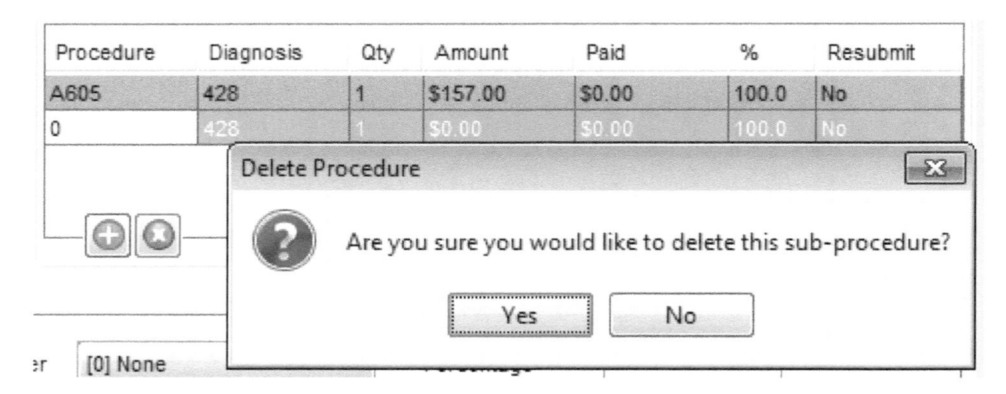

NEW PATIENT RECORD (Page 10)

After you have added in all the procedures and sub-procedures for this patient, you will have four choices:

- Save
- Save and New
- Save and Close
- Cancel

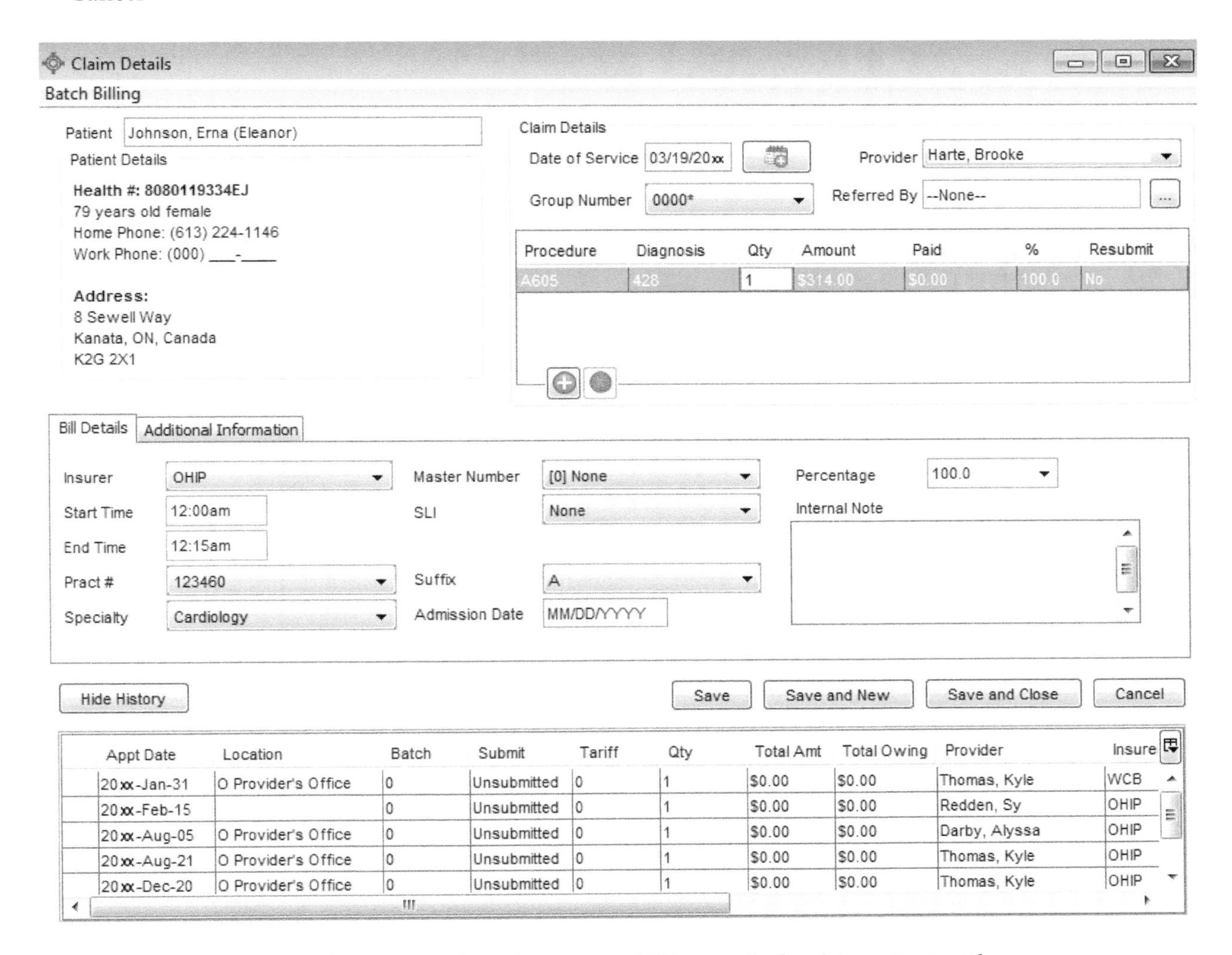

Save: You would choose this option if you have more billing to do for this patient with a different service date. This will allow you to right click on the claim and choose "copy claim to above." This will save you from having to select the patient again and complete the **Bill Details** window again before proceeding to complete the **Claim Details** window. In this way, you will only need to complete the Claim Details window with the new billing information (i.e., service date, procedure and sub-procedure).

Save and New: You would select this option if you have more claims to generate for a new patient.

Save and Close: You would select this option if you had no other claims to generate.

Cancel: You would select this option if you do not want to save any of this information.

NEW PATIENT RECORD (Page 11)

If you are doing hospital billing, you may want to **add multiple dates for the same billing codes**. For example, if the physician is the **Most Responsible Physician (MRP)** for a patient, and sees the patient every day for one week, multiple dates can be added for the same codes. In this case, C602 and E083 (cardiology in-patient, hospital visit with the **MRP** premium code) would be the codes used. Go to the field – **Date of Service** – and to the right you will see a ⊕ green button. Click on this button and you will see a dropdown, which will include another small ⊕ green button attached to a small calendar. Once you have selected this button, a dropdown calendar will appear. Select the appropriate multiple dates for these same codes. Once done, select **OK** and then **Save, Save and New, Save and Close** or **Cancel** as explained above.

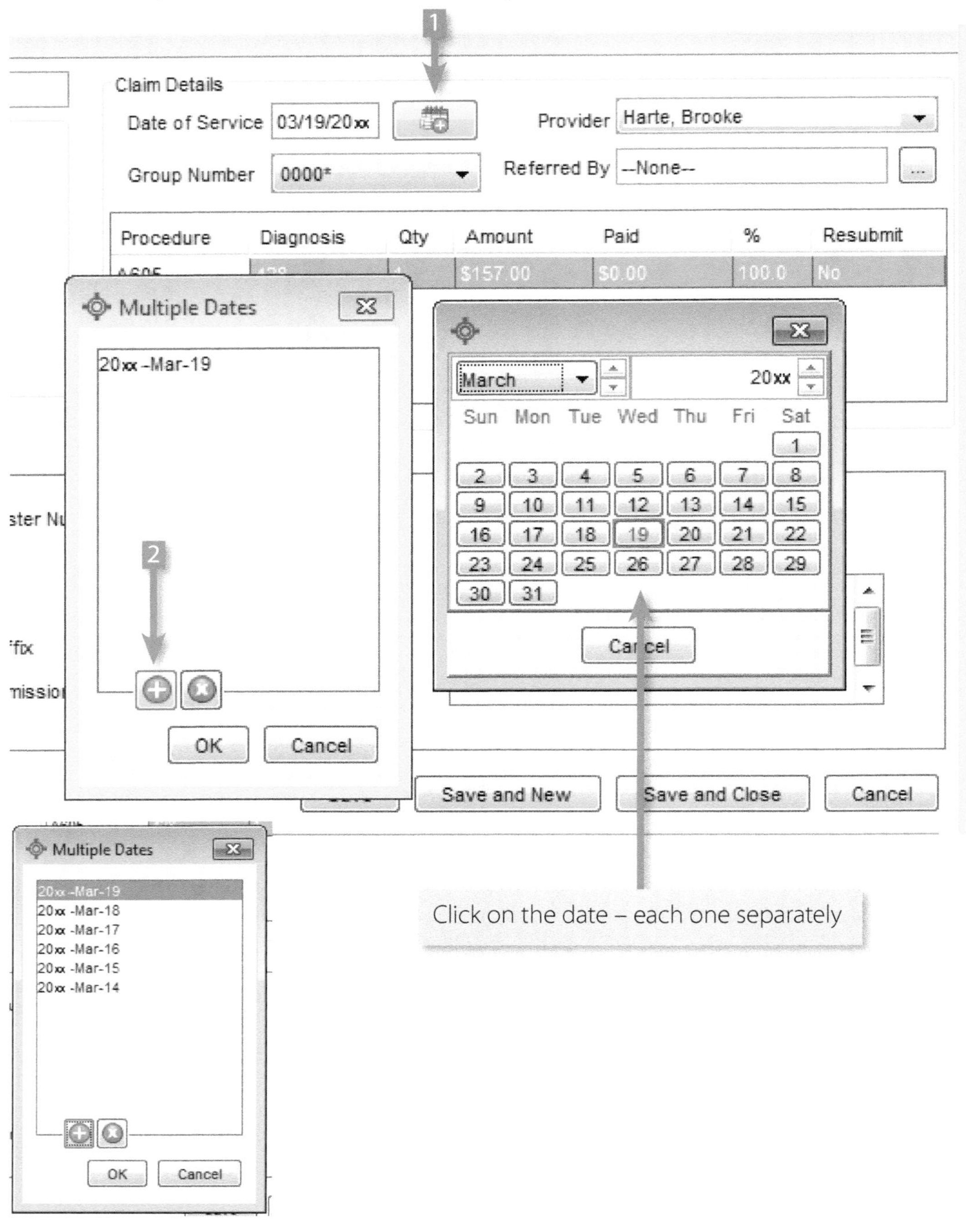

Appendix H

Ministry Claims Submission Software

PAGE 1

MC EDT Connection

Prerequisites:

-In order to complete this process, you must have a Go Secure ID and password.
-The ministry recommends that you use Google Chrome to access the Go Secure website: https://www.edt.health.gov.on.ca
-**Do not** create a book mark to go back to the MC EDT web page; this has been known to cause errors that prevent you from being able to log in.
- There are Settings in Google Chrome that you may want to set to help with using the web browser with Accuro and the Go Secure website (See Appendix)
- Alternately, instead of modifying the Google Chrome settings, you can begin to type in the URL above into the address bar of the internet browser, and once you have already visited the site once, the website will show up as on option to select from.

Step 1 – Before you Connect to MC EDT

Create your OHIP submission file in Accuro

If you want to send an OHIP submission file then you must first create the OHIP submission file in Accuro. Make sure that you are in the "Unsubmitted Claims" Tab and that you have selected the correct Provider that you would like to submit for. Click on the "Submit Claims" button. A screen that looks like the following is displayed. Remember the file name, eg. HA123456.008:

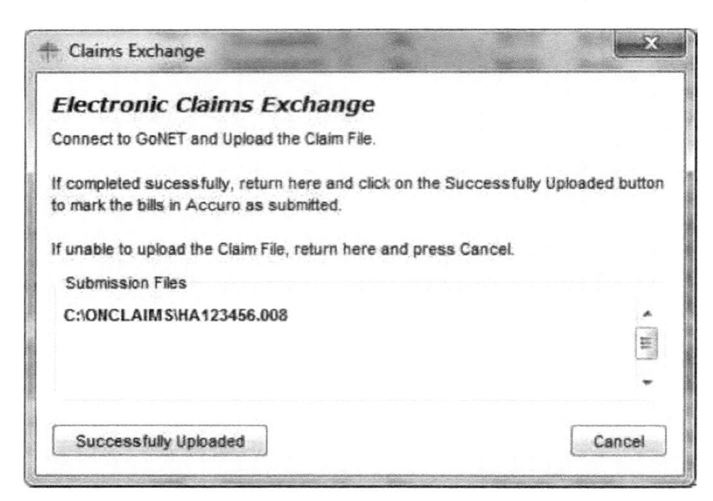

Minimize your active windows so that you can see your Windows Desktop, by clicking on your "Show the Desktop" icon or holding down (the Windows button on your keyboard) and while holding it down, type the letter M.

PAGE 2

Step 2 – Connect to MC EDT Service

Double click on the Google Chrome icon on your desktop and Log In to MC EDT

For detailed instructions please refer to the MC EDT Reference Manual available at:

http://www.health.gov.on.ca/english/providers/pub/ohip/edtref_manual/mc_edt_reference_manual.pdf

2a. Upload Files to the Ministry (Submission)

Once you are logged in, click on "MC EDT Service (Upload/Download)". The next screen appears as below.

MINISTRY OF HEALTH AND LONG-TERM CARE

Français

MAIN | DESIGNATED ACCOUNTS | ADD DESIGNEE LOGOUT

MEDICAL CLAIMS ELECTRONIC DATA TRANSFER

Upload

Download

CONTACT US | PRIVACY | IMPORTANT NOTICES

© © QUEEN'S PRINTER FOR ONTARIO, 2012 | LAST MODIFIED: 2012-05-17

PAGE 3

Click on Upload to send your claim file(s). The File Upload screen similar the one below is displayed.

If the "Select a Billing number field is blank", click on the Drop Down list and click on the appropriate Physician Billing Number.

Click on Choose File. A screen similar to the one below is displayed:

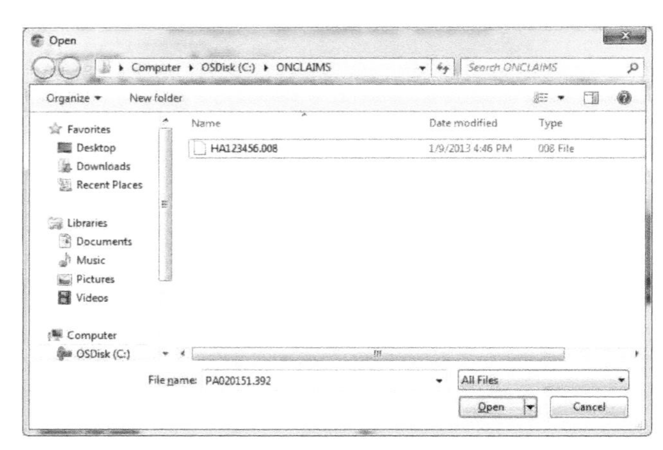

PAGE 4

If the location at the top of the screen is not "Computer \ C: \ONCLAIMS", Navigate to C:\ONCLAIMS by:

Click on Computer on the left side. Click on your (C:) drive.

Click on the ONCLAIMS folder

Double-click on your submission file.

Once the file has been selected, then click on the "Select File Type" dropdown and choose "Claim File".

Click on Upload. Make sure to see the confirmation message similar to the following,

File 'HA123456.008' has been successfully uploaded.

If you have more than one file to send, click on "Upload Another File" and repeat this process until all claim files have been sent.

Once done, click Home.

2b. Receive Files from the Ministry (Download)

Click on Download. A screen similar to the one below is displayed. If you are authorized for more than one provider you may have to select your Physician from the Physician drop down list first and click Download to get to this screen.

MINISTRY OF HEALTH AND LONG-TERM CARE

Français

MEDICAL CLAIMS ELECTRONIC DATA TRANSFER

List of Reports/Files for Billing Number 112383

File Type	Subject	File Name	Date	Status	
RA	Remittance Advice	RA_AUGUST_2012.TXT	2012-08-10	Available	Download
ES	Enrolment Report Patient Summary	PCRM60.TXT	2012-08-10	Available	Download
OU	Outside Use Report	PCRM70.TXT	2012-08-10	Available	Download

Sort by File Type Home Refresh

CONTACT US | PRIVACY | IMPORTANT NOTICES

© QUEEN'S PRINTER FOR ONTARIO, 2012 | LAST MODIFIED: 2012-05-17

PAGE 5

Download all files that are Status 'Available'. Click on Download next to the file you wish to download. If the location at the top of the screen is not "Computer \ C: \ONCLAIMS", Navigate to C:\ONCLAIMS by:

Click on Computer on the left side. Click on your (C:)drive.

Click on the ONCLAIMS folder

Click Save, if required. (Based on your Internet settings)

Repeat the process until you have downloaded all files with the status "Available".

If you have more than one provider you will click on "Select another Billing Number" to repeat the process for all of your providers.

You will not see the status change to 'Downloaded' unless you press the "Refresh" button at the bottom of the screen.

When you are done, click on Logout and close your browser.

Step 3 - After Connecting to MC EDT; Return to Accuro

If you successfully uploaded your submission files, click on "Successfully Uploaded" in the Claims Exchange window. If you were unable to log in or submit your claim files, click Cancel.

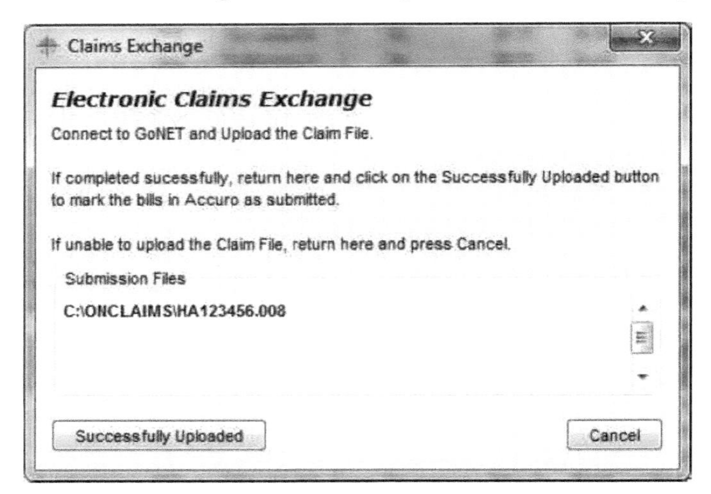

PAGE 6

If you downloaded files, to process them, click on the "Assessments" button within Accuro in the Claims section.

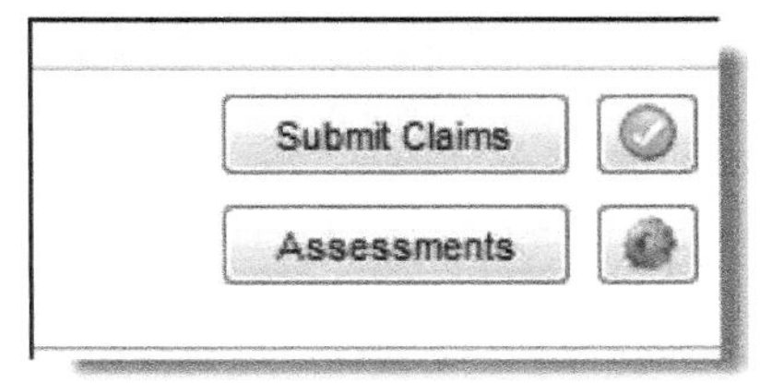

A screen similar to the one below will be displayed:

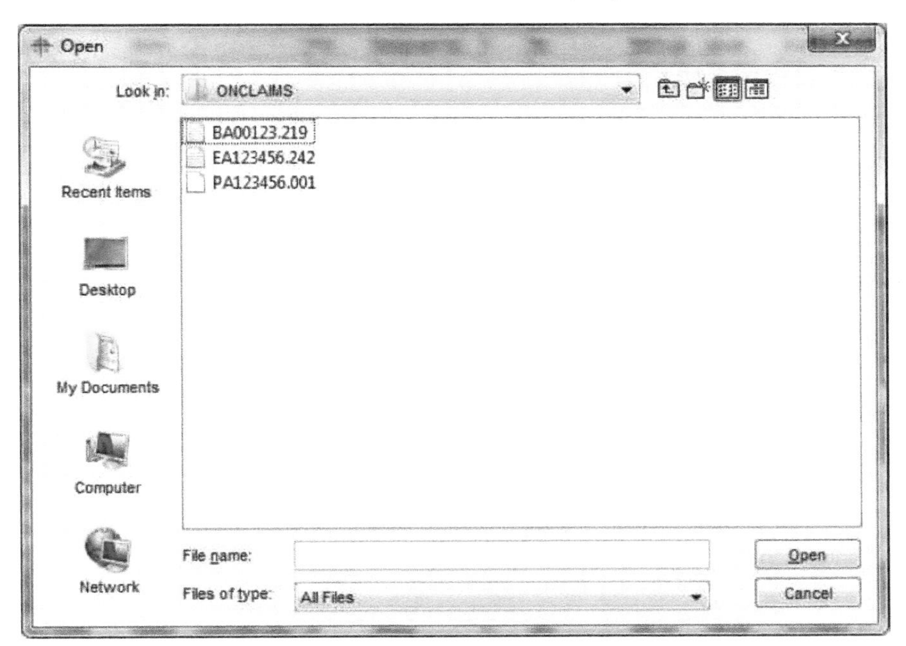

Click on any file to highlight it. Hold down the Ctrl key and while holding it down, type A to select all files. Click on Open. The files will be processed into Accuro and removed from the ONCLAIMS folder.

PAGE 7

To verify if your previous submissions have been processed by the Ministry, click on Manage Submissions (the gear icon to the right of the Assessments button).

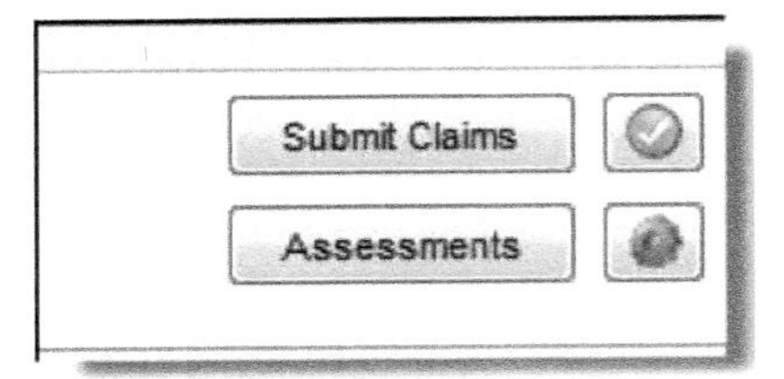

Click on the "Batch Status" tab. All submissions that were marked as "Successfully Uploaded" in Accuro will be listed in here. Every submission line with a date prior to today should have a Processed Date. The Ministry generally releases the "Batch Edit" files within 24 to 72 after a submission has been completed. The Batch Edit files are what give the processed date in the Batch Status tab of Submission Management.

To verify if you have rejected claims and to correct them, click on the "Not Reconciled" tab.

PAGE 8

Appendix – Browser settings for Google Chrome

If you choose to use Google Chrome as the Internet Browser with MC EDT, here are some settings that may assist you with using the browser with Accuro and the Ministry's website:

When you first launch Google Chrome, click on the icon on the far right of the address bar that looks like 3 horizontal lines.

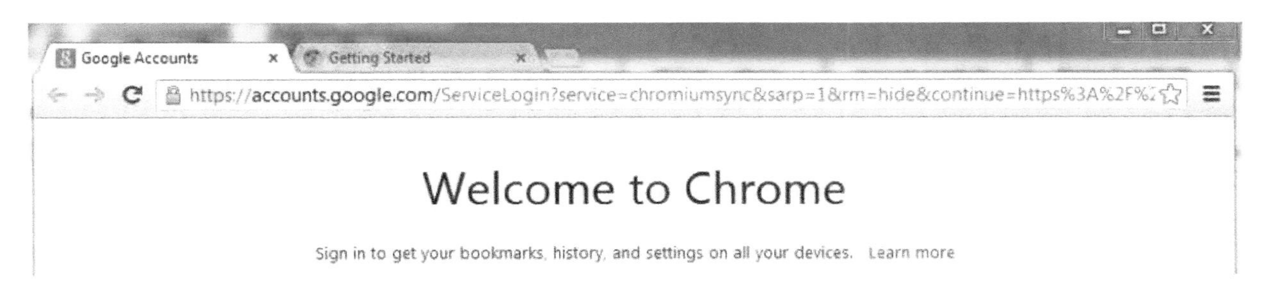

Then choose "Settings"

Since sometimes creating a bookmark for the MC EDT website causes an error when logging in, you can avoid having to type the website each time by setting Chrome to open a specific page on start-up. Please find the setting below and click "Set pages"

On start-up

- Open the New Tab page
- Continue where I left off
- Open a specific page or set of pages. Set pages

Type the MC EDT website as one of the pages to open on start-up.

https://www.edt.health.gov.on.ca

You can also go into the advanced settings to set up a default save location when downloading your claim files:

+ Show advanced settings

PAGE 9

Find the setting for "Downloads"

Downloads

Download location: C:\ONCLAIMS Change...

☐ Ask where to save each file before downloading

Click "Change" and ensure that the Download location is C:\ONCLAIMS
To choose the location select "Computer \ C: \ONCLAIMS", Navigate to C:\ONCLAIMS by:

Click on Computer

Click on your (C:)drive.

Click on the ONCLAIMS folder

Now if you close your browser and relaunch, it should open right to the GO Secure (MC EDT) website so that you may sign in.

Appendix I

Electronic Documents

ELECTRONIC DOCUMENTS

The following files have been made available electronically to complete the tasks within the workbook:

- Billing Scenario Template
- Error Code Template
- Error Report Messages Template
- Healthy Life Extended Health Care Template
- Healthy Life Public Service Health Care Plan Form (PSHCP)
- Healthy Life University Health Insurance Plan Form (UHIP)
- Invoice – Brooklane Medical Centre
- Invoice – Hope General Hospital
- MOHLTC Resource Manual for Physicians Familiarization
- MOHLTC Schedule of Benefits Familiarization
- Organization Chart
- Patients – BMC and Student Spreadsheets
- Provincial and Territorial Health Cards Template
- Receipt – Brooklane Medical Centre
- Receipt – Hope General Hospital
- Workplace Safety and Insurance Board Form 8 (WSIB)

Appendix J

Related Task Documents

MOHLTC SCHEDULE OF BENEFITS FAMILIARIZATION (Page 1)

Section	Search Item	Answer	Page No.
General Preamble	List and explain the age definitions.		
General Preamble – Assessments	Are chronic diseases eligible for premium billing? Provide three examples of chronic diseases and their codes.		
Consultations and Visits – Family Practice & Practice in General	What is the house call assessment code?		
Appendices	There are exclusions or uninsured services not covered by the Schedule of Benefits. Which appendix covers this area?		
Consultations and Visits – Endocrinology & Metabolism	What is the billing code for diabetes management by a specialist (maximum of one service per patient for a 12-month period)?		
Consultations and Visits	Does the MOHLTC provide a payment rate with the code?		
Spinal Surgical Procedures	What is the vertebrae needle biopsy code?		
General Preamble	What is a referral?		
Female Genital Surgical Procedures	What is the code for a hysterectomy (excision) with or without adnexa (unless otherwise specified) abdominal code?		
Consultations and Visits – Geriatrics	What is the code for geriatrics telephone support – initiated by a caregiver where a physician provides telephone support to a caregiver(s) for a patient with an emphasized, established diagnosis of dementia?		
Digestive System Surgical Procedures	What is the code for a biopsy using a needle in the pancreas?		
Respiratory Surgical Procedures	What is the code for a single nasal polyp excision (nose)?		
General Preamble	What does Schedule of Benefits mean when referring to the Act?		

MOHLTC SCHEDULE OF BENEFITS FAMILIARIZATION (Page 2)

Section	Search Item	Answer	Page No.
General Preamble	What does Schedule of Benefits mean by medical consultant?		
Consultations and Visits – Pediatrics	What is the code for a periodic health visit for someone 12 to 17 years of age?		
General Preamble	What do specific elements of a direct physical encounter with a patient include?		
Urogenital and Urinary Surgical Procedures	What is the code for a catheterization in the hospital?		
Endocrine Surgical Procedures	What is the code for a thyroid gland excision biopsy?		
General Preamble	List the time definitions.		
General Preamble	What is the definition of Most Responsible Physician?		
Consultations and Visits – Family Practice and Practice in General	List the units of time in case conferences.		
Diagnostic and Therapeutic Procedures	What is the code for the Hepatitis B (HB) injection?		
Obstetrics	What is the code for a caesarean section?		
Musculoskeletal System Surgical Procedures	What is the code for a knee amputation through knee disarticulation?		
Integumentary System Surgical Procedures	What is the code for operations of the breast – mastectomy – simple – female – with or without biopsy?		
Cardiovascular Surgical Procedures	What is the code for a one-coronary artery repair?		
Ocular and Aural Surgical Procedures	What is the code for an inner ear intra-cochlear?		
Neurological Surgical Procedures	What is the code for a peripheral nerve graft – minor sensory/cutaneous nerve?		
Haematic and Lymphatic Surgical Procedures	What is the code for a bone marrow transplant infusion into a recipient?		
Consultation and Visits – Family Practice and Practice in General	What must be documented in order to be eligible for payment for a telephone consultation?		

MOHLTC SCHEDULE OF BENEFITS FAMILIARIZATION (Page 3)

Section	Search Item	Answer	Page No.
Consultations and Visits – Family Practice and Practice in General	What is the code for interviews with relatives or a person who is authorized to make a treatment decision on behalf of the patient in accordance with the *Health Care Consent Act*?		
Consultations and Visits – Family Practice and Practice in General	What is the code for a general listing consultation?		
Appendix Q – Summary of Acronyms	Provide the acronyms for the following: Comprehensive Care Model Family Health Group Family Health Network		
Appendix C	When is prior approval required from the Ministry for payment to be rendered outside of Canada when there is an illness, disease, or injury?		
General Preamble	Psychotherapy, Hypnotherapy, Counselling, Primary Mental Health, and Psychiatric Care services are calculated in time units. 1 unit = 20 minutes. Explain the remainder.		
General Preamble	What is a General Assessment?		
Dermatology	What is the code for ultraviolet light therapy?		
Appendix D	Is surgery to alleviate physical symptoms that have not responded to six months of active treatment billable?		
General Preamble – General Information	All insured services must be documented in appropriate records. What does the Act require?		
General Preamble – Anesthesiologists' Services	What does the general anesthesia service include?		
Numeric Index	Why would this be useful?		
Surgical Preamble	What is the allowable procedure fee percentage for a surgeon for morbidly obese patients?		

MOHLTC SCHEDULE OF BENEFITS FAMILIARIZATION (Page 4)

Section	Search Item	Answer	Page No.
General Preamble – Definitions	What does "P" represent?		
General Preamble – Definitions	What does "T" represent?		
Appendices	Which appendix indicates time units for surgery and anesthesia?		

MOHLTC RESOURCE MANUAL FOR PHYSICIANS FAMILIARIZATION (Page 1)

Section	Search Item	Answer	Page No.
Physician Payment	What is the purpose of the general preamble?		
Claims Submission	What are the three types of claims a physician may submit?		
Physician Registration	Which regulation states that claims must be submitted by electronic data transfer (EDT)?		
Physician Payment	What is the purpose of InfoBulletins?		
Claims Submission	What are the Specialty Codes for Midwife and Nurse Practitioner?		
Claims Submission	What is the diagnostic code for an in-laws problem?		
Claims Submission	What is the diagnostic code for a mole?		
Claims Submission	What is the diagnostic code for difficulty at work?		
Claims Submission	Are all diagnostic codes alphabetical in one list?		
Claims Submission	What is the code for a viral disease?		
Claims Submission	What is the code for dislocating a finger in an accident?		
Claims Submission	What is the code for chickenpox?		
Claims Submission	What is the code for schizophrenia?		
Claims Submission	What is the code for immunizing for MMR?		
Claims Submission	What is the monthly cutoff date for claims submission?		
Claims Submission	What is the code for physiotherapy for tendinitis?		
Claims Submission	What is the code for low birth weight in an infant?		
Claims Submission	What is error code V22?		
Claims Submission	What is error code MY?		
Physician Payment	Are the Appendices with the Schedule of Benefits? Are they all part of the Schedule of Benefits? What is their purpose?		

MOHLTC RESOURCE MANUAL FOR PHYSICIANS FAMILIARIZATION (Page 2)

Section	Search Item	Answer	Page No.
Payment Integrity	What is PPRB?		
Physician Registration	Who must a physician register with in Ontario?		
Physician Registration	What must be completed to get an OHIP billing number?		
Physician Payment	Can physicians propose changes to the Schedule of Benefits?		
Claims Submission	What is the form to complete for inquiries about benefits?		
Claims Submission	What is the proper format for a patient's date of birth?		
Claims Submission	What is the error code for OHIP records that show corresponding procedure(s) on this day were claimed previously by another physician?		
Claims Submission	What is the diagnostic codes for blindness?		
Claims Submission	What is the error code for a practitioner not registered with OHIP?		
Claims Submission	Are error codes and error report messages reasons for rejected claims?		
Claims Submission	When is a claim considered stale dated?		
Claims Submission	Claims Error Report – What is a Remittance Advice Report?		
Physician Registration	What must a physician have with the College of Physicians and Surgeons of Ontario (CPSO) in order to apply for an OHIP billing number with the Ministry?		
Physician Payment	Special visit premiums – What is a non-elective visit?		
Claims Submission	What is the error code for an invalid or missing province code?		
Claims Submission	What is the error report message for resubmit as an RMB claim?		

MOHLTC RESOURCE MANUAL FOR PHYSICIANS FAMILIARIZATION (Page 3)

Section	Search Item	Answer	Page No.
Claims Submission	What is the error report message for number of services exceed maximum allowed?		
Claims Submission	What is the explanatory code for service is not an OHIP benefit?		
Claims Submission	What is the explanatory code for not allowed in addition to visit fee?		
Claims Submission	Are explanatory codes reasons for reduction or disallowment as a result of medical rules?